A Kansas Snake Community:

Composition and Changes over 50 Years

A Kansas Snake Community:
Composition and Changes over 50 Years

Henry S. Fitch

KRIEGER PUBLISHING COMPANY
MALABAR, FLORIDA
1999

Original Edition 1999

Printed and Published by
KRIEGER PUBLISHING COMPANY
KRIEGER DRIVE
MALABAR, FLORIDA 32950

Copyright © 1999 by Krieger Publishing Company, Inc.

Library of Congress Cataloging-in-Publication Data

Fitch, Henry Sheldon, 1909–
    A Kansas snake community : composition and changes over 50
years / by Henry S. Fitch.
        p.   cm.
    Includes bibliographical references and index.
    ISBN 0-89464-996-5 (hardcover : alk. paper)
    1. Snakes—Kansas—Lawrence.   2. Snakes—Ecology—
Kansas—Lawrence.   3. Animal communities—Kansas—
Lawrence.   4. University of Kansas.   Natural History
Reservation.   I. Title.
QL666.O6F5368   1999
597.96′09781′65—DC21   97-49063
                                                              CIP

10 9 8 7 6 5 4 3 2

Dedication

To my family, for all of whom natural history became a way of life. To my wife, Virginia (Ginger), and my daughter, Alice, who often worked with me in the field and scribed thousands of records of snakes. To my son Chester, who distinguished himself as a snake photographer, and my son John, who often contributed live snakes to the cause.

Contents

Acknowledgments

My study was part of the Experimental and Applied Ecology Program of the University of Kansas, and nearly all of the fieldwork was done on the Kansas Ecological Reserves (KER) belonging to the University under this program. I thank Drs. Kenneth B. Armitage and W. John O'Brien, past and present directors of the program, for their cooperation. Dr. W. Dean Kettle, associate director of the program, Galen Pittman, manager, and Bruce Johanning, research associate, also were helpful in many ways. The late Professor E. Raymond Hall of the University's former Department of Zoology deserves credit for acquiring some of the land now included in KER for the University to use in field research.

University of Kansas students who carried on fieldwork for me or for their own projects on the KER contributed many snakes and much information about them. My list of helpers includes: Rex O. Bare, James W. Bee, William N. Berg, W. Leslie Burger, Donald R. Clark, Robert R. Fleet, Howard Freeman, Richard S. Funk, Harry W. Greene, Hank Guarisco, Russell J. Hall, Donna M. Hardy, John Hawkins, Robert M. Hedrick, Robert W. Henderson, Dale L. Hoyt, Larry Hunt, Richard Lattis, Julian Lee, John M. Legler, Warren Legler, Richard B. Loomis, Luis Malaret, Anthony N. McFarland, Robert M. Packard, William S. Parker, David Pennock, David Pippitt, Dwight R. Platt, Michael V. Plummer, Dennis G. Rainey, Randall Reiserer, Eric Rundquist, Richard A. Seigel, Kenneth E. Shain, Eric Shulenberger, Arnold K. Smith, Donald Troyer, Robert G. Webb, Pennie von Achen, and Robert B. Wimmer. Deborah F. Cowman, graduate student from Texas A&M University, helped me with fieldwork in the spring of 1995.

Neighboring farmers and landowners contributed substantially. To all I am deeply indebted. The prevailing attitude of suspicion and hostility toward my snake study in its early years gradually changed to one of interest and support. Many live snakes were contributed especially by Mr. and Mrs. Kevin Brock, Mr. and Mrs. Harold Brune, Mr. And Mrs. Roger Christie, Steve Purdy, Mrs. J. F. Morgan, Dr. Chester Sullivan, and Mr. and Mrs. Robert Thiry.

Special collaborators who made important contributions to my study include Dr. Hampton W. Shirer, who devised and constructed radio transmitters that served for telemetric studies of several kinds of snakes; Patricia Pisani, who participated in the telemetric trailing of snakes; Stanley D. Roth, biology teacher of Lawrence High School, who contributed live snakes; Joseph T. Collins and Suzanne L. Collins, who contributed photographs of several uncommon species, and Errol D. Hooper, Jr., who kindly provided the drawings for Figure 8.

Special thanks are due to all members of my family for their longtime support and assistance: my wife, Virginia, my sons, John and Chester, and my daughter, Alice. Virginia often accompanied me in the field and recorded the data that I obtained while examining live snakes. Alice also often recorded for me in the field in the early years of the study. My granddaughter, Lena M. Echelle, my son-in-law, Dr. Anthony A. Echelle, and Alice also typed parts of the manuscript. Chester was especially helpful in photographing the live snakes.

Introduction

My study of Kansas snakes involved the monitoring of local populations over 50 consecutive seasons from 1948 to 1997, with mark-and-recapture procedures. Because of the locale near the geographical center of the United States, the 18 species are in general those kinds best known to science, and for each there is abundant literature extending back into the previous century. However, my intensive and continual monitoring has revealed previously unknown aspects of the ecology and demography of most species. Five of the species were at the edges of their natural ranges and were so uncommon that records averaged less than one per decade and very little was found out about them, but their presence in low densities is of interest in demonstrating biodiversity. For the remaining 13 species the amount of data obtained varied enormously. In some instances it is not evident whether findings apply to an entire species, to a geographic population or subspecies, or only to the local population studied.

The objectives of my study were to clarify the ecology and demography of each species, its phenology, responses to weather and climate, day-to-day and seasonal movements, reproduction, growth, food habits, numbers and population structure, and to determine how these traits vary temporally and how they are affected by ecological succession. It is anticipated that the large amount of data representing a specific locality will be useful for comparison and contrast with other localities and areas or regions in future studies of local and geographic variation in ecological traits.

Areas of especially concentrated field work included House Field (with adjunct Horse, Picnic and Vole fields), Quarry Field, Biotic Succession Area (BSA), and on the Nelson Environmental Study Area (NESA) the northwest area of rodent enclosures (see Figure 1). Each of these was used for census calculations from capture-recapture ratios and for estimates of population density for one or more snake species. Measurements made from the maps of these areas varied somewhat according to the species—the estimated boundaries of its habitat and the layout of traps or shelters serving for captures, resulting in areas of similar but slightly different sizes for different species.

Of the 18 species of snakes included in my study, four are absent from the Fitch Natural History Reservation (FNHR) but occur on adjacent areas. Eight other species of the local ophifauna were not found in the course of my study; these were the eastern hognose snake, *Heterodon platirhinos,* rough green snake, *Opheodrys aestivus,* plainbelly water snake, *Nerodia erythrogaster,* diamondback water snake, *Nerodia rhombifer,* Graham's crayfish snake, *Regina grahamii,* western ribbon snake, *Thamnophis proximus,* plains garter snake, *Thamnophis radix,* and massasauga, *Sistrurus catenatus.* These are species of lowland habitats—sandy bottomland, marsh, river's edge or streamside thicket—habitats poorly represented or lacking in the upland terrain where my study was made.

The 18 species studied represent only two of the many snake families—Viperidae, including the venomous copperhead and timber rattlesnake, and Colubridae, the dominant family of snakes, including the remaining 16 species. There are, however, three distinct lineages within the local colubrids. The subfamily Colubrinae includes the genera *Coluber, Elaphe, Lamropeltis,* and *Pituophis,* large, active snakes, oviparous, mainly constrictors (except for *Coluber*). The subfamily Xenodontinae includes *Carphophis, Diadophis,* and *Tantilla,* small, secretive, oviparous snakes having enlarged fanglike teeth (grooved in some) at the posterior end of each maxillary bone. They prey mainly on invertebrates. Finally, members of the subfamily Natricinae, including the genera *Nerodia, Storeria, Thamnophis, Tropidoclonion,* and *Virginia,* range from small to large, are mostly aquatic or secretive, have heavily keeled dorsal scales (unless they are burrowers) and in North America all are live-bearers (contrasting with their Old World counterparts, nearly all oviparous). They are more cold-hardy than most snakes. The species and subspecies of snakes studied are listed below. Names follow Collins (1997).

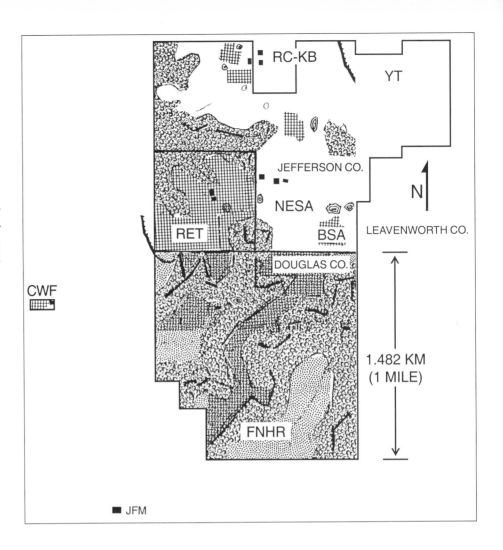

Figure 1. Map of areas and habitats where population studies of snakes were pursued from 1948 to 1997, with mark-and-recapture procedures. FNHR = Fitch Natural History Reservation; RET = Rockefeller Experimental Tract; NESA = Nelson Environmental Study Area; BSA = Biotic Succession Area; YT = Yelton Tract; RC-KB = Roger Christie and Kevin Brock farms; CWF = Chester Fitch property; JFM = J. F. Morgan farm.

OLD FOREST
NEW FOREST (OLD FIELD, PASTURE, PRAIRIE)
POND
STREAM
BUILDING
LINE OF TRAPS OR SHELTERS
TRAP COVERAGE

Species and Subspecies of Study

Agkistrodon contortrix phaeogaster Osage copperhead

Carphophis vermis Western worm snake

Coluber constrictor flaviventris Yellowbelly racer

Crotalus horridus Timber rattlesnake

Diadophis punctatus arnyi Prairie ringneck snake

Elaphe emoryi Great Plains rat snake

Elaphe obsoleta obsoleta Black rat snake

Lampropeltis calligaster calligaster Prairie kingsnake

Lampropeltis getula holbrooki Speckled kingsnake

Lampropeltis triangulum syspila Red milk snake

Nerodia sipedon sipedon Northern water snake

Pituophis catenifer sayi Bullsnake

Storeria dekayi texana Texas brown snake

Storeria occipitomaculata occipitomaculata Northern redbelly snake

Tantilla gracilis Flathead snake

Thamnophis sirtalis parietalis Red-sided garter snake

Tropidoclonion lineatum Lined snake

Virginia valeriae elegans Western earth snake

Site of Study

The area of my study was in northeastern Kansas in the vicinity of the point where Douglas, Jefferson, and Leavenworth counties abut on the northern edge of the Kaw River Valley from 268 to 332 meters above sea level. The terrain was varied with flat hilltops and tributary valleys, mainly pastureland, and steep slopes, mostly wooded, with seral and climax tree species in varying proportions. Valleys and ravines had intermittent streams and there were numerous artificial ponds. Flat hilltop "cuestas" had shallow soil underlain by rock, and outcrops of the Oread limestone were prominent at hilltop edges. The occupied and abandoned farmsteads had buildings including residences, barns, sheds, and silos.

Fieldwork centered on the Fitch Natural History Reservation (FNHR), the northeasternmost section of land in Douglas County which was a major source of data throughout the span of my study (Figure 1). Adjacent neighboring areas that were added and were also significant sources of data include the Rockefeller Experimental Tract (RET), a quarter section (65 ha) in

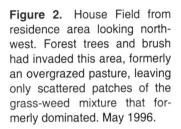

Figure 2. House Field from residence area looking northwest. Forest trees and brush had invaded this area, formerly an overgrazed pasture, leaving only scattered patches of the grass-weed mixture that formerly dominated. May 1996.

Figure 3. West edge of Quarry Field looking north beyond northern boundary of FNHR onto RET which was then a privately owned farm with fields under cultivation. At the time of this photo, Quarry Field was overgrazed, relatively barren, and had few if any snakes. FNHR, 7 December 1948.

Jefferson County adjoining the western half of FNHR on its northern edge, acquired by the University of Kansas in 1956. The Nelson Environmental Study Area (NESA) with RET comprised the southeasternmost section of land in Jefferson County, and was acquired in 1970. The Biotic Succession Area (BSA) was a large upland field in the southeastern part of NESA, regularly mowed except for islands of natural vegetation. The Yelton Tract was a rectangular block (61 ha) in Leavenworth County opposite the northeastern part of NESA. Substantial amounts of data also were obtained through the courtesy of neighboring landowners. The Chester Fitch (CWF) property of 4.2 ha, purchased in 1986, was 1.6 km west of FNHR headquarters. Artificial shelters were distributed on CWF and checked from time to time. The John F. Morgan (JFM) farm of

16 ha adjoined the FNHR section on the southwest. The Roger Christie and Kevin Brock (RC-KB) properties with small acreages adjoined NESA on the north. The Ruby Wiggins (RW) farm occupied land between FNHR and CWF. The Harold Brune (HB) farm was 1 km north of NESA. Occasional records of snakes found farther afield on roads or in woodlands or grasslands were included for some purposes.

During the period of the study some of these areas underwent major changes as ecological succession occurred, especially on FNHR where trees steadily invaded and dominated former croplands, pastures, and prairie (Figure 2). By the 1990s former pastures had only isolated patches of grassland while croplands and prairie had reverted to forest (Figures 3 & 4). Less

Figure 4. West side of Quarry Field from approximately the same spot as Figure 3. After removal of grazing livestock, the field developed a crop of thick grass and weeds in the first growing season, as shown here, and several species of snakes became abundant in the following years. By the 1990s trees and brush dominated the field with only small open patches remaining. FNHR, 21 June 1949.

Figure 5. Double-funnel wire trap placed to intercept snakes at base of hilltop limestone outcrop where many species of snakes come in search of hibernacula. FNHR, 15 October 1949.

striking succession occurred in the woodlands; when livestock were removed, a denser growth of understory shrubs developed. Also, the American elm, the dominant tree species, underwent a drastic decrease, with the largest and oldest trees especially subject to the ravages of phloem necrosis and introduced elm bark beetles (*Scolytus multistriatus*) leaving gaps in the canopy, which eventually were filled by other tree species such as the American ash.

On RET, regenerated and original prairie tracts were maintained by controlled burning. On NESA, blocks of former pasture and cultivated land were subjected to regular mowing, preventing the invasion of woody vegetation. On CWF (prior to the 1986 purchase), and on JFM and RC-KB, horses, cattle, pigs, and poultry were kept. The maintenance and feeding of these domestic animals and the presence of numerous outbuildings, some in disrepair, provided food and shelter for house sparrows, barn swallows, pigeons, and house mice. Colonies of these commensals in turn provided food for some snake species. Henderson (1974) published a brief preliminary account of resource partitioning in the snakes of FNHR.

Figure 6. Site of abandoned limestone quarry and rock-crusher, a habitat for several kinds of snakes. A colony of flathead snakes was present here in the early years of the study, but was eliminated as succession progressed. FNHR, 21 June 1949.

Figure 7. Hilltop escarpment of the Oread limestone, with southwest exposure, and many crevices and fissures providing hibernacula. FNHR, 1 November 1951.

Methods and Materials

Snakes were obtained for study by a variety of methods. Use of wire funnel traps and artificial shelters (both metal and wooden) comprised the most successful methods, which combined yielded more than 95% of the records obtained. From 1949 through 1956 funnel traps (Fitch, 1951, 1987) were used in fall, distributed along the hilltop outcrops where snakes came to hibernate (Figure 5). Each trap was placed at the base of a vertical rockface of the limestone escarpment and could intercept snakes moving in either direction. Fourteen such outcrops with a linear distance of 3.25 km were sampled (Figures 6 & 7). Species differed in their times of retirement into hibernation, but with broad overlap. Beginning in 1957 summer trapping was carried on, using drift fences of scrap lumber, screen or sheet metal, and funnel traps in pairs; each trap at the end of a fence barrier which was 5 to 8 m in length.

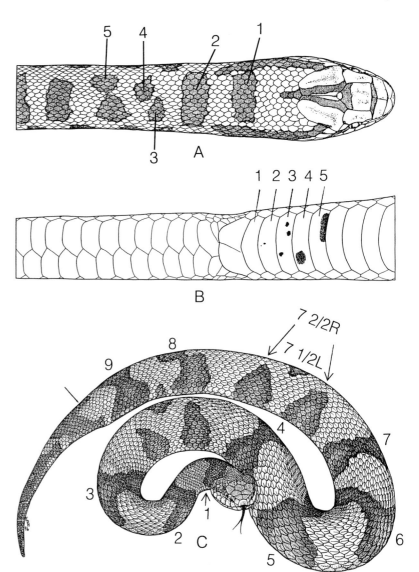

Figure 8. Natural markings of snakes that supplemented scale-clipping as means of individual identification, with combinations not likely to be duplicated: A. Prairie kingsnake, with dorsal blotches numbered from the anteriormost as follows: No. 1—Blotch contacts neck stripe on left; No. 2—Typical blotch, nothing distinctive, not included in the identifying formula; No. 3—Right side only; No. 4—Left side only; No. 5—Double. B. Ringneck snake, ventral aspect of end of body and base of tail, ventral scutes numbered, beginning with the first anterior to the anal plate: No. 1—Clear; No. 2—Center dot; No. 3—Spot left, 2 spots right; No. 4—Blotch left; No. 5—Bar right. C. Copperhead showing dorsal "hourglass" markings, 9 of them complete (9 CM) and with 2 half marks on the left side and 1 on the right following complete mark number 3, and with 1 half mark on the left side and 2 on the right following complete mark number 7. Formula: 9 CM + 3 2/2 L, 3 1/2 R, 7 1/2 L, 7 2/2 R. Artwork by Errol D. Hooper, Jr. Permission for artwork sources granted by KU Herpetology and JTC.

Intensive sampling extended over an area of about 3 × 2 km but was concentrated within 28 sampling units of only a few hectares each and few of these units were sampled in any one year. The areas sampled and the methods and intensity of sampling varied, and did not correspond exactly in any two years of field work.

The 18 kinds of snakes that comprise the local ophifauna differ greatly in abundance and the species samples obtained varied from only one in *Storeria occipitomaculata* to more than 22,800 in *Diadophis punctatus*. As a general rule every snake that could be captured was individually marked by scale-clipping and was measured, weighed, sexed, checked for food in the stomach, reproductive condition, injuries or parasites, and then released within a few meters of the capture point. In some species the artificial identification marks derived from scale-clipping were supplemented by recording individual peculiarities in pattern as a means of positive identification. In the copperhead, for instance, the serial dorsal hourglass markings with frequent assymetry between left and right sides are such that no two individuals are exact matches and a system was devised for classifying variants and using their distinctive patterns for identification. In the ringneck the presence and distribution of bands, blotches, spots and dots on the posterior ventrals were found to be highly variable, with distinctive combinations in individuals. In Figure 8 the variable patterns used as an aid to identify individuals are illustrated for the prairie kingsnake, ringneck, and copperhead.

Snake trapping (Fitch, 1970, 1987) was sustained and increased through 1963, but from 1964 through 1976 relatively little trapping was done. Instead, fieldwork was concentrated on the diminutive species, mainly ringnecks, worm snakes and brown snakes. In 1965, 1966 and 1967 major efforts were devoted to radiotelemetric studies of the larger snake species. In 1977 large-scale live trapping was resumed and continued through 1997, with a gradual shift of operations in the 1980s from FNHR to NESA. During this period there was increasing reliance on artificial shelters vs. live traps. In the 8-year period 1990 through 1997, funnel traps were operated on NESA set along the snake-proof fences of former rodent enclosures, from which sections had been removed, permitting free ingress and egress of snakes and other animals.

Over the 50-year span of fieldwork (1948 through 1997) a total of approximately 32,160 capture records of 18 species were accumulated. Recaptures of individually marked snakes yielded essential information concerning growth, day-to-day and seasonal movements, longevity, and population density. The longtime program of capture and marking failed to achieve fully marked populations of any species, even in small areas under intensive study. The ratio of marked to new snakes differed according to the abundance, secretiveness, and mobility of the species: *Lampropeltis triangulum* 85%, *Elaphe emoryi* 58%, *Lampropeltis calligaster* 37%, *Agkistrodon contortrix* 30%, *Thamnophis sirtalis* 27%, *Pituophis catenifer* 25%, *Elaphe obsoleta* 23%, *Diadophis punctatus* 16%, *Nerodia sipedon* 13.3% (Fitch, 1992).

Occasionally snakes were found in the act of capturing or swallowing prey, but food habits were studied mainly by palpating prey from the stomachs of those that had fed recently. Each snake handled was checked for any discernible bulge of the abdomen that might indicate recent feeding. Some food items recovered in intact condition were examined and weighed, but most were forced up into the gullet only far enough to be identified, then squeezed back into the stomach so that the snake was not deprived of its meal. Only a small percentage of the snakes captured had detectable food items in their stomachs, especially those captured in funnel traps. Those found beneath shelters were more likely to be digesting a meal. In the 1950s and 1960s fecal material was collected from many of the snakes handled, and prey was identified to species from the residues of bone fragments, hairs, feathers, scales, or chitin. Scats have the advantage that they can be collected in much larger numbers than stomach items. However, a major disadvantage is that the actual number of prey animals cannot be determined; an individual of the prey may leave traces in several successive scats, and one scat may contain residue from several prey individuals. Some soft-bodied prey animals may be digested so thoroughly that little or no residue remains to be identified in a scat.

The reproductive ecology of each species was given special attention. Females were palpated to detect and count eggs or embryos. The sex of each snake, usually obvious in adults, was verified by pressing one side of the tail base exposing the edge of the inverted hemipenis, or by probing into the tail in males or palpating the thickened cloacal capsule in adult females. Cloacal smears from snakes of both sexes were checked for sperm, indicative of sexual maturity in males and recent copulation in females.

Growth was studied from the increments in length and weight gained by marked individuals during the intervals between captures, and the individual and mean sizes of young belonging to cohorts of known age, compared with hatchlings or neonates. In all species growth seems to continue throughout life, becoming progressively slower in older snakes. Size provides a clue to age, but the correlation decreases as age increases. As an age cohort grows older the size disparity widens. In older adults many annual age cohorts overlap in size.

For the common species attempt was made to analyze population structure — ratios of the sexes and of successive annual age cohorts, with due allowance for differences in the activity and distribution of these various categories. A sexual size difference was found in each species; males are larger than females in *Agkistrodon contortrix, Crotalus horridus,* and in the colubrid genera *Elaphe, Lampropeltis,* and *Pituophis,* whereas females are larger in all other local kinds of snakes. Small sample sizes in older cohorts and the influence of good or bad years on individual growth rates have sometimes led to anomalous figures, with a younger cohort averaging larger than an older one. On average, with each successive year the growth increment should become smaller and the sexual size difference should widen.

Insofar as data is available, topics are discussed in the following order in each species account: (1) A summary of the species' morphological and ecological traits over its range as a whole, and distinctive traits of the local population. (2) Behavior, including response to seasonal change, to conspecifics as potential mates or competitors, to prey and to natural enemies. (3) Responses to ecological succession. (4) Spatial relationships including home ranges or activity ranges, seasonal movements, and longtime wandering. (5) Food habits as affected by sex, size, and season, and the effect of successional changes. (6) Reproduction, including seasonal cycles, time of oviposition, hatching or birth, numbers per clutch or litter, and the year-to-year variation caused by weather. (7) Growth, determined from individually marked snakes and from annual age cohorts when recognizable; age at sexual maturity. (8) Composition of the population in ratio of the sexes and of successive annual age cohorts. (9) Population density on specific areas, as indicated by numbers actually observed, and the ratios of recaptured previously marked individuals in samples (Fitch, 1982). (10) Intraspecific geographic variation in ecological traits including body size, sexual dimorphism, frequency of reproduction, and number of eggs or young in clutch or litter.

Attempts were made to determine the abundance of snakes on specific areas, not only by counting those actually seen or captured, but by Petersen Index calculations based on the ratios of recaptures to original captures, for the four most numerous species. Population densities varied in the habitat mosaic of the study areas, and for each species an attempt was made to select an area of fairly uniform favorable habitat and sample it thoroughly and uniformly. Selected census areas were not exactly the same for different species, but they overlapped. House Field, Quarry Field, and the NESA pens area were delimited somewhat differently for the four species censused. Although the less numerous species could not be censused by Petersen Index because captures and recaptures were too sporadic, their densities could be guessed by the ratios of their captures to those of the censused species (*Agkistrodon contortrix, Coluber constrictor, Diadophis punctatus,* and *Thamnophis sirtalis*).

In Table 2 for *Agkistrodon,* as in similar tables for *Coluber* (Table 23), *Diadophis* (Table 40), and *Thamnophis* (Table 81), some years' records were omitted when their data were too meager for meaningful comparison. Every year from 1948 through 1997 produced some records, but including them all would needlessly lengthen the table and obscure the more significant comparisons where large series were available.

In all instances where adequate series were available, means are shown with one standard error.

Scientific names, both binomial and trinomial, and their vernacular equivalents have been used where appropriate. The list on page 2 shows the applicable trinomials and their vernacular equivalents for the species studied, but in the species accounts I have used the binomial species name for each, feeling that subspecies should be deemphasized. Subspecific status is automatically indicated by the geographic location — in this case the tri-county area of Douglas, Jefferson and Leavenworth in northeastern Kansas.

In the species accounts, after having established what kind of animal is being discussed, I have often referred to it in general terms, as racer, ringneck, rattlesnake, or garter snake, rather than using the long, unwieldy formal name each time, but it was necessary to distinguish between the two kinds of rat snakes and the two kinds of kingsnakes that were included.

Agkistrodon contortrix

Traits of the Species

The copperhead is a medium-size pit viper characteristic of deciduous forests in the eastern United States. There is geographic variation in size, color pattern, and ecological traits. The basic pattern of chestnut-colored hourglass dorsal markings on a tan ground color is effectively cryptic against a background of leaf litter. (See Plates 1 & 2.) Juveniles differ from adults in having the distal half of the tail greenish-yellow and, like the young of some other vipers, they have been observed to lure certain kinds of prey within striking range by holding the tail erect with squirming movements that imitate a worm or grub (Ditmars, 1907; Neill, 1948). Such luring behavior is only weakly developed in the local population. Copperheads are mainly nocturnal during hot weather but are diurnal in the cool weather of spring and fall. As sit-and-wait predators that capture their prey by ambush they are remarkably sluggish in behavior. With body looped in an S-shaped coil ready to strike, the copperhead may spend days at a time in a potential ambush site with no perceptible movement. The average meal is about 20% of the snake's weight and 10 to 12 meals annually are considered to be typical (Fitch, 1960). Parturient females are somewhat emaciated from fasting and nourishing their embryos. In late summer females laden with embryos cease to feed and retreat to rock outcrops or similarly sheltered places, often gathering in small groups that confer mutual security during the final weeks of pregnancy.

In the local population near the northwestern extreme of the species' range, copperheads average markedly smaller than those of the Northeast or Southeast but larger than those of the Southwest. In local adults mean snout-vent length (SVL) ranged from 610 to 719 mm (males) and 560 to 631 mm (females) in different years. Locally the prairie vole is the chief prey species, followed by the white-footed mouse, but any mammals of a size that can be swallowed are potential prey. First-year young too small to take the kinds of prey eaten by adults feed upon small snakes (*Diadophis, Carphophis*),

skinks (*Eumeces, Scincella*), narrow-mouthed frogs, certain smooth-skinned moth larvae, and cicada nymphs which are vulnerable when they emerge on the soil surface. First-year young tend to stay in woodlands near limestone outcrops where adults come to hibernate and females come to give birth, but adults, especially males, disperse into grassland habitats in summer. The Petersen Index census of copperheads indicated densities of 3.9 to 34.6 per ha with much overlapping of activity ranges between individuals.

The pattern of hourglass-shaped, chestnut-colored dorsal markings on a tan ground color was highly variable, with irregularities in the markings and asymmetry between markings of left and right sides, and these irregularities aided in the identification of individuals marked by scale-clipping. A more striking variant was the complete absence of the dark markings in occasional individuals (all males) that were of uniform tan color. Three young of two litters born in captivity, one first-year young trapped, and one adult male trapped were of this patternless phase, believed to involve a sex-linked mutation. Mothers and sisters of the patternless males born in captivity had normal patterns (Fitch, 1959). (See Plates 3 & 4.)

Behavior

As sit-and-wait predators, copperheads are slow and sluggish in their routine movements. Shifting from one station to another the snake employs rectilinear locomotion and its movement is so slow as to be almost imperceptible with frequent long pauses. However, a startled copperhead may escape by rapid crawling, with lateral wriggling replacing the usual rectilinear movement. Snakes interrupted in the course of nocturnal movements are most active in escaping, usually heading for shelter such as a thick bush, burrow, or rock crevice. The first response of one disturbed in its natural surroundings is a jerk of the head turning to confront the disturbance and this may be followed by a strike if the snake is touched or further disturbed. The snake may vibrate its tail, producing a rattling or whirring

9

sound, and may make a sudden lunge for shelter. Individuals are usually solitary, and even when two or more are together their interactions are not prominent.

In courtship the male either follows the female or crawls over her, rhythmically nudging her sides with the tip of his snout. The male "combat dance" in which rivals rear with their ventral surfaces in contact, each trying to throw down his opponent, has often been observed in both free and captive copperheads (Schuett & Gillingham, 1989). After losing such a contest the defeated male is disinclined to courtship, even in the absence of a dominant male. The female seems to exercise some choice of mates; when approached by a courting male she rears her forebody mimicking the male challenge display that precedes combat, and this suffices to discourage and intimidate males that have been losers in recent combats (Duvall, Schuett & Arnold, 1993).

Capture of prey is usually accomplished with a close-range strike from ambush. The snake may instantly retract to a coiled position or cling to the prey holding it down and injecting more venom, depending on whether or not the victim is large and active and is perceived as a potential threat.

Reactions to disturbance varied according to the sex, age, and activity of the snake. Sluggishness and reliance on the cryptic pattern for concealment characterized behavior. Most often a snake would allow close approach of a person, with no perceptible movement. Even those exposed by raising shelters usually remained immobile, at least for a few seconds.

Size Relationships

Table 1 compares sizes of adult copperheads on NESA, BSA, an area of food abundance (high population of prairie voles), with the adjacent area of FNHR having a relatively meager food supply over a 12-year period, 1986 through 1997. Of the 78 copperheads captured on NESA, BSA, 31 (40%) had food in their stomachs, and all but 3 of these prey items were prairie voles. Of 209 copperheads captured on FNHR, 14 (6.7%) had food

in their stomachs—3 jumping mice, 3 short-tailed shrews, 2 prairie voles, 2 glass lizards, and one each of white-footed mouse, ring-necked snake, brown snake, and cicada. Adult copperheads were significantly larger on NESA, BSA; males were 13% longer and females 9% longer than their counterparts on FNHR. There were only 4 immature snakes (5.1%) in the NESA, BSA sample, but there were 67 (32%) in the FNHR sample. On NESA, BSA 8 gravid females averaged 7.13±1.15 embryos, 2.02 (39%) more than the overall average of 5.11 young per litter.

Replacement of Fangs

Copperheads shed their teeth, including the fangs, frequently. Each maxillary bone ordinarily bears a single tooth—the tubular fang, but on each maxillary there are two sockets side by side, and they are occupied alternately as old fangs are shed and new ones replace them. When a new fang has completed its growth, its base coalesces with the maxillary bone in its socket, and for several days both the old and the new fang may be functional.

In a captive copperhead I found that ". . . for the seven-weeks observation period, left and right sides alternated in replacement of the fangs with approximately a 33-day cycle on each side, and with known replacement periods extending over five, six and eight days, during which both new and old fang were in evidence on the same side. The new and old fangs were simultaneously functional during only a small part of the replacement period" (Fitch, 1960). After its pedicel erodes, the old fang breaks off and lies loose in its sheath. Eventually it adheres to prey that is being swallowed, passes through the digestive tract and is voided intact, embedded in fecal matter.

Of 1285 newly captured copperheads examined, 804 (62.6%) had only one fang on each side while 481 (37.4%) were in the process of fang replacement. Within this group 439 (34.2%) were replacing a fang on either the left or the right side, whereas 41 (3.2%) were replacing fangs on both sides simultaneously, but replacement was not necessarily at the same stage on the left and right. The rate of replacement seemed to be similar in young and adults. Even neonates that have not yet taken food have been observed to be replacing fangs. The relative scarcity of snakes replacing fangs on both sides indicates a strong tendency for alternate rather than synchronous replacement.

Responses to Succession

Table 2 shows mean size (SVL and weight) of adult copperheads of both sexes in annual samples over a 50-

TABLE 1. Sizes of Adult Copperheads on Two Adjacent Areas, One (NESA, BSA) Having an Abundant Food Supply, the Other (FNHR) Having a Relatively Meager Food Supply, 1986–1997

	N	SVL (mm)		Weight (g)	
NESA, BSA					
Males	45	708.9±17.2	(500–908)	259.2±17.3	(106–500)
Females	33	644.8±8.3	(530–825)	271.2±20.8	(160–718)
FNHR					
Males	119	636.2±8.7	(503–840)	152.8±7.0	(77–381)
Females	90	590.2±5.5	(500–755)	137.9±5.3	(70–240)

TABLE 2. Sizes of Adult Copperheads in Annual Samples

Year	Males			Females		
	N	SVL (mm)	Weight (g)	N	SVL (mm)	Weight (g)
1949	15	629±14.4	156±0.96	12	568±11.5	143±1.08
1950	35	614±23.6	181±1.35	38	580±6.6	147±0.83
1951	47	680±14.6	253±1.48	32	592±8.3	178±0.90
1952	28	719±15.5	248±1.63	15	681±8.7	217±1.30
1953	19	710±16.3	206±1.09	9	621±11.5	267±1.90
1954	21	669±23.8	190±2.12	21	621±14.3	141±1.35
1955	34	641±17.6	167±1.33	19	575±12.3	138±0.91
1956	36	641±15.0	160±1.38	19	562±5.6	119±0.92
1957	57	630±13.0	169±1.15	31	586±10.5	148±0.86
1958	128	639±8.5	166±7.2	97	584±5.6	146±0.43
1959	91	636±10.3	155±1.18	72	584±6.5	145±0.73
1960	40	671±17.6	155±1.18	40	596±9.8	142±0.73
1961	56	642±11.1	173±0.97	82	560±5.6	155±0.60
1962	65	626±10.0	159±0.37	26	616±12.0	134±0.68
1963	41	614±11.9	142±1.63	30	598±9.1	144±0.83
1964	34	645±13.9	133±1.81	30	599±9.4	130±0.71
1977	101	610±6.4	132±1.69	74	575±5.5	135±0.44
1978	48	619±12.8	156±1.09	55	588±7.0	136±0.70
1979	11	665±24.4	179±2.30	23	580±12.3	133±0.55
1980	23	668±18.2	164±1.0	13	587±13.7	120±0.83
1981	27	651±19.1	153±1.36	23	561±11.8	146±0.99
1982	47	670±13.3	163±0.88	29	606±12.4	156±1.13
1983	43	635±12.8	155±1.13	27	584±11.6	135±0.65
1984	47	676±14.3	159±12.1	30	621±6.3	126±0.49
1985	27	710±18.8	191±16.2	18	591±11.5	133±6.1
1986	26	662±17.3	200±18.4	23	610±13.9	134±8.6
1987	24	650±18.1	170±15.3	16	595±16.8	188±20.6
1988	30	682±18.3	204±19.1	11	596±23.2	169±10.6
1989	17	695±25.5	203±21.5	11	592±10.8	162±10.6
1990	31	669±36.0	200±13.0	18	630±11.3	174±17.4
1991	29	660±22.2	195±15.8	21	597±15.3	192±31.1
1992	22	684±22.7	190±26.8	18	602±13.7	129±15.1
1993	9	645±36.1	183±29.4	16	614±13.8	188±15.7
1994	10	612±27.4	160±10	10	621±12.2	183±15.4
1995	3	643	213	20	613±10.7	211±13.8
1996	11	698±21.3	243±25.7	15	642±15.4	225±22.6
1997	9	632±32.0	169±30.2	11	615±21.4	176±19.1

year period. In each sample males are larger than females; for the combined samples they average 8% longer (SVL) and 12% heavier. In these samples 500 mm SVL was arbitrarily considered the minimum adult length in both sexes. The variance for males is greater than that for females since they grow to be larger. Both length and weight changed markedly from year to year; in the "best" years weight in both sexes was about twice as great as in the "worst" years. Males averaged about 18% longer in the best year, compared with the worst, and for females the corresponding figure was 13%.

At the start of the study in 1949 and 1950 sizes were small, but with the successional changes that resulted from removal of livestock, luxuriant annual crops of herbaceous vegetation provided a surplus of food and shelter for small mammal prey (*Microtus* and *Sigmodon*) and they underwent a population explosion. From 1951 through 1955 the snakes were thriving, with rapid increase in numbers, and attainment of relatively large size. By 1956 succession had entered a new phase, with woody vegetation encroaching and numbers of small mammals much reduced. As a result of the

curtailed food supply copperheads became scarcer and no longer attained the sizes characteristic of the early 1950s. Suboptimum habitat, low densities, and relatively small adult size characterized the 1960s and 1970s. By the mid-1980s NESA, recently acquired by the University and subjected to management practices with formerly cultivated fields and pastures producing abundant crops of herbaceous vegetation, resembled the early successional stages of those on FNHR 35 years earlier — higher densities of small mammals and thriving copperhead populations.

Variance in weight and SVL was increased by differences in seasonal distribution of the annual samples. Some samples were mainly from spring whereas in others summer and fall were well represented. The great gain in weight experienced by gravid females during the course of the summer and their weight loss when young were born caused considerable fluctuation in the weight ratios between the sexes.

The largest female captured (on 25 May 1991; BSA) had SVL of 825 mm and weighed 540 g (gravid). The largest male also on BSA, was 960 mm and weighed 530 g on 11 July 1994.

Spatial Relationships

Table 3 shows movements (distances between successive capture points) of individually marked copperheads of various categories. Time elapsed between successive captures ranged from a few days to many years. The first two columns show movements of adult males and females in summer habitat, presumably within their normal ranges. In both sexes relatively short movements are most numerous and are fairly evenly distributed up to 150 m, then they taper off abruptly, but on occasion much longer movements occur — up to 500 m. This pattern suggests that activity ranges normally consist of areas up to 150 m in diameter but that snakes occasionally make longer exploratory or wandering movements beyond their activity range.

The occasional long movements increase the average substantially; an estimate of activity range size probably should include only those movements concentrated in the range 0 to 150 m.

In this concentrated range the average distance for male movement is 70.3 ± 6.1 m, and for females 77.5±7.5 m. Assuming that ranges tend toward circular shape, and that movements within them are random and are equivalent to an activity range radius, a mean range of 1.63 ha for males (N=43), and 1.85 ha for females (N=43) are calculated (πr^2).

In an earlier discussion of copperhead movements comparing mobility in the sexes, I noted that male

TABLE 3. Distances Travelled by Individually Marked Copperheads

Meters	Within Summer Ranges					Between Summer Range & Hibernation Outcrops		At Hibernation Outcrops	
	Adult Male	Adult Female	1st Year	2nd Year	3rd Year	Adult Male	Adult Female	Adult Male	Adult Female
0–10	4	6	1	1	1	—	—	12	10
11–20	1	1	2	—	2	—	1	7	4
21–30	3	—	—	—	3	1	1	11	8
31–40	3	2	—	1	1	2	1	7	2
41–50	4	4	4	2	—	—	1	7	6
51–60	3	1	—	—	2	—	1	2	4
61–70	4	6	1	2	1	1	1	7	2
71–80	3	4	—	1	—	—	1	—	1
81–90	5	0	1	—	2	—	—	—	2
91–100	1	5	—	—	1	1	—	3	4
101–120	5	3	—	1	—	1	1	3	1
121–140	5	8	—	—	1	—	—	4	2
141–160	3	3	2	1	2	1	1	1	—
161–180	—	2	—	—	—	—	—	—	—
181–200	2	1	1	—	—	—	—	—	1
201–220	2	—	1	1	1	5	—	2	—
221–240	—	1	2	2	1	3	—	1	—
241–260	4	1	1	—	—	—	—	—	1
261–280	—	—	—	—	—	1	—	1	—
281–300	2	1	—	—	3	1	—	—	—
301–350	2	2	1	5	3	1	—	—	—
351–400	1	—	4	—	—	1	—	—	—
401–450	1	1	2	—	1	3	—	1	—
451–500	—	1	—	1	—	—	—	1	—
>500	—	—	4	1	2	9	7	—	1

ranges averaged substantially larger than those of females (Fitch 1960). However, that statement was based on data which included the records of many gravid females associated with other females at birthing dens. For these individuals day-to-day movements were short consisting chiefly of thermoregulatory shifts to or from the shelter of the den or in proximity to it. Inclusion of these short movements resulted in a low mean for female movements. For the present reappraisal, records of the females associated with dens were omitted from the calculations. Activity ranges of about the same size for males and females are indicated.

Also, in Table 3 immatures of three size groups corresponding approximately with first-, second-, and third-year young are compared with adults in their movements. These young show a higher proportion of relatively long movements, and obviously are more inclined to wander than adults. First-year young, especially, made several movements as far as 1 km, and showed little or no tendency to stay within a small familiar area identifiable as an activity range. Partly grown young also made several long movements and were more inclined to wander than adults but less inclined to do so than first-year young.

Many adults were captured both in fields assumed to represent their summer ranges, and at hilltop rock outcrops where presumably they had come to hibernate; the intervening distances representing seasonal

shifts between summer ranges and hibernacula. These seasonal shifts varied from only a few meters to well over a kilometer in different individuals. The mean shift for females (209 m) was substantially shorter than the mean for males (369 m).

Copperheads living on the upland cuesta often have ranges that include hilltop limestone outcrops or are adjacent to them, and these snakes have to do little travelling to reach their hibernacula. Others living in the lowlands need to leave their summer ranges and climb wooded slopes to reach the limestone outcrops.

In many instances an individual was caught repeatedly at the same hibernation outcrop; in some cases a snake was caught at approximately the same date and location in several successive years, but the exact site of the hibernaculum was not known. A snake was rarely recaptured at a hibernation outcrop different from the one of its previous capture(s). After travelling to an outcrop in fall, a snake may spend 2 weeks or more exploring the vicinity before retiring for the winter. Recorded male movements at the outcrop (N=75), averaged approximately 100 m, and female movements (N=48) averaged 65.5 m.

Copperheads that were tracked from day to day while carrying radio transmitters were usually found in tight coils on the soil surface, but concealed in sites well situated for ambushing prey. Most day-to-day move-

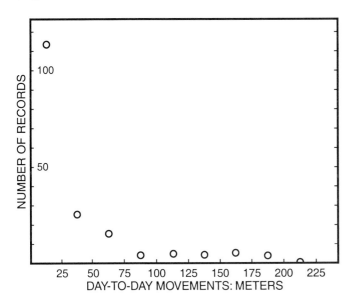

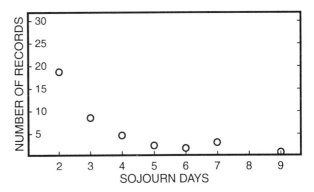

Figure 9. Numbers of records of day-to-day movements of different lengths in adult copperheads carrying radio transmitters. Usually the snake moved only a few meters or did not move at all from one day to the next.

Figure 10. Numbers of sojourns (stopovers from 2 to 9 days duration at specific locations) recorded in adult copperheads carrying radio transmitters.

ments were short—less than 5 m (Figure 9). Whether sites were chosen with reference to actual runways of prey, detected by olfaction, is unknown. On the few occasions when the snakes were found undisturbed but in the act of moving from one resting site to another, they progressed slowly with the head close to the substrate moving back and forth in an arc and the tongue constantly testing, perhaps for prey odor. On 27 (11.2%) of 241 occasions when copperheads were located by radiotelemetry (excluding females at birthing dens), they were not seen; either they were underground or hidden beneath a mat of surface vegetation.

As sit-and-wait predators copperheads were found to spend most of their time lying motionless at potential ambush sites and relatively little time in any sort of activity. Often on successive days a snake was found to be still in the same place and in what seemed to be exactly the same position. Such a sojourn might last for several days, but 82 of 117 sojourns did not last more than one day. Of 37 sojourns that lasted more than one day 18 were 2-day, 8 were 3-day, 4 were 4-day, 2 were 5-day, 1 was 6-day, 3 were 7-day, 1 was 9-day, and 1 was 14-day.

Usually an individual snake was checked at approximately the same time each day, and a 2-day sojourn meant that it spent at least 24 hours (and up to 48 hours) at a given spot. Likewise, a 3-day sojourn indicated an occupancy of 48 to 72 hours. For 119 sojourns the mean was 1.7 days (Figure 10).

Most shifts between sojourns were short; 43% were less than a meter, but with a mean of 15.7 m and a

maximum of 22.9 m. For 18 radio-equipped copperheads (not including those in female aggregations) that were recorded 241 times, 66% of the records were in fields and 34% were in forests. However, the fields had brush clumps and young trees, and none of the snakes was more than a few meters from some type of woody vegetation or from dense concealing cover. Several of those trailed had a tendency to stay at or near the line of contact between trees and grassland. Of the 12 snakes followed the longest, 8 stayed in fields throughout the time of surveillance (one for 38 days), while 4 were found in both field and forest (three of them were found mostly in forest).

In autumn when copperheads leave the areas of their summer activities and travel to hilltop outcrops of the Oread Limestone in search of hibernacula, they favor sites where the outcrop is prominent with deep fissures and the exposure is mainly southward.

Snakes that have reached the limestone outcrop follow along its lower edge searching for deep crevices that might serve as hibernacula. There are no large aggregations, and many hibernate solitarily. On FNHR there are probably hundreds of hibernacula that are used by copperheads, distributed linearly along several kilometers of limestone outcrops on both the Plattsmouth member at the 317 m contour, and the Toronto member some 6 m below it. A high proportion of the total of copperhead records in my study were obtained by intercepting such hibernation-bound snakes with wire funnel traps placed along the limestone face. Activity is most concentrated about mid-October, and in some years captures have continued through mid-November. Two snakes that were equipped for radiotelemetry were trailed into their hibernacula. A male released at its capture point on 6 October moved 21 m in 45 minutes to a deep hibernaculum and did not reemerge. A female trapped at an outcrop and released on 15 October remained at the same spot for 4 days, then shifted 3.5 m and was located deeply buried

TABLE 4. Distances (m) Traveled Day to Day by Copperheads Monitored by Radiotelemetry

	N	0	1–2	3–4	5–6	7–8	9–10	11–12	13–14	15–16	17–18	19–20	21–22	23–24	≥25
Males	140	41.4	15.0	7.1	7.1	2.8	3.7	3.7	2.1	2.8	2.1	1.4	3.6	–	6.4
Females	187	41.7	14.4	10.2	5.3	5.9	2.1	2.1	1.0	1.6	.5	2.1	1.6	.5	7.5
Combined	327	41.6	14.7	8.9	6.1	4.6	3.4	4.3	1.5	2.1	1.2	1.8	2.5	.3	7.1

beneath an accumulation of dry leaves. Over a 2-week period she made shifts of 3.5, 6, and 6 m, and by 7 November had finally reached a deep hibernaculum where she spent the winter. Another female released with a transmitter in a bottomland field on 6 October, made successive daily movements of 58 and 70 m northeast to the edge of woodland, stopped there for 5 days, then continued northeast up a wooded slope to a southwestern exposure of the Oread Limestone, and on 14 October had entered a deep fissure concealed by a thick layer of dry leaves. She spent the next 3 days there but by 7 November had shifted 11 m to another deep fissure where she hibernated.

Most copperheads that were caught in live traps were alone; 92.7% of total captures were singles. Occasionally, two or more might be caught in the same trap, and obviously the prospects of this happening purely by chance were remote. Probably in most instances double or multiple captures resulted from snakes following scent trails. There is little social interaction between individuals, but trailing may occur primarily to bring the sexes together for mating, secondarily to bring together small aggregations at hibernacula or to bring together small aggregations of females in late pregnancy. On 138 occasions traps were found to have caught more than one copperhead; there were 108 cases of double, 25 cases of triple, 4 had four each and 1 had five. In 59 instances traps contained snakes that could be interpreted as pairs—an adult male and female; in seven of these cases there were two adult males with the female, in another case three males and the female, and in still another four males and the female. In three instances the combination was a male and two females. In two other instances there was a pair accompanied by an immature. Pair captures, like other plural captures, occurred mostly in October and May; 54.6% of all plural captures were in October. Next to pair captures, those with two or more adult males were most frequent with a total of 20; 15 in October, 3 in September, and 2 in May. Adult females were caught together in eight cases: two in June, one in July, two in September, two in October, and one

in November. First-year young were caught together and/or with older young on 10 occasions (once each in June, September, and November with all others in October). One- and 2-year-olds were caught with each other on 14 occasions, and with adults on 19 occasions, mostly in October.

Records of the copperheads (8 males and 10 non-gravid females) monitored by radiotelemetry on their summer ranges are summarized in Tables 4 and 5. Movements were sporadic and unpredictable. Often a snake stayed at the same place for a day or more (up to 14 days), but once it left a spot it rarely returned and tended to wander indefinitely. Grassland (70%) was favored over woodland, but with a tendency to follow along the line of contact between them. Day-to-day movements were usually shorter than 5 m, but occasionally much longer movements up to 146 m were made. Males were somewhat more vagile than females, and made the three longest movements. On many occasions the snakes located were not actually seen, as effort was made to avoid disturbance that might alter behavior, because they were usually sheltered in dense concealing vegetation. The snakes that were seen were usually coiled in ambush positions, which sometimes were maintained for days at a time with no discernible shift. Few were found with their bodies extended, and even fewer were actually moving; 6.9% were underground or beneath objects.

In 1966 and 1967, 12 gravid females were equipped for radiotelemetry, and their associations with other females and dens were observed. One of these females monitored in an upland grassy field could not be found on 15 July, and when relocated on 18 July was found to have made an unusually long shift of approximately 100 m, and joined an aggregation in a den in the south-facing limestone outcrop of an old quarry site. She was recorded there every day until 4 August. Attachment to a denning aggregation was less consistent in some others. One from a denning aggregation was monitored daily from 6 August to 5 September and she shifted 17

TABLE 5. Habitats, Postures, and Activities of Copperheads Monitored by Radiotelemetry

	N		Habitat		Posture & Activity				
	Individuals	Records	%Fields	%Woods	%Not Seen	%Coiled	%Extended	%Moving	%Underground
Males	8	75	66	34	32	48	4.7	2.7	2.7
Females	10	98	73	27	37.7	42.8	6.1	3.0	10.1
Combined	18	173	70.1	29.9	36.3	45.0	9.8	2.9	6.9

times during that month. She visited a crevice 9.1 m ESE of the main den seven times, a third site 2.4 m east four times, and the main den six times. It is not definitely known whether the second and third sites that she returned to were used by other females. A female trailed at the south end of a hilltop field in late June 1967, moved to the hilltop outcrop and visited the 1966 den site on 28 June, and after moving away, returned there briefly on 29 June. At this relatively early date the den was probably not being used by other females. Still another female captured from a denning aggregation in early September was held in confinement until birth of her litter, then released with her young, and she was equipped with a transmitter for radiotelemetry. She was recorded at the den on each of the next 12 days. On 15 and 16 September she was lying at the entrance in contact with, or adjacent to, neonates which may have been her own or from different mothers.

In northeastern Kansas birthing dens are typically at hilltop limestone outcrops with south-facing exposures, at sites similar or identical to those used for hibernacula. One aggregation was found in a hilltop field beneath a strip of corrugated metal. Another was found at a rock fill below a pond. For several years in succession, the late Dr. Robert Mengel had aggregations beside his house on a north-facing wooded slope in the northwestern outskirts of Lawrence, 10 km west-southwest of FNHR. The snakes had a retreat in a hole beneath the concrete slab of a sidewalk. When emerged they could be observed at eye level at distances of less than a meter through a basement window. This den was used for at least 3 successive years, although the females found there were captured and removed from time to time. On various occasions lone females have been found with their newborn litters or obviously near parturition; evidently a substantial proportion of them do not join aggregations to give birth.

Kinds of Prey

In my earlier study of copperhead ecology (Fitch, 1960) I recorded 512 prey items from FNHR and adjoining areas; of these 450 were identified from scats whereas 62 were palped from stomachs. Comparison of trends for the scat and stomach items showed that they were similar for most kinds of prey. However, the stomach items are considered to be more useful because identifications from scats, based on dissociated parts such as wads of fur or fragments of chitin do not show the numbers of prey animals eaten. The prey sample presented here consists entirely of stomach items including the original 62 from the 1950s and 233 collected subsequently.

The total of 295 food items palpated from copperhead stomachs included: 107 *Microtus ochrogaster,* 46 *Peromyscus leucopus,* 16 *Blarina hylophaga,* 14 *Cryptotis parva,* 10 *Zapus hudsonius,* 5 "mice" unspecified, 4 *Synaptomys cooperi,* 3 *Sigmodon hispidus,* 3 *Microtus pinetorum,* 3 *Reithrodontomys megalotis,* 1 *Peromyscus maniculatus,* 1 *Mus musculus,* 16 *Diadophis punctatus,* 8 *Ophisaurus attenuatus,* 6 *Eumeces fasciatus,* 2 *E. obsoletus,* 5 *Carphophis vermis,* 1 *Storeria dekayi,* 1 *Cnemidophorus sexlineatus,* 1 *Coluber constrictor,* 10 *Rana blairi,* 3 *Gastrophryne olivacea,* 1 *Rana catesbeiana,* 1 *Pseudacris triseriata,* 12 *Magicicada septemdecin,* 7 *Tibicen pruinosa,* and 8 moth larvae. Most of the animals eaten were adults; 10 of the voles were immature, as were all 11 of the frogs (*Rana blairi* and *R. catesbeiana*). Lepidopterans were taken only as larvae and cicadas only as nymphs. Two of the five-lined skinks and the racer were juveniles.

Almost all items were taken singly, but immature voles that seemed to be littermates were found in combinations of 5, 4, 4 and 2 in different stomachs, and one snake contained 2 adults. Seventeen-year cicadas also were exceptions to the usual finding of one prey item per snake; there were seven in one stomach and two in another.

In terms of biomass the composite prey sample was estimated as 58.3% *Microtus ochrogaster,* 15.6% *Peromyscus leucopus,* and *P. maniculatus,* 4.4% *Ophisaurus attenuatus,* 3.9% *Blarina hylophaga,* 2.7% *Zapus hudsonius,* 2.7% *Sigmodon hispidus,* 2.2% *Synaptomys cooperi* 2.1% *Rana blairi* and *R. catesbeiana,* 1.6% *Microtus pinetorum,* 1.3% *Cryptotis parva,* 1.2% *Diadophis punctatus,* and less than 1% apiece for 16 other prey species.

During the 50 consecutive years of field studies on FNHR great changes in habitats overall and in the distribution and abundance of nearly every plant and animal species were observed. It was anticipated that ecological succession with changing availability of prey species might result in marked changes in the food habits of resident predators such as the copperhead. To test this idea 295 food records from FNHR and adjacent areas were divided by decades, 1950s, '60s, '70s, '80s and '90s (Table 6).

Several of the prey species recorded in the food during the early years of fieldwork disappeared from FNHR as succession proceeded, and hence were absent from the diet during the latter decades of fieldwork—*Gastrophryne olivacea, Cnemidophorus sexlineatus, Sigmodon hispidus,* and *Synaptomys cooperi,* but these were not the chief food species. In each decade the prairie vole and white-footed mouse combined comprised approximately half of the items taken, with the vole as a grassland inhabitant dominating in the first

TABLE 6. Food of Copperheads Over Five Decades Showing Changing Percentages

Kinds of Prey	N	Numbers & Percentages of Decade's Prey Items				
		1950s	1960s	1970s	1980s	1990s
Microtus ochrogaster	107	14(19.2%)	18(31.9%)	18(32.2%)	23(39.8%)	34(66.6%)
Peromyscus leucopus	46	13(17.8%)	11(19.3%)	9(16.0%)	11(19.1%)	2(3.8%)
Cicada (*Tibicen, Magicicada*)	21	3(4.1%)	10(17.5%)	5(9.0%)	1(1.7%)	2(3.8%)
Blarina hylophaga	16	8(11.0%)	2(3.5%)	1(1.8%)	4(6.9%)	1(2.0%)
Diadophis punctatus	16	5(7.0%)	4(7.0%)	4(7.1%)	2(3.4%)	1(2.0%)
Cryptotis parva	14	3(4.1%)	2(3.5%)	3(5.4%)	5(8.6%)	1(2.0%)
Frog (*Rana blairi* and *R. catesbeiana*)	11	1(1.4%)	4(7.0%)	5(9.0%)	—	1(2.0%)
Zapus hudsonius	10	3(4.1%)	—	2(3.5%)	4(6.9%)	1(2.0%)
Ophisaurus attenuatus	8	2(2.8%)	1(1.8%)	1(1.8%)	2(3.4%)	2(3.8%)
moth larva	7	—	2(3.5%)	4(7.3%)	1(1.7%)	—
Eumeces fasciatus	6	3(4.1%)	—	—	2(3.4%)	1(2.0%)
"Mice" and *Mus musculus*	5	2(2.8%)	—	1(1.8%)	1(1.7%)	1(2.0%)
Carphophis vermis	5	3(4.1%)	1(1.8%)	1(1.8%)	—	—
Synaptomys cooperi	4	2(2.8%)	—	—	1(1.7%)	1(2.0%)
Sigmodon hispidus	3	2(2.8%)	—	—	1(1.7%)	—
Microtus pinetorum	3	1(1.3%)	—	2(3.6%)	—	—
Reithrodontomys megalotis	3	1(1.3%)	2(3.5%)	—	—	—
Gastrophryne olivacea	3	3(4.1%)	—	—	—	—
Eumeces obsoletus	2	1(1.3)	—	—	—	—
Coluber constrictor	1	1(1.3%)	—	—	—	1(2.0%)
Cnemidophorus sexlineatus	1	1(1.3%)	—	—	—	—
Pseudacris triseriata	1	1(1.3%)	—	—	—	—
Storeria dekayi	1	—	—	—	—	1(2.0%)
Peromyscus maniculatus	1	—	—	—	—	1(2.0%)

TABLE 7. Frequency of Different Prey Types in Copperheads, According to Age-Size and Sex of Snake

	Adult Male		Adult Female		2nd-Year Young		1st-Year Young		Combined	
	N	%	N	%	N	%	N	%	N	%
Mammal										
Microtus ochrogaster	54	55.1	36	36.7	17	27.0	—	—	107	36.3
Peromyscus	12	12.2	24	24.5	10	15.9	1	3.0	47	16.0
Blarina	3	3.1	6	6.1	3	4.5	4	11.0	16	5.7
Cryptotis	2	2.1	2	2.0	6	9.5	4	11.0	14	4.7
Zapus	3	3.1	4	4.1	2	3.3	1	3.0	10	3.3
Sigmodon	2	2.1	1	1.0	—	—	—	—	3	1.0
Reithrodontomys	1	1.0	1	1.0	1	1.6	—	—	3	1.0
"mice"	3	2.1	1	1.0	1	1.6	—	—	5	1.7
Synaptomys	2	2.1	—	—	2	3.3	—	—	4	0.9
Microtus pinetorum	1	1.0	1	1.0	1	1.6	—	—	3	1.0
Combined mammals	83	83.9	76	77.4	43	69.3	10	28.0	212	71.6
Reptile										
Diadophis	3	3.1	3	3.1	2	13.3	8	22.0	16	5.4
Ophisaurus	4	4.1	3	3.1	—	—	1	3.0	8	2.7
Eumeces fasciatus	—	—	1	1.0	1	1.6	4	11.0	6	2.0
Eumeces obsoletus	1	1.0	1	1.0	—	—	—	—	2	0.7
Storeria dekayi	—	—	—	—	1	1.6	—	—	1	0.3
Carphophis	—	—	—	—	2.0	3.3	3	8.0	5	1.7
Coluber	—	—	—	—	1	1.6	—	—	1	0.3
Cnemidophorus	—	—	—	—	1	1.6	—	—	1	.3
Combined reptiles	8	8.2	8	8.2	8	13.0	16	44.0	40	13.4
Amphibian										
Rana	3	3.1	2	2.0	5	7.8	1	3.0	11	3.7
Pseudacris	—	—	—	—	—	—	1	3.0	1	.3
Gastrophryne	—	—	—	—	—	—	3	8.0	3	1.0
Combined amphibians	3	3.1	2	2.0	5	7.8	5	14.0	15	5.0
Insect										
Cicada	3	3.1	10	10.2	2	3.3	5	14.0	20	6.7
Moth larva	1	1.0	2	2.0	5	7.8	—	—	8	2.7
Combined insects	4	4.1	12	12.2	7	11.1	5	14.0	28	9.4

three samples, but the mouse as a woodland inhabitant, becoming the most frequent prey in the 1980s. Actually, the trends of prey taken were remarkably similar in all four decades of the study. The copperhead seems to respond to successional changes in the habitat by adjusting its numbers and by withdrawing to those situations within the habitat mosaic that retain essential resources.

In contrast, copperheads of different age classes showed striking differences in the composition of their food (Table 7; Figure 11). For first-year young the food consisted of the small secretive snakes (*Diadophis* and *Carphophis*), small, smooth-skinned subterranean anurans (*Gastrophryne, Pseudacris*), shrews (*Cryptotis, Blarina*), five-lined skinks, and cicada nymphs. All of these were represented in the prey of adults, but they made up only a small percentage of it. For second-year young, mice, shrews, and voles all were important; small snakes, skinks, frogs, and cicadas also were eaten, but were less important than in first-year young. In third-year young, intermediate in size between neonates and adults, the food composition was similar to that of adults, with voles and mice making up most of the food, but leopard frogs were 7.9% and one snake (racer) was eaten that was larger than any of the snakes taken by juveniles. For adults the vole *Microtus ochrogaster* made up approximately two-thirds of the

total with other small rodents making up about half of the remainder and shrews, lizards, small snakes, leopard frogs, cicadas, and moth larvae each making up only very small percentages. Judging from the wide variety of prey species recorded here (with 10 species of mammals, 4 of lizards, 4 of frogs, and 4 of snakes), copperheads in general, take whatever kinds of small vertebrates are available to them, but they undoubtedly avoid toads (*Bufo* sp.) because of their poisonous dermal secretions. Although there were no birds in my sample, captives fed upon them readily, and other investigators have found birds in the diet. In contrast, copperheads were highly selective in their feeding on invertebrates, limiting themselves to two kinds of cicadas (nymphs) and several kinds of large, smooth-skinned moth larvae.

Adult males and females were essentially similar in their diets, but males took a higher proportion of voles (53.5% vs. 36.8%), and took a lower proportion of white-footed mice (11.6% vs. 23.5%), weighing on the average about 18 g. Voles averaging about 30 g are easily swallowed by adult male copperheads, but are too large for some females. Also, males tend to disperse farther and to invade grassland habitat where voles occur, whereas females tend to remain in woodland where white-footed mice occur.

In a study carried on at the Catoosa Wildlife Management Study Area of the Cumberland Plateau in central Tennessee, Garton and Dimmick (1969) indicated differences between the sexes in prey taken. Adult males dispersed from woodland hibernacula to open fields and preyed mainly on voles (especially *Microtus ochrogaster*) whereas adult females tended to remain in the woodland, fed mainly on lepidopteran larvae such as those of *Citheronia regalis* and *Automeris io,* but also on white-footed mice (*Peromyscus*), lizards, and shrews. No anuran prey were recorded in this Tennessee study. In my earlier study (Fitch, 1960) I summarized literature records from various parts of the range. Microtines, especially *Microtus ochrogaster* and *M. pennsylvanicus* are favorite prey (*M. pinetorum, Synaptomys cooperi,* and *Clethrionomys gapperi* are also commonly taken). Other than microtines *Peromyscus leucopus, Blarina hylophaga, Cryptotis parva,* and *Zapus hudsonius* are among the mammals most often taken. In the Appalachian region salamanders (*Plethodon* sp. and *Pseudotriton*) are eaten. In Pennsylvania young opossums, squirrels, and chipmunks have been found in stomachs. Unusual items include a hummingbird (*Archilochus colubris,* Virginia), moles (*Condylura cristata,* and *Parascalops breweri,* Virginia), spiders (Maryland and Oklahoma), and a mantis (*Stagomantis,* Georgia). Seemingly the only invertebrates regularly taken are cicadas of several genera, both nymphs and newly emerged adults, and larvae of

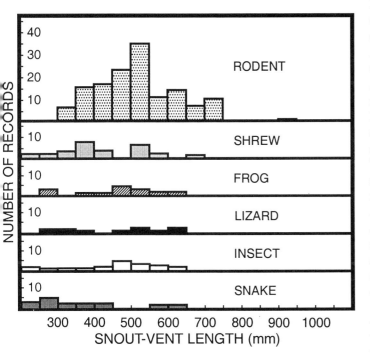

Figure 11. Numbers of records of different types of prey animals eaten by copperheads of different sizes. Small snakes (*Diadophis, Carphophis*) are especially important in the food of first-year young, and rodents are taken mainly by adults. Frogs, lizards, and insects are taken by copperheads of all sizes.

large moths, *Saturnidae, Sphingidae, Citheroniidae,* and *Ceratocampidae.*

Lung Fluke Infestations

Many of the live copperheads examined were infested with lung flukes (Plagiorchidae). These parasites live and feed in the lungs of the ophidian host; their reproduction involves migrating up the trachea into the buccal cavity where oviposition occurs. Eggs laid in the snake's mouth pass through the digestive tract and are voided with the feces, but development can occur only in an aquatic environment. In a snake's mouth the flukes are seen as minute, dark, leechlike bodies, either alone or in clusters. When the snake's feces are deposited in wet places, microscopic, active ciliated larvae (*miracidia*) hatch, but to develop further the miracidium must find an aquatic snail of the host species. The parasite then bores into the tissues of the snail, transforms and grows, and eventually reproduces asexually by releasing large numbers of redia into the water. These, in turn, must find the right species of tadpole to develop further, and can attain the adult stage only if, after its metamorphosis, the infested frog is eaten by the host species of snake.

Of 504 copperheads checked for flukes, 177 (35.2%) had the parasites in their mouths; others may have been infested with flukes that were out of sight in their lungs. Unlike the plagiorchids of some other local snakes, those of the copperhead were not sharply limited seasonally. The percentage of observed infestation varied seasonally as follows: May 31.4% (N=83), June 21.4% (N=103), July 29.2% (N=89), August 18.2% (N=33), September 34.6% (N=52), and October 23.4% (N=94). Usually there were several flukes; a few snakes had many, 13 each had only one, and this group was represented in each month that the snakes were active.

Copperheads of different age-size classes differed somewhat in their incidence of recorded infestation as follows: first-year 5.4% (N=39), second-year 25.8% (N=89), third-year 23.2% (N=108), fourth-year 41.3% (N=75), fifth-year 32.0% (N=78), sixth-year 27.2% (N=33), seventh-year 33.3% (N=12), eighth-year or older 38.0% (N=21). These figures suggest that infestations are usually not acquired until the second year, and that they are variable in adults, not tending to build up in relatively old snakes. Details of the parasites' life history remain unknown. *Rana blairi* is the most probable frog host since it occurred twice as often as all other anurans combined in the copperhead's food. Since the copperhead does not ordinarily frequent wet places, a major hurdle for the fluke must be making its way from snake defecation sites to the aquatic snail habitat.

Reproduction

Mating of the copperhead has been described in detail, both under natural conditions and in the laboratory (Fitch 1960; Duvall et al., 1993). There are two distinct periods when mating occurs: late summer-early fall, and spring, typically in May at about the time of ovulation. Females may mate with more than one male and some litters have multiple paternity. The male initiates courtship by nudging the female's side with his snout, and then mounting and pressing his chin against the female's neck. The female may respond negatively to the male's nudging by bumping him vigorously with a lateral coil. Also, females sometimes respond with a head-lifting display similar to the challenge display of rival males. This aggressive action seemed to involve female choice as it was effective in discouraging presumably less fit males that had lost bouts with other males, and, as a result, were disinclined to behave aggressively, even toward smaller opponents (Duvall et al., 1993).

Like some other pit vipers, female copperheads in late gestation are known to aggregate, and groups of 2 to 11 have been reported (Allen, 1868; Finneran, 1953; Fitch, 1960; Gloyd, 1934). There is little or no feeding in the weeks before young are born, and aggregation may confer some degree of security; a predator attacking a female would probably be at risk from the bites of others in the immediate vicinity disturbed by the commotion. Females weighed down by their fetuses are relatively slow and clumsy in escaping when danger threatens. The female aggregations are always associated with "dens", holes or crevices where the snakes can escape danger or avoid extremes of weather. When temperature and humidity are favorable, the snakes emerge and may be found lying in contact with each other or even piled up at the den's entrance. They also may settle and coil at separate spots within an area of several square meters.

Table 8 shows the incidence of fecundity in 186 female copperheads on the basis of palpation and weight (whether above or below average for their length). Of the 186 snakes, 52% were found to be gravid. Thus it

TABLE 8. Fecundity Determined by Palpation in 186 Female Copperheads 1963–1978

Probable Age in Years (on Basis of SVL)	Number Gravid	Number Not Gravid	Mean Litter Size in Fecund Females
3+	17(41.5%)	24	4.75 (3–6)
4+	37(55.1%)	30	5.00 (3–8)
5+	28(45.2%)	23	5.50 (4–10)
6+	10(62.1%)	6	6.25 (5–7)
7+	1	5	
8+	3(75.0%)	1	
10 and over	1		

seems that approximately half are reproductive each year, with essentially a biennial cycle. Less than half of females reach sexual maturity by their third year in time to give birth as 3-year-olds. Those that do presumably remain unproductive the following year, while the majority (55%) give birth for the first time as 4-year-olds. Litter size increases with age and size of female. Also there seems to be a tendency for large and old females to produce more often than biennially. However, only one of six of the presumed 7-year olds was gravid.

For 75 female copperheads captured late in pregnancy, parturition dates in confinement ranged from 14 August, 1971 to 7 October, 1950, with a mean date of 9 September. Time of birth is affected by the annual weather cycle; early spring emergence may result in early birth dates, and persistently cloudy weather in spring and summer may reduce basking and delay birth. In 1950 and 1951 females captured early in pregnancy and confined through the summer, with no opportunity to bask, had their young weeks later than normal, in late October or even November.

"Relative clutch mass" determined from the weight loss in females at the time of parturition was 36.1%±1.6 of gravid weight, with much variance between individuals. In some the loss was as much as 50%.

Beginning in 1959 embryo counts were obtained by palpating females captured in late May, June, or July. Counts were obtained in each of 28 years and totalled 103. Counts ranged from three to thirteen and averaged 5.64, but five was by far the most frequent number. In each of 26 years gravid females (N=187) were retained in captivity until birth of their litters, and young totalled 946 with an average of 5.06 per litter. Five was the most frequent litter size with a range from 1 to 13 (Table 9). An average loss of 0.58 embryos during gestation is implied. Of the young born to captive females, 7% including entire litters of 7, 5, and 3 were stillborn, but usually there were only one (N=10) or two (N=6) casualties per litter. Occasionally in giving birth females expelled infertile eggs and these would have been counted as embryos in females palpated before parturition. A 10% loss between ovulation and birth is indicated.

The 946 young born in confinement ranged from 150 to 263 mm (SVL), but most were in the range of 200 to 240. Some of them were definitely stunted. In 1950 especially, females were captured early in the season and retained many weeks until they gave birth. Prolonged confinement, limiting opportunity to bask, or to feed normally, resulted in delayed births and stunted neonates. Females feed little or not at all during late pregnancy. About mid-July they abandon summer

TABLE 9. Reproduction in Copperheads

Year	Number of Young per Litter		N	Mean SVL of Neonates (mm)
1949	3.7		3	198.6
1950	4.8±0.38		15	195.2
1951	6.67	3–11	6	216.4
1953	5.4	4–7	5	223.0
1954	6.6±0.44	3–10	10	214.9
1957	4.3	3–6	6	248.6
1958	4.8	3–7	6	211.0
1959	4.0±0.23	3–5	11	209.8
1961	5.5±0.46	3–7	8	210.0
1964	4.8±0.47	2–6	11	214.5
1965	4.6±0.20	4–5	11	211.4
1966	4.4±0.29	3–6	9	211.6
1969	5.0±0.42	3–7	10	230.1
1970	4.3	3–5	4	223.0
1973	4.7	4–6	3	219.1
1974	5.8	4–7	4	222.8
1977	4.5±0.40	2–6	13	207.8
1978	5.2±0.31	4–6	6	226.9
1979	5.4±0.55	5–6	5	229.8
1985	4.9	4–7	6	223.5
1986	3.8	2–5	6	219.0
1987	5.9±0.55	5–8	9	
1988	4.5		6	
1990	5.6	4–6	3	237.6
1991	7.7±1.28	4–13	7	
1992	4.75±1.31	1–7	4	199.0

ranges and make their way back to shelters such as hilltop rock outcrops to gather in small groups awaiting birth of their young. The aggregations usually consist of 3 to 9 females. They gather in a mass beneath a flat rock or in a hole or crevice, and spend most of their time under shelter, but when surface conditions are favorable they may emerge and scatter over an area of several square meters.

In some instances captive females produced entire litters of stunted young, some or all of them dead, suggesting that the trauma of capture or captivity was injurious. However, many litters with seemingly normal and full-size young included a runt much smaller than the others and sometimes stillborn, and evidently such occurrences are frequent in nature. In adversity, such as food shortage preventing the development of normal litters, the strategy seems to be to decrease both the number of young and their size.

The ratio of neonate weight to weight of parturient female is unusually high in the copperhead, i.e., parental investment per offspring is higher than in most snakes. A gravid female copperhead is relatively secure from predation and accident. Because the species is a sit-and-wait predator, a heavy burden of embryos does not seriously interfere with securing prey during early pregnancy, and during late pregnancy females take little or no food. The potential to deliver a venomous bite doubtless deters predators, and the aggregations that form during late pregnancy must provide some mutual security. Activities of gravid females seem to be

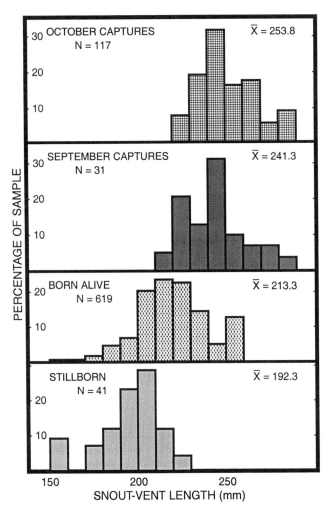

Figure 12. Sizes (SVL) of neonate copperheads. Undersized young often are stillborn. Surviving young undergo rapid growth in fall.

controlled chiefly by thermoregulation. They retreat into a den to avoid ambient temperatures that are often above and occasionally below their preferenda, or emerge to bask near the den entrance, maintaining a high body temperature to expedite development of their embryos. When captured, gravid females are relatively passive, with little of the violent twisting, jerking, and thrashing employed by others, especially adult males.

Growth, Sex and Age Ratios

For 145 young captured in fall, minimum SVL was 213 mm (September) and 217 mm (October), but 46.6% of the young born in confinement were shorter than 213 mm suggesting stunting because of confinement of the pregnant females (Figure 12). Under suboptimum conditions females usually bring their litters to term, but the neonates are undersized. Among 144 of the

litters born in captivity 84 had at least one young that was stunted (less than 213 mm SVL). In some litters all young were approximately the same size, with less than 1% variation, whereas in others the largest was up to 23% larger than the smallest. The mean difference between largest and smallest in a litter averaged approximately 7%, and it was not clearly correlated with size of female, number of young in litter, or any particular year. Presumably the undersized young were somewhat handicapped, and had shorter life expectancies than normal-size young. However, substantial numbers of them survived. Many of them were recaptured as adults. Each captive-born young released was force-fed a small chunk of raw meat beforehand, and probably this initial meal improved survival.

Birth dates of 98 litters ranged from 8 August to 31 October, but were concentrated in the period 4–27 September, with an average date of 12 September. Six of seven October birth dates were in 1950 when females were subjected to relatively long confinement, and probably free-living females rarely, if ever, retain their young so long.

Table 10 shows growth in the copperhead as revealed by the records of individuals marked and recaptured. It is evident that the sexes are approximately the same size at birth, and males are only slightly larger than females as 1-year-olds and 2-year-olds. At maturity males are substantially larger than their female counterparts; by age 6 they are more than 12% longer. The largest male (SVL 960 mm) was 16% longer than the longest female (825 mm). Many of the marked snakes recaptured as large adults were originally caught and marked when they were immature and small enough so that their ages could be estimated with accuracy. Aging the snakes is facilitated by the fact that births are limited to a brief period at the end of summer and early autumn, and there are discrete annual age classes.

The 378 neonates, and first- and second-year young included in Table 11 were unmarked young whose ages could be deduced from their sizes. For marked adults recaptured in spring or early summer, increments were added to their actual measurements to represent the additional growth they would have made if they had gained at the average rate of their age-group and were recaptured on 1 September. The small samples available for the older age classes show several discrepancies. Year-to-year gains are small in snakes that are more than 10 years old, and are obscured by individual differences. It is obvious that growth slows progressively with age. Table 12 represents an attempt to show size-age correlation more accurately than shown by the records which were the basis for Table 13. In the fall sample of Table 13 sex and age groups may be represented in their true proportions—in contrast to spring and summer samples,

TABLE 10. Growth and Survival in Marked Copperheads

Sex	Span of Records	SVL at First & Last Capture	Prob Age at First & Last Capture	No. of Captures	Remarks
♀	11/5/58–6/13/72	585–642	4–18	3	Attained maximum age without growing to be unusually large
♂	5/11/73–8/27/85	710–793	6–18	3	
♀	5/16/65–10/3/78	556–665*	4–17	2	Retaken as roadkill with part of body missing
♀	10/20/58–6/5/71	445–670	2–15	3	
♂	10/4/53–9/22/59	793–838	9–15	2	Already a large adult at first capture
♂	10/6/61–9/8/67	783–796	9–15	3	As above
♀	10/17/81–7/10/93	487–650	3–15	4	
♂	10/24/51–10/24/57	765–955	8–14	2	
♂	10/7/51–9/20/58	715–873	6–14	7	
♀	9/29/67–8/27/77	565–625	4–14	2	Growth relatively slow
♂	10/11/49–5/14/57	663–890	5–13	5	
♂	10/11/75–9/10/84	621–868	4–13	2	
♂	6/1/77–6/3/88	460–807	2–13	4	
♂	7/17/51–10/28/58	615–836	4–11		
♂	10/19/50–10/16/57	617–801	4–11	4	
♂	5/19/71–5/2/81	392–795	1–11	8	
♂	9/30/72–6/6/82	232–728	0–10	2	Born in captivity
♀	8/29/77–9/4/86	238–638	0–9	4	

*Estimated from tail length.

which are obviously biased because of behavioral differences.

When young are born, they disperse slowly and may remain associated for periods of days or even weeks. The normal sluggishness and low vagility delay dispersal, but also there seems to be a sibling bonding that holds such groups together. Often litters have been found still associated although abandoned by the mother. Presumably early dispersal would confer selective advantage in improving each neonate's chances of obtaining prey. On the other hand, collective security like that gained by aggregations of gravid females prevails also in litters of young as long as they stay together; a predator attacking one individual exposes itself to the venomous bites of others lying within striking range. Feeding is generally postponed until after the first ecdysis has occurred and abdominal yolk is used up. For example, on 14 August 1964 a female was released at her point of capture with her litter of six young recently born in confinement. On 18 September when the site was checked, two of the young were coiled in contact, partly in sunshine, beneath the edge of an overhanging rock. A third was in a similar position 0.5 m south. A fourth was coiled beneath a small, flat rock, and a fifth was coiled 3.1 m north. Thus after 35 days the group was still nearly intact, lacking one neonate and the mother.

Table 14 shows sizes of copperheads whose ages were known because they were recaptured after being marked early in life, or in the case of 1- and 2-year-olds, they comprised distinct size cohorts. The figures show relatively rapid growth in the first 2 years, slackening

TABLE 11. Age-Size Groups in Juvenile Copperheads

Time	N	Age (Months)	Mean SVL (mm)	Size Range
At birth	90	0	222.7±1.6	177–250
September	24	1	233.3±3.3	201–261
October	69	2	249.6±2.3	213–297
April	4	8	248.7±5.3	233–255
May	17	9	262.0±4.2	228–293
June	11	10	290.1±7.7	244–317
July	9	11	282.9±7.7	241–308
August	6	12	313.5±5.9	309–343
September	27	13	359.3±5.8	310–408
October	121	14	362.6±2.6	300–418

TABLE 12. Typical Sizes of Copperheads of Different Ages

Age in Years	Males (SVL, mm)	Females (SVL, mm)
1	320 (303–398)	320 (264–396)
2	460 (391–505)	440 (390–479)
3	550 (506–600)	510 (480–555)
4	625 (601–650)	573 (556–592)
5	675 (651–708)	610 (593–637)
6	715 (709–733)	640 (638–651)
7	748 (734–760)	660 (652–667)
8	770 (761–781)	675 (668–679)
9	790 (782–800)	685 (680–690)

TABLE 13. Composite (1949–1995) Fall Sample of Copperheads Divided According to Sex and Probable Age Cohort (on the basis of SVL)

	Males		Females		Total	
Age in Years	N	%	N	%	N	%
0 (Neonate Born in Lab)	336	24.3	241	24.5	577	24.4
Captured	116	8.4	77	7.8	193	8.2
1	137	9.9	112	11.4	249	10.3
2	187	13.5	116	11.8	303	12.8
3	163	11.8	130	13.2	296	12.5
4	150	10.8	114	11.7	264	11.2
5	109	7.9	105	10.7	214	9.1
6	68	4.9	31	3.1	99	4.2
7	29	2.3	25	2.5	54	2.3
8	19	1.4	11	1.1	30	1.3
9	17	1.3	13	1.3	30	1.3
10	13	1.0	3	0.3	16	0.7
11–20	34	2.5	6	0.6	40	1.7

TABLE 14. Sizes in Recaptured Copperheads of Approximately Known Ages

Age in Years	Male			Female		
	N	SVL (mm)		N	SVL (mm)	
0	49	222.0±2.14	(177–250)	41	223.6±2.40	(183–248)
1	17	324.9±13.4	(235–404)	20	334.0±13.2	(253–413)
2	23	460±5.0	(423–490)	16	456.6±4.5	(419–481)
3	15	527.1±4.54	(501–550)	10	510±4.89	(490–525)
4	19	611±7.1	(570–625)	5	534±7.3	(534–580)
5	17	658±12.0	(618–722)	10	584±9.1	(574–625)
6	11	677±8.8	(625–702)	11	604±7.9	(551–642)
7	11	702±11.9	(634–795)	9	623±10.0	(588–632)
8	5	734±28.4	(760–828)	8	650±11.2	(610–696)
9	3	784	(738–864)	4	680±29.5	(635–883)
10	11	830		5	657	(613–727)
11	4	809	(785–836)			
12	1	840				
13	1	807				
14	2	854	(840–868)	2	664	(625–700)
15				2	662	(653–670)
17				1	665	
18	1	793		1	642	

TABLE 15. Copperheads Recaptured During Decades of 1960s, 1970s, 1980s, and 1990s

Year	Span of Individual Records	Number of Calendar Years in Which Individual Was Captured	Captures per Individual	Total	Number within a Calendar Year
1	321	76	0	—	476*
2	102	212	1	—	495
3	57	27	2	241	110
4	37	6	3	48	15
5	31	3	4	20	7
6	14		5	5	2
7	22		6	5	
8	9		7	1	
9	10				
10	5				
11	4				
12	1				
13	2				
14	2				
15	—				
16	1				

*Indicates snakes' absence from the records in years in which they were believed to be present, because they were recorded in both earlier and later years.

after adolescence. At all ages males grow faster than females, and the differential is greatest after sexual maturity is attained. The oldest snakes recaptured were markedly smaller than the maximum, suggesting that the largest unmarked snakes were much older or else had experienced accelerated growth.

Table 11 shows growth of young copperheads from birth up to the time of second hibernation on the basis of the records of first-year young collected over the entire span of the study. Even with the combination of many year's data, summer samples are small leading to an irregular growth curve. In a year, from one September to the next, average gain in SVL was 126 mm, indicating an average gain of about 18 mm per month for a typical juvenile during the 7-month growing season. In fall at the end of the growing season, there is the possibility of size overlap between the most retarded second-year young, and the most accelerated first-year young, 2 to 3 months old and approximately 300 mm SVL.

Summer trapping in areas away from hilltop, limestone outcrops seldom yielded first-year copperheads (1.5%); second-year young also were relatively scarce (6.6%), and third-year young (11.9%) were thought to be underrepresented. Adult females also were not adequately represented since those that are gravid travel back to the outcrops to aggregate for several weeks before young are born. These factors no doubt biased the figures used for my previous estimate of population composition (Fitch, 1960).

In the fall sample, believed to be relatively free from behavioral bias, the 2365 snakes had 41.5% females. Only the oldest age groups deviated significantly from this ratio. In the 170 snakes believed to be 7 years or older, (on the basis of the age-size correlation shown in

Table 12) females were reduced to 34.2%. The fall sample included 577 neonates from females briefly held in confinement, and in these litters the sex ratio was 41.8% females to 58.2% males; for another 223 neonates captured at or near birthing sites the female: male ratio was 40%:60%.

Table 15 shows figures for copperheads that were marked and recaptured over a 30-year period. It shows that most were captured few times (those caught only once are not included), that individual records often spanned many years (up to 16), but often individual snakes were missing from some of the intervening years. In contrast to more active species—racers, garter snakes, and kingsnakes—copperheads were never caught many times even though their records spanned many years; 8 captures was the maximum, and most of those recaptured were taken only 2 or 3 times. Table 16 compares the sexes in frequency of capture and time spans of records. In general they are remarkably similar. Individually females were captured a little more often than males and males were a little more likely to miss a year.

Table 17 compares age categories and sex ratios in two major samples of copperheads, one consisting of those trapped in fall along the hilltop rock outcrops where they come to hibernate and the other consisting of those obtained in summer, mainly in open fields away from the outcrops. The fall sample is nearly twice as large as that for summer, and it was assembled mainly in the early years of field work, mostly on FNHR, whereas the summer sample was mainly from later decades and included data from RET and NESA. In nearly all subsamples males outnumber females, and in the combined

TABLE 16.   Patterns of Recapture in 332 Individually Marked Copperheads 1966–1995

Percentages of Samples

Number	Captured 2 or More Times ♂	♀	Both	Year Span of Records ♂	♀	Both	Years Captured ♂	♀	Both	Captures per Year ♂	♀	Both	Years Missed ♂	♀	Both
1				2.6	9.2	6.5	23.6	24.2	23.9	79.4	78.6	79.0	38.8	33.8	36.0
2	75.9	73.0	74.3	41.4	26.4	33.8	64.0	64.6	64.3	17.7	17.3	17.5	25.8	16.9	21.0
3	16.1	14.3	15.2	20.7	15.9	18.2	8.7	8.5	8.6	2.3	2.5	2.4	12.9	16.9	15.0
4	4.0	7.1	5.5	9.5	12.1	10.9	1.9	2.0	1.9	0.3	1.2	0.8	9.7	8.5	10.1
5	1.7	1.3	1.5	6.9	9.1	8.1				0.3	0.3	0.3	9.7	12.7	11.3
6	0.6	1.3	0.9	5.3	6.0	5.6							1.6	2.8	2.3
7	0.6	1.9	1.2	6.9	5.3	6.0							1.6	5.6	3.8
8	1.1	1.9	1.9	2.6	4.5	3.6								1.4	
9				—	5.3	2.8									
10				2.6	1.1	1.6									
11				1.8	4.4	2.8									

TABLE 17.   Comparison of Sex and Age Ratios in Two Population Samples of Copperheads: from Hilltop Rock Outcrops in Fall and Fields in Summer, 1948 to 1995

Age Class	Fall Sample Male N	%	Female N	%	Combined N	%	Summer sample Male N	%	Female N	%	Combined N	%
First Year	143	8.1	90	5.1	233	13.2	47	4.1	37	3.8	84	8.5
Second Year	106	6.0	98	5.5	204	11.5	26	2.6	29	2.9	55	5.5
Third Year (adolescents)	165	9.4	70	4.0	235	13.3	57	5.7	46	4.6	103	10.4
Fourth Year (young adults)	196	16.1	136	7.7	332	18.8	116	11.7	85	8.6	201	20.2
Fifth Year and Older	445	25.2	314	17.8	759	43.0	285	27.0	263	26.5	548	55.3
Combined Sample	1055		708		1763		531		460		991	

sample 57.5% were males, but there were no clear-cut age-specific differences in sex ratios except in the oldest snakes. In 170 large adults, all thought to be at least 7 years old (on the basis of the age-size correlation shown in Table 12) females were only 33.8%. The most significant difference between the fall and summer samples is the better representation of immatures in fall. Adults were 56.2% of the fall sample but 75.5% of the summer sample. The young (especially neonates) doubtless have higher rates of mortality in the interval between fall and summer sampling; also they seem to be less inclined to disperse from the rock outcrops where seasonal concentrations occur. In a natural population each successively older age cohort should have fewer individuals than the next younger cohort, but in my samples this trend tends to be reversed with relatively few snakes in the younger cohorts. No doubt behavioral differences are involved, with small snakes less susceptible to trap capture than larger ones. If distance travelled is directly proportional to length of the snake, and if likelihood of capture depends on vagility, the trends shown by my records are to be expected.

Numbers

In an earlier account of the copperhead on FNHR (Fitch, 1960), I presented many sets of figures for the Petersen Index Census and discussed the factors affecting their accuracy. For the small valley on the west side of FNHR encompassing about 10 hectares, a density of 13.1 per ha was calculated and a density between 12.3 and 17.2 per ha was considered typical. The relatively long time required to gather a sample, and the difficulty in defining and uniformly sampling a specific area that contains a discrete population has prevented obtaining highly reliable figures. However, better and more recent samples have tended to bear out in a general way the figures obtained in my earlier study.

Sluggishness, with short and infrequent movements, and long, continued occupancy of a chosen area were the most notable traits of the copperhead revealed by years of field study. Live-trapping operations would have had to be much more concentrated, with more traps per unit area to achieve a fully marked population. Because of sedentary habits some individuals were evidently able to live for many years on the most intensively sampled areas without being captured. For others that were captured and marked many years elapsed between successive captures in some cases.

One clue to population density is the number actually trapped on a specific area, but the calculated density would be too high if ranges overlapped adjacent areas, or it might be too low if some of the snakes present

TABLE 18. Numbers of Copperheads Captured in House Field (10.0 ha lowland) and Quarry Field (3.45 ha Hilltop) in Different Years

Year	House Field		Quarry Field	
	No. Captured	Est. Density/ha	No. Captured	Est. Density/ha
1977	81	8.1	74	21.6
1978	36	3.66	27	7.8
1979	13	1.3	28	8.1
1980	17	1.7	15	4.4
1981	—		22	6.4
1982	21	2.1	25	7.3
1983	26	2.6	32	9.3
1985	24	2.4	16	4.6
1986	11	1.1	10	2.9
1987	17	1.7	9	2.6
1988	20	2.0	5	1.4

TABLE 19. Petersen Index Census Calculations for Copperheads in House Field and Quarry Field in 1977

	Number Caught in First Sampling Period	Ratio of Recaptures in Resampling Period	Estimated Population	Estimated Density/ha
House Field	30 (May)	44/12 (June–Sept.)	110	11.0
	39 (May–June)	35/7 (July–Sept.)	195	19.5
	65 (May–June–July)	9/4 (Aug.–Sept.)	146	14.6
	12 (May 1–13)	62/13 (May 15–Sept. 24)	57	5.7
	30 (May)	9/7 (June)	39	3.9
Quarry Field	22 (May)	50/12 (June–Oct.)	92	26.6
	33 (May–June)	39/12 (July–Oct.)	107	31.0
	9 (May 1–13)	12/2 (May 16–28)	54	15.7
	42 (May–June–July)	30/11 (Aug.–Oct.)	119	34.6
	22 (May)	11/3 (June)	81	23.6

were not captured. Table 18 shows numbers of copperheads captured over a period of years on two of the many study areas sampled—House Field (with Horse Field, Vole Field, and Picnic Field), a 10.0 ha block of former pastureland extending from a pond east of FNHR headquarters to the west boundary; and Quarry Field, a 3.45 ha triangular hilltop area of former pasture. Both were surrounded by areas of less favorable habitat. In 1977 the trapping effort was more intensive and extensive than in any other year, and the numbers of copperheads captured then are believed to show the best approximation of numbers actually present. The smaller numbers captured in later years are believed to reflect reduced sampling effort more than changes in population levels.

The actual number present probably varied less and some individuals were known to be present in several different years. Table 19 shows census figures based on recapture ratios in 1977 (the year in which sampling was most intensive). For both House Field and Quarry Field a wide range of census figures was obtained, depending upon how the season's data was divided for the preliminary sample and resample: the later the resampling, the fewer the recaptures from the first sampling, and the larger the census figure calculated. Fifteen calculations each for House Field and Quarry Field using the same data set but dividing it in different ways indicated a mean of 155.5±18.5 (15.6/ha) for House Field and 97.95±10.6 (22.5/ha) for Quarry Field.

The progressive increase in the census figure as the ratio of the presampling to resampling periods is increased, evidently results from some instability of the population sampled, with individuals crossing boundary lines to leave or enter the area sampled. As the presampling period is lengthened, the area's total of sometime occupants is increased. At the same time absenteeism of the area's former occupants (including

marked snakes) increases, so the ratio of marked to new snakes dwindles and calculated population becomes more inflated. It seems that this effect was more pronounced for the House Field sampling, with a relatively elongated area, than for Quarry Field with a more compact shape. In Table 19 the third census calculation for Quarry Field, based on May records exclusively, was much lower than other census figures.

Geographic Differentiation

The population studied, the Osage copperhead, *Agkistrodon contortrix phaeogaster,* differed from other geographic populations in many characteristics some of them subtle. Over the copperhead's extensive range the most obvious differences between populations are in body size and in pattern. The largest copperheads (*A. c. contortrix*) are in the southeastern United States and those of the northeastern United States (*A. c. mokeson*) also average considerably larger than those from Kansas. The smallest copperheads are those of Oklahoma and Texas (*A. c. laticinctus, A. c. pictigaster*). The number of young per litter is closely correlated with body size. Mean litter sizes for geographic populations have been recorded as follows: 6.6±0.9 (3–11) in 10 from Ohio, Illinois, and Kentucky; 6.4±0.35 (2–14) in 41 from northeastern states, Massachusetts to Virginia; 6.65 (5–11) in 17 in Georgia, Mississippi, and Louisiana; 3.8±0.5 (1–7) in 17 in Oklahoma and North Texas; and 3.1 (2–4) in 8 in West Texas (Fitch 1985).

Mitchell's (1994) figures for Virginia copperheads contrast with mine for Kansas as follows: litter size 7.6 vs. 5.34; size of neonate 196.5 SVL, 7.0 g vs. 222.7 SVL, 11.1 g; adult male 733 SVL, 273 g in Virginia, 656 mm SVL and 119 g in Kansas; adult female 598 SVL, 178 g in Virginia vs. 595 SVL and 154.5 g in Kansas.

Carphophis vermis

Traits of the Species

The western worm snake is a diminutive xenodontine relative of highly fossorial habits, reflected in its cylindrical muscular body with thickened neck, small wedge-shaped head, countersunk lower jaw, tiny eyes, cephalic shields including preoculars, temporals, nasals and labials reduced from a typical colubrid formula, teeth small and numerous, tail short and muscular, body scales smooth and polished, reduced to 13 longitudinal rows. (See Plate 5.) In all these traits *C. vermis* shows evolutionary convergence with other fossorial snakes, including many that are not closely related to it. Food consists mainly or entirely of earthworms. Loose, loamy soil is preferred. Ordinarily the snake does not show itself but moves through the soil or over its surface beneath a layer of leaf litter. The habitat is in open woodland or woodland edge. Flat rocks are preferred for shelter, and the snakes are able to attain some thermoregulation by contacting their sun-warmed undersurfaces, or withdrawing to deeper burrows to avoid unfavorably warm or cool temperatures at the surface. In an area of favorable habitat on a rocky, wooded slope worm snakes were found to attain densities up to 119/ha, but because of secretive and subterranean habits they are seldom seen by casual observers, even where they are most abundant. Compared with most other snakes worm snakes are active at relatively low temperatures often in the range of 23° to 26°C. Mean sizes of adults were 245 (216–288)mm SVL in males and 287 (250–344)mm SVL in females. Males attain sexual maturity in the second year, females in the second or third. Mating occurs in both fall and spring. Eggs average 2.5 per clutch.

Clark (1970) explained in detail the habitat requirements that limit the occurrence and abundance of *Carphophis.* These fossorial snakes prefer a clay-loam soil where earthworms are abundant. They cannot penetrate soil that is dry and packed, and are active mainly when moisture content is between 21 and 30%. They avoid low places where water collects, and are most often found on slopes, especially where there are trees and ground vegetation is sparse. On Clark's NESA study area habitat conditions may have been nearly optimum. Using a capture-recapture Petersen Index, Clark obtained census figures indicating 119 per ha in 1966, and 61 per ha in 1967 after a period of severe drought. With the same data set, but utilizing the supposedly more refined Hayne method, he obtained figures indicating 90 per ha in 1966 and 55 per ha in 1967. These figures indicate that the worm snake is the second most abundant species locally, but much less numerous than *Diadophis* which attains densities of more than one thousand per ha.

In several areas both species were found in substantial numbers, and their changing ratios over time reflect ecological succession (Table 20). House Field (FNHR) became a favorable habitat in 1950 when dense herbaceous vegetation accumulated to provide ground cover in this formerly heavily grazed pasture. The changed ratio probably reflects buildup in number of ringnecks which, in 1965–7 were censused at 774 to 1808 per ha while worm snake numbers changed relatively little, and they were found mostly along edges that were partly shaded by trees. The quarry area had much loose rock, and was being invaded by trees and brush with woodland on three sides. The habitat was favorable for both species, and their ratio did not change. Rat Woods, having a sparse, open stand of small trees and rock-strewn slopes with southern exposure, had the highest densities of ringnecks found

TABLE 20. Relative Number of *Carphophis vermis* and *Diadophis punctatus arnyi* in Several Study Areas

| Time of Sampling | House Field | | Quarry Field | | Rat Woods | | Skink Woods | |
	N	%Carphophis / Diadophis	N	%Carphophis / Diadophis	N	%Carphophis / Diadophis	N	%Carphophis / Diadophis
1950–54	60	3.3	156	5.1	219	8.8	146	65.0
1957	57	1.8	80	5.0	76	26.8	58	43.2

TABLE 21. Tentative Age Groupings in 426 Worm Snakes 1949 through 1997

Most Probable Age in Years	Males			Females			Male/Female %	
	N	Mean SVL (mm)	Range	N	Mean SVL (mm)	Range	Numbers	SVL
1st	31	125	(107–167)	41	132	(110–158)	76	94.8
2nd	39	182	(173–205)	31	196	(173–224)	126	93.0
3rd	45	215	(206–229)	26	247	(224–263)	173	87.0
4th	32	233	(230–242)	31	270	(265–277)	103	86.3
5th	28	246	(242–253)	27	282	(278–286)	104	87.5
6th	23	260	(254–263)	14	295	(290–305)	164	88.0
7th	18	270	(265–274)	17	311	(306–317)	106	87.0
8th	4	277	(275–280)	7	322	(318–325)	57	86.0
9th	1	288		—	—			
10th				3	335	(334–338)		90.5
Combined sample (adults only)	190	229.4	(173–288)	125	280.7	(224–338)	152	81.7

anywhere on FNHR during the early 1950s, but after livestock were removed and brush invaded, shading the substrate, both species became scarcer with ringnecks affected earlier and more severely than worm snakes. By 1965 both species had become much scarcer in Rat Woods and were no longer hunted regularly. The drastic decrease in numbers was attributed to the spreading of brush and trees, and the accumulation of herbaceous vegetation. Skink Woods, a rock-strewn, upper slope of western exposure in open woodland dominated by Chestnut Oak and grazed through 1948, seemed to be prime habitat for *Carphophis* which in annual samples outnumbered *Diadophis* 19 to 8 in 1950, 54 to 16 in 1951, and 18 to 17 in 1953. However, by 1954 the ratio had declined 4 to 10, and by 1957 it was 25 to 33. Over the years of observation both species became much scarcer on the area, but the decline was gradual.

Growth, Sex and Age Ratios

A total of 417 worm snakes were recorded on FNHR and nearby areas. Table 21 shows tentative allocations by sex, size (SVL), and most probable age. Small snakes that were evidently first-year young constituted the most numerous group and the larger sizes were progressively scarcer. Clark (1970) traced the trend of growth in marked individuals, more than 30 in all, of both sexes, that were recaptured after periods of weeks, months, or years, up to an age of 4 years. Beyond the age of 4 years individual ages were not definitely known, and projections were made on the

basis that each year survivors in any annual cohort become progressively fewer and growth becomes progressively slower. The largest individuals recorded, a female of 344 mm (SVL) and a male of 288 mm were interpreted as being 10 years old and 9 years old respectively, but if they had made unusually rapid growth, they might have been younger.

Clark found active sperm in males as small as 177 mm SVL, but many that were larger still lacked sperm, and he concluded that 216 mm SVL was the most typical size of maturity in males, and 250 mm SVL in females. In my records means for adults were 245.4 mm SVL (216–288), N=120 for males, and 286.9 mm (250–344) N=106 for females.

Table 22 shows weights in 125 worm snakes grouped according to sex and most probable age. Ages of individuals were not definitely known. Age allocations were made on the basis of the age-length correlations shown in Table 21. Males and females are not significantly different in weight at first, but in the second-year young females are definitely heavier, and the disparity increases. In large adults, males are only about two-thirds of the weight of their female counterparts.

Behavior

Clark's (1970) intensive field study from 1964 to 1967 was concentrated on a wooded east-facing slope (RW) near the west boundary of FNHR, and on a wooded, south-facing slope of NESA (0.8 ha) before the area was acquired by the University of Kansas. On RW

TABLE 22. Weights of Worm Snakes According to Age and Sex

Most Probable Age in Years	Male			Female			Male/Female %
	N	X̄ Weight	(g)	N	X̄ Weight	(g)	
1st	14	1.19±.098	(0.70–1.85)	11	1.16±0.124	(0.75–1.60)	102
2nd	14	3.25±0.18	(2.0–4.6)	12	3.46±0.17	(2.5–4.5)	94
3rd	13	5.30±0.27	(4.1–5.9)	9	5.60±0.58	(4.8–8.6)	95
4th	9	5.60±0.58	(4.5–7.1)	13	7.90±0.41	(6.4–9.8)	71
5th and 6th	16	7.26±0.63	(4.2–10.1)	9	10.0±0.10	(5.8–14.5)	72
7th and older	13	8.00±0.65	(6.5–10.1)	7	13.7±1.17	(11.7–19.9)	58

(0.465 ha) 604 worm snakes captured at various places in Douglas and adjoining counties were introduced and 88 were recaptured 104 times. On NESA 153 snakes were captured, marked, and released, and 36 were recaptured a total of 50 times.

Clark's (1970) thoroughgoing study brought out the following facts about worm snake ecology, which are accepted here with minor qualifications. Compared with its more eastern relative *C. amoenus, C. vermis* is more fossorial in its adaptation, is larger, more brightly colored, and has a narrower head, shorter tail, and smaller eyes. Worm snakes spend most of their time underground or beneath shelter but occasionally emerge and travel short distances on the surface. Individual ranges from 0.016 to 0.173 ha were calculated for various sex and age classes; adult males have the largest areas and juvenile females have the smallest. Mating occurs in both fall and spring. Adult females annually produce about three eggs ovulated in late May; by the time of laying, some 37 days later, clutches are reduced to a mean of 2.5 and to only 1.73 at hatching after another 50 days. During incubation eggs increased by an average 152% (100–205%) in weight. Mature size is attained by males most often in the second year and females in the third. Earthworms are the main food, especially the introduced European *Allolobophora.* Males shed about four times annually, females only about half as often.

Seldom emerging onto the surface, worm snakes do not bask in direct sunshine, but they may thermoregulate by maintaining contact with the undersides of sun-warmed surface objects. Obviously body temperature is more affected by substrate temperature than by air temperature. The preferred body temperature is low compared with other kinds of snakes. Twenty-one body temperatures obtained in my study averaged 25.7 °C and ranged from 19.0° to 31.7 °C. Evidently worm snakes are active over this wide range and do not have narrow preferenda. Sixteen of the 21 records were above 24 °C.

Clark's (1970) conclusion that the preferendum was between 23° and 24 °C was based on body temperatures of the snakes he captured and the behavior of those confined in an enclosure having a temperature gradient. However, the 23°–24 °C range seems too low and may have been influenced by the timing of field work with records obtained mostly between 7.00 and 9.30 hrs. before air and soil were warmed to typical daytime levels, so that snakes had little opportunity to thermoregulate. Somewhat higher body temperatures were obtained in my study (Figure 13).

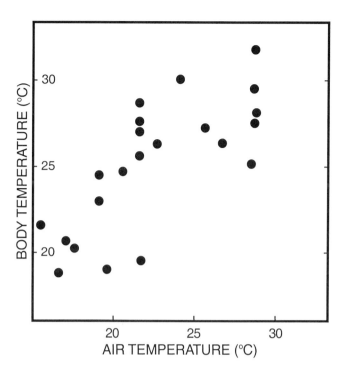

Figure 13. Body temperatures in worm snakes; they are influenced by ambient air temperatures and even more by soil temperatures. Active worm snakes are usually several degrees cooler than other kinds of snakes active at the same time and place.

In the worm snake the tail is relatively short compared with other snakes that are not fossorial. Also, the difference between the sexes in relative tail length is unusually great in *Carphophis vermis.* In male hatchlings tail length averages about 18% of SVL whereas in females it is about 13%. Through allometric growth the tail becomes relatively longer in males, approximately 20% in adults, but there is very little increase in females. The tail is relatively thick and muscular and it is used to propel the body forward as the snake forces its way through loose soil.

Eleven (5.3%) of 209 adult worm snakes lacked their tail tips presumably as a result of attack by predators. However, none of 118 immature snakes had lost part of their tail.

Geographic Differentiation

In Arkansas, Trauth, Cox, Meshaka, Butterfield, and Holt (1994) found mean adult SVL (222.6±22.3, 186–263 in 17) to be significantly smaller than in my Kansas sample, but found clutch size to be larger than in Kansas (3.4±0.5, 2–5 in 17).

Coluber constrictor

Traits of the Species

As a polytypic, transcontinental species the racer is subject to much variation in ecology and morphology, some of it subtle. The most striking geographic variation is in body size and color. Subspecific vernacular names reflect such variation in the "black," "blue," "green," and "speckled" racers. In the local population the dorsal ground color is usually a uniform grayish brown and the venter is pale grading from white on the chin to shiny yellow posteriorly. However, there is a wide range in shade of dorsal color, from pale gray to almost black (resembling other subspecies, *C. c. constrictor* and *C. c. priapus*). (See Plates 6 & 7.) Hatchling racers are strikingly different in appearance from adults. They have a pattern of chocolate brown mid-dorsal rhombs on a pale, bluish-gray ground color. The rhombs are wider than long; on the posterior one-third of the body they are progressively fainter, shortened and crowded with dusky interspaces, becoming indiscernible on the tail, which is uniform brown dorsally. (See Plate 8.) Low on each side of the body are two rows of brown spots alternating with the dorsal rhombs. Each supralabial bears a dark mark, and there are other dark marks on the top and sides of the head separated by white areas creating a distinctive facial pattern, and there are dark reddish brown spots on the ventrals. The pattern fades gradually. In year-old racers the dorsal rhombs are faint but discernible. In newly matured racers traces of the juvenile pattern remain, mainly as a faint speckling on the ventrals.

The preferred habitat is tall-grass prairie or pastureland. Racers are strictly diurnal, and have a relatively high body temperature preferendum, between 34° and 35 °C, maintained by thermoregulatory behavior in basking. High body temperature promotes rapid movement in pursuit of prey or escape, rapid digestion, and rapid growth. Food habits overlap those of most other local snakes. Large insects, including grasshoppers, crickets, katydids, and cicadas make up an important part of the food, especially for young, but as larger size is attained, vertebrates including frogs, lizards, other snakes, birds, mice, voles, and shrews become increasingly important. Females grow larger than males, are less scansorial, and take a higher proportion of mammalian prey (76.5% of 81) than adult males (51.3% of 39) or immatures (21.0% of 38). The average prey item is relatively small (usually less than 5% of snake weight), hence, racers that have ingested prey are little affected in their speed of movement or degree of activity and feeding is frequent even while digestion is in progress. Sexual maturity is attained in the second year and reproduction is annual. In the local population, eggs averaging 11.8 (5–21) per clutch are laid in abandoned mammal burrows at about the end of June and hatch in late August or early September. Clutch size is proportional to female size. Hatchlings are about 220 mm SVL. At an age of a year they have more than doubled in length and females are about 13% longer than males. Racers tend to stay in areas that average 2.5 to 3.0 ha but leave them to make seasonal shifts averaging approximately 300 m to hibernacula at hilltop outcrops. In favorable habitats racers attain densities up to 20/ha. Natural losses in adults may approximate 40% annually. Occasionally individuals may survive for 10 years of even more. Major predators include the striped skunk and red-tailed hawk.

Determinants of Size

Tables 23 and 24 show the remarkable size range of racers in the local population. In both sexes the largest adults are more than 10 times the bulk of newly matured individuals. Male and female hatchlings are similar in size, but at an age of 1 year females are substantially larger than males, are 2.5 times their original length and more than 11 times hatching weight. The means of 34 annual means indicated male length of 708 mm and female length of 800.

Table 25 suggests a rapid turnover since most racers recorded were captured only once, and those recaptured more than once were mostly captured in just one year. Rapid turnover involves both a high rate of mortality and individual shifts. The table suggests that

TABLE 23. Mean Sizes in Annual Samples of Adult Racers 1949 to 1997

	Males				Females		
Year	N	SVL (mm)	Weight (g)		N	SVL (mm)	Weight (g)
1949	24	645.2±19.3	100.4±7.3		24	778.8±28.5	184.6±3.2
1950	38	622.2±21.5	87.4±6.5		36	755.0±22.4	143.8±13.1
1951	16	705.6±29.2	103.8±8.0		14	812.9±32.6	205.6±21.0
1952	19	641.2±18.7	100.8±8.9		13	831.2±38.4	205.6±21.1
1953	31	690.0±24.2	106.0±12.3		18	868.1±35.8	185.0±31.0
1954	24	665.9±20.5	105.4±10.8		30	797.3±22.0	172.0±13.9
1955	38	687.4±15.0	107.9±7.2		31	787.6±19.6	178.3±12.9
1956	33	701.4±17.5	130.8±7.6		34	777.6±28.0	141.8±10.1
1957	34	710.3±18.1	135.6±8.5		44	805.5±14.9	167.5±13.0
1958	116	726.9±12.6	131.1±5.0		93	802.6±13.8	174.2±8.5
1959	119	748.6±10.3	141.9±5.2		82	854.5±19.2	191.7±9.7
1960	128	721.7±9.3	115.2±4.9		69	841.2±17.2	171.9±13.4
1961	130	690.9±9.2	149.2±4.0		110	830.5±14.6	167.5±8.2
1962	87	691.4±10.4	103.7±4.9		56	785.7±20.3	134.6±7.95
1963	103	683.3±9.3	102.2±4.75		60	772.5±16.2	143.9±10.9
1964	55	676.1±12.5	94.6±6.5		17	757.6±27.3	122.5±15.1
1965	47	692.6±10.0	89.5±8.6		28	792.9±17.6	148.1±15.8
1966	30	722.4±15.2	119.9±7.9		11	788.6±27.5	152.8±18.7
1977	98	708.4±9.7	103.8±8.0		75	751.1±28.5	148.4±16.0
1978	81	676.0±16.8	99.4±8.6		45	791.8±17.4	167.3±16.7
1979	27	705.0±24.8	110.7±11.9		20	817.0±30.8	155.3±20.2
1980	45	685.9±14.4	103.2±6.2		41	836.3±19.7	141.2±8.6
1981	19	714.5±22.0	108.8±8.1		32	820.9±26.0	161.4±26.4
1982	57	681.7±29.5	109.5±5.1		59	796.9±17.2	151.2±8.9
1983	40	743.5±17.3	133.7±8.8		21	794.6±23.2	183.8±23.5
1984	27	771.3±16.4	131.3±10.5		25	795.2±29.0	158.3±15.1
1985	17	671.5±5.3	115.1±10.9		28	792.9±23.0	155.6±12.7
1986	24	766.0±20.1	149.9±15.0		23	826.4±27.1	194.0±36.0
1987	9	817.7±23.3	157.0±24.2		25	844.9±28.2	163.2±24.8
1988	17	743.7±19.7	130.7±12.1		24	742.4±21.6	136.0±12.8
1989	9	723.3±31.6	120.4±17.8		25	785.6±70.6	202.3±19.9
1990	45	749.7±12.6	143.0±7.1		51	803.4±16.3	151.6±12.7
1991	55	750.5±11.5	131.9±7.2		28	773.1±18.1	160.2±11.6
1992	29	720.3±15.1	137.8±11.2		33	741.3±27.8	155.9±12.9
1993	16	740.6±21.4	138.3±12.8		17	829.6±32.7	206.2±16.0
1994	26	732.1±6.1	114.5±11.2		15	803.0±31.0	173.6±21.7
1995	14	630.0±14.3	92.7±14.3		12	717.2±29.6	144.3±24.9
1996	18	664.7±13.2	95.0±6.4		10	844.6±36.8	228.0±27.2
1997	10	687.3±28.9	119.9±12.1		13	838.2±38.0	208.0±28.1

tenure is more ephemeral for females than for males; a higher percentage of females were caught only once, or in only one year. However, the greater activity of males may put them at greater risk of capture, especially in the spring breeding season.

Behavior

Alertness and speed characterize the behavior of active racers. One that has detected prey will move briskly with forebody elevated ready to pursue with a sudden forward dash and lunge. In finding prey vision is relied upon more and olfaction less than in most snakes. A person on foot approaching a racer usually causes it to dart away and the person may be aware of the snake's proximity only from the waving tops of the grass. Unlike most other snakes, racers approached by cars while crossing a road may dart away in time to avoid becoming traffic casualties. One caught in a wire funnel trap usually struggles frantically to escape when approached by a person, and may strike at the person even when he is still several meters away. On many occasions when I have approached trapped racers, the snakes have darted out through the funnel opening and escaped. Others, left in traps for periods of hours after their discovery also sometimes escaped without such stimulus. Racers cornered or injured or too cold to escape, rely instead on their foul-smelling musk to repel predators. The snake coils with rapid movements hiding its head and forebody and sliding its vent over its dorsal surface to smear itself thoroughly. Squirming movements of the tail help to spread the musk. Often in fall trapping operations, along the hilltop outcrops

TABLE 24. Sizes of Racers in a Local Population of Northeastern Kansas

	N	SVL (mm)	Weight (g)
Adult Male	1715	714.9±10.9 (500–1110)	123.6±3.17 (34–430)
Adult Female	1349	822.2±5.3 (600–1210)	165.7±3.75 (52–538)
Hatchling Male	72	218.1±2.0 (178–250)	4.7±0.09 (3.2–6.3)
Hatchling Female	36	223.1±2.52 (193–249)	4.61±0.13 (2.9–6.1)
1-Year-Old Male	24	529.0±6.3 (466–577)	49.5±2.36 (22–68)
1-Year-Old Female	27	556.4±6.3 (488–600)	53.4±2.20 (35–71)

TABLE 25. Incidence of Recaptures in Racers Individually Marked and Released

No. of Captures per Snake	Males				Females			
	N	% Times Captured	% Years Captured	% Years Spanned	N	% Times Captured	% Years Captured	% Years Spanned
1	590	66.7	75.2	78.0	642	69.4	80.6	80.8
2	147	16.8	17.8	12.7	101	10.9	13.8	9.3
3	70	7.9	4.9	4.8	127	13.8	3.4	4.5
4	37	4.2	1.4	2.6	33	3.6	0.8	2.6
5	12	1.3	0.7	1.6	12	1.3	0.3	1.3
6	6	0.7	—	0.2	6	0.7	0.8	0.2
7	10	1.1	—	0.1	1	0.1	0.3	0.7
8	4	0.4	—	—	2	—	—	0.2
9	2	0.2	—	—	—	0.2	—	0.3
10 or More	1	0.9	—	—	—	—	—	0.1

where racers come to hibernate, the snakes were encountered and they always escaped by instantly turning downslope and gaining high velocity coasting downhill. Compared with other local snakes, racers are fast-moving and maintain a high level of activity. Annual migrations are made in fall from summer ranges to the hilltop limestone outcrops that provide hibernacula, and back again in spring.

Responses to Succession

The racer is a nearly ubiquitous and abundant species, and an ecologically important member of the local fauna. Its numbers and local distribution changed drastically during the course of my study In 1948 major habitats on FNHR consisted of formerly cultivated fields, woodland, and open pastures, heavily grazed by livestock. All three were deficient as racer habitat, and few racers were present. These were found in the more open types of woodland and along the edges where thickets of weeds or shrubs bordered on open land. In 1949, with cessation of grazing, the formerly pastured areas developed a dense grass-weed mixture that provided shelter. Concurrently, exploding populations of small mammals supplemented high populations of crickets and grasshoppers already present on the pastures as the snakes' food supply. Under these improved habitat conditions racers thrived and increased for several years. By 1952 the ratio of broad-leaved forbs to grasses in the former pastures had begun to decrease. Throughout the 1950s and 1960s this trend continued, with a few species of grasses, mainly *Bromus inermis* and *Poa annua* replacing many species of broad-leafed forbs. With the trend from highly diverse to more uniform ground vegetation the food supply for small mammals deteriorated and their numbers declined. The snakes, in turn, had their food supply sharply curtailed, and they decreased. During the 1970s and 1980s habitat deterioration continued as shrubs and trees encroached on formerly open areas, replacing the grass-forb mixture, which was fragmented into a mosaic, with residual patches steadily shrinking and eventually disappearing. By 1990 the pasture vegetation was reduced to remnants and racers had almost disappeared.

On the adjacent NESA, former farmlands were subjected to diverse management practices with burning, grazing, and especially mowing serving to maintain some diversity of habitat and prevent a successional sequence such as occurred on FNHR. Much of the area is grassland but with different assemblages of species and amounts of cover. Racers have remained abundant, with numbers comparable to those on FNHR in the 1950s.

On FNHR the trend was one of rapid increase in the early 1950s with subsequent gradual decline over the next three decades as the grassland habitat shrank and was replaced by woody vegetation. Trapping efforts influenced the trends. Few racers were caught in the years 1967 through 1976, when relatively little snake trapping was done. If the meager data from these years are omitted, the records show a gradual decline from the peak in the mid-1950s through the 1960s and 1970s, accelerating in the 1980s and 1990s until the species was almost gone from the area.

Spatial Relationships

Racers tend to stay within familiar areas. In the course of trapping operations it was common experience to catch the same individual over several successive years in the same general area, either in fields that were in the snakes' summer range or along hilltop outcrops where hibernacula were situated. I attempted to sort recorded movements into distinct categories as follows: those within a summer range; those at the hilltop outcrops where snakes come to hibernate; those between summer range and hibernaculum; and occasional relatively long shifts not belonging to any of the first three. Several movements of more than a kilometer were recorded. At the other extreme were occasional "non-movements" when a snake was caught at precisely the same place on successive occasions. After processing, each snake was released several meters away to prevent re-entry into a trap and in most instances there were substantial intervals—weeks, months, or even years between non-movement captures and obviously the snake had travelled extensively before returning.

Figure 14, with both sexes combined, shows relative frequency of movements of different lengths, within supposed home ranges. It is shown that regardless of elapsed time, most distances between capture points are less than 180 m and that there is no decrease in frequency up to this level. Numbers of records decrease rapidly for distances from 180 to 300 m, then taper off gradually to zero. Racers seem to move about at random within their chosen areas which average about 180 m in diameter (up to 300 m), and the average movement between random points may be equated with a home range radius. For a circular range of 180 m diameter an area of 2.54 ha (πr^2) is calculated, and for the extreme size of 300 m an area of 7.06 ha is implied. However, racer ranges probably are never perfect circles but deviate toward elliptical or irregular shape even in homogeneous habitat and may be highly irregular where barriers or habitat borders impose constraints on free movements. The narrow elongate hilltop field extending diagonally from the northeastern to southwestern portions of FNHR provided examples of unusually elongate ranges; five between 300 and 400 m, two between 500 and 600 m, and one between 600

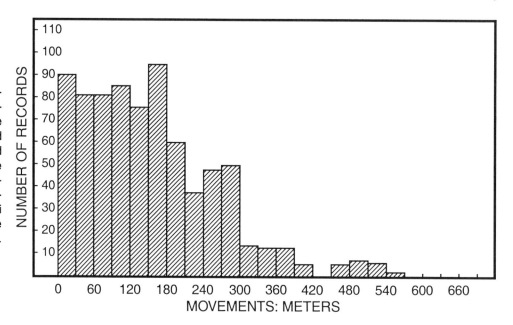

Figure 14. Relative frequency of distances of different lengths between capture points in individually marked racers that were recaptured after varying intervals. The records are construed to indicate that movements are often limited to ranges with radii of about 180 m, but with some larger, up to 300 m in radius.

and 700. On NESA, where the partially snake-proof fences of enclosures were used for trap sites, ranges must have been highly irregular. One complex consisted of two adjacent square enclosures each 84 m per side, adjoining each other as a T-shaped block. Individual racers were often trapped on two or more sides of these enclosures and presumably passed under, through, or over the fences to enter them in most cases. Some enclosure fences were made of half-inch wire mesh; wide enough for adult racers to pass through.

Table 26 shows increasing distance between successive capture points with elapsed time. After an interven-

ing hibernation the distance averaged more than twice as far as that within a season. After two or more hibernations the distance nearly tripled. The figures indicate that home ranges tend to change over time as the snake abandons parts of its range and moves into new areas. When fields of wheat or alfalfa adjoining FNHR were mowed, racers moved from them onto the study area. Males' movements averaged a little longer than those of females; doubtless the burden of eggs in early summer restricted female movement somewhat.

Table 27 shows movements of racers in the vicinity of their hibernacula, or between their hibernacula and

TABLE 26. Distances Between Successive Captures in Individually Marked Racers on Summer Ranges

	Males		Females		Combined	
Within a Season	N	Distance of Movement (m)	N	Distance of Movement (m)	N	Distance of Movement (m)
>300 m	156	89	82	71	238	82
All Movements	267	155	157	155	424	155
After 1 Hibernation	149	184	74	168	223	179
After 2 or More Hibernations	35	290	41	238	76	218
Combined Samples	451	175	272	169	723	173

TABLE 27. Mean Distances between Successive Captures in Individually Marked Racers Associated with Hibernacula

	Males		Females		Combined	
Hibernaculum to Summer Range	N	Distance of Movement (m)	N	Distance of Movement (m)	N	Distance of Movement (m)
Same Season	34	354	37	276	71	313
After 1 Year	12	278	22	382	34	344
After 2 or More Years	8	314	9	420	17	367
Combined Samples	54	332	68	332	122	332
At Hibernacula						
Same Season	26	97	28	156	54	99
After 1 Year	11	53	11	171	22	111
After 2 or More Years	4	342	5	138	9	230
Combined Samples	41	76	44	163	89	118

summer ranges. All hibernacula are at hilltop outcrops of the Oread Limestone where there are deep fissures and crevices. In some instances the hibernaculum was within the snake's summer range or adjacent to it, but usually it was disjunct involving migratory movements between them in both spring and fall—rarely as much as a kilometer. The second part of the table is based on distances between successive capture points both of which were at the hilltop limestone outcrops. Most of these captures were made in October. In many instances a snake was caught at the same spot or only a few meters away in 2 or more years, indicating fidelity to specific hibernacula. However, the capture points were often farther apart, indicating either that the snake was using a different hibernaculum or that it was following the outcrop, returning to its former hibernaculum.

Radiotelemetry revealed aspects of behavior that were not evident from mark-and-recapture studies. Twelve racers (seven males and five females) were equipped with radio transmitters and monitored daily for intervals up to 102 days (combined total 523 days). More than 90% of the time these snakes were in grassland but occasionally they shifted to open woodland or brush thickets. Unlike other kinds of snakes that were similarly instrumented, racers that were approached by the investigator tended to move away, avoiding proximity to humans. Efforts were made to avoid disturbing the snakes, but on two occasions when retreating snakes were followed they travelled distances of 64 m and 51 m within a few minutes, exceeding the distance normally covered in an entire day. Sometimes the snake trailed was underground in a mammal-made tunnel, or in a tree, but most often it was on the soil surface. Mean movement per day (linear distance between sites occupied) was 33.8 m (29.6 in males, 41.4 in females). There was no movement on 21.4% of the days, with

females (26.4%) more inclined than males (20.0%) to be sedentary. Racers that remained at the same place on successive days were usually hidden beneath the surface layer of old vegetation; some were underground. Suspected causes of such sojourns were preparation for ecdysis and digestion of unusually large meals. The longest 1-day movement was 370 m but more than half of all movements were less than 20 m (Figure 15).

The greatest difference between the sexes was in scansorial behavior; six of the seven males were found in trees and these records constituted 14.1% of the male total, whereas only one of the five females was found above ground constituting 1.5% of the female total. On the 35 occasions that racers were found in trees or bushes height ranged from 0.8 to 3.6 m above ground. The female climbed for 3 days, the males for 32 days. The racers found in trees and bushes were either coiled or extended in well-concealed spots, usually in leafy clusters on outer twigs. When closely approached, they usually remained motionless depending on concealment; sometimes they glided away silently. Males, being relatively light and slender, climb more easily than females. The racers that were found in trees seemed to be in sites well adapted to ambushing prey such as katydids, cicadas, tree frogs, and small birds.

Kinds of Prey

Prey totalling 184 separate items were found in the stomachs of 145 captured racers. Vertebrates and invertebrates occurred in almost equal numbers but the vertebrates were estimated to comprise more than 95% of the total biomass represented. The snakes which were found to contain prey were only 3.6% of the total captures. Most of the snakes examined had not fed

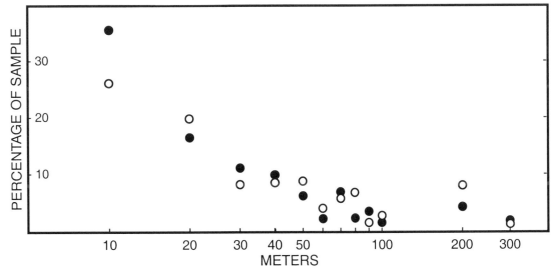

Figure 15. Relative frequency of day-to-day movements of different lengths in adult racers carrying radio transmitters; males shown as dots, females as open circles.

recently or at least were not noticeably distended with prey that could be palpated from the stomach. Racers are adapted to feed frequently on relatively small prey that is rapidly digested. None of the racers captured was severely handicapped in locomotion by having ingested a relatively large food item. Total prey biomass was estimated at 1850 g, with a mean of only 11.3 g per item.

Prey identified consisted of 40 *Microtus ochrogaster*, 34 acridid grasshoppers (including *Melanoplus bivittatus, Arphia simplex, Melanoplus differentialis, Chortophaga viridifasciata, Melanoplus femurrubrum, Dissosteira americana* and *Sphargemon equale* in that order of importance), 27 crickets including 21 *Acheta affinis*, 2 *Nemobius fasciatus*, and 2 unspecified, 11 *Reithrodontomys megalotis*, 9 *Ceuthophilus pallidus*, 9 *Peromyscus leucopus*, 7 katydids (*Neoconocephalus robustus* and *Orchelimum vulgare*), 6 moths and moth larvae, 5 *Peromyscus maniculatus*, 5 *Rana blairi*, 4 *Thamnophis sirtalis*, 4 cicadas (*Tibicen pruinosa* and possibly others) 3 *Eumeces fasciatus*, 3 *Storeria dekayi*, 2 each of *Cnemidophorus sexlineatus, Eumeces obsoletus, Hyla chrysoscelis*, and unspecified "mice" and 1 each of *Blarina hylophaga, Coluber constrictor, Cryptotis parva, Diadophis punctatus, Ophisaurus attenuatus*, unspecified "snake," *Synaptomys cooperi, Tropidoclonion lineatum*, and *Zapus hudsonius*.

There were some significant trends in the distribution of these prey items. Small mammals were eaten much more often by adults (68) than by immatures (2), because most immatures were not large enough to ingest even shrews or small mice. Food items recorded from first-year young included 10 grasshoppers, 9 crickets, 2 cave crickets 2 moths and one each of mouse, five-lined skink, Great Plains skink, and six-lined racerunner. Adult racers take these same kinds of prey but also take a variety of much more bulky vertebrate prey, and insects are a relatively minor part of their diet. Of the adult racers that yielded food items, 79 (71%) were females. Of the small mammals eaten 52 (76%) were taken by females; no doubt bias is due to the fact that females more often grow to a size at which they can readily ingest voles and white-footed mice. Some seasonal change in diet is evident, based on changing availability of prey. Mammals were taken in greatest numbers in spring (35) less in summer (27) and least in fall (5) but for insects the trend was just the opposite: 16 in spring, 23 in summer and 29 in fall. Doubtless the great abundance of orthopterans and other large insects in fall causes the snakes to prey more on them and less on mammals at that time of year.

In an earlier study (Fitch, 1963a) I listed prey items identified from both scats and stomachs. Scats can almost always be obtained from newly caught racers, whereas only a small percentage of them have detectable stomach items. However, the scat material is fragmentary and does not show well the bulk of the food ingested or even the number of items; fur or feathers or scales in a scat may represent a single prey animal or several of the same species. Amphibians seem to be digested completely leaving no clue except perhaps their stomach contents—the chitinous remains of small arthropods that probably would not be taken as prey by the snakes, because of minute size or noxious qualities. In a sample of 479 scats 1008 food items were identified, and 76.8% were insects; approximately 92% of these were orthopterans with acridid grasshoppers of 11 species making up the largest component, followed by gryllids and tettigoniids in almost equal numbers. Besides grasshoppers, crickets, and katydids, the insects taken are mostly cicadas, and moths and their larvae—taken in much smaller numbers than the orthopteran prey.

The racer's wide range of food species, including insects, amphibians, reptiles, and mammals, buffers it against times of prey scarcity. Environmental changes may reduce populations of one type of prey (e.g., drought reducing frogs) but may favor another type of prey such as grasshoppers.

Reproduction

Racers attain sexual maturity at sizes well below the averages for adults. Males a little more than 1 year old, in fall after their first full growing season, were found to have active sperm (e.g., SVL 461 mm, 29 October, 1959; 515 mm, 14 October, 1959; 503 mm, 12 September, 1960; 533 mm, 7 September, 1959; 540 mm, 13 September, 1960). These males were thought to be 12 to 14 months old, and would be potential breeders the following spring at an age of 19 months. Their age cohort is the largest group of sexually mature males, but perhaps active competition for mates and aggression by larger and older males prevents them from siring litters in proportion to their actual numbers.

Sexual maturity in females was determined from the presence of oviductal eggs or enlarged ovarian follicles detectable by palpation, and/or by a thick-walled cloacal capsule, palpable as a rubbery lump anterior to the vent. Females of slightly less than 600 mm occasionally have incipient cloacal capsules. Of 118 females that were gravid the smallest was 600 mm in SVL; others were 630, 640, 643, 653 and 671 mm. It seems that in some females sexual maturity is postponed until the third year so there is a surplus of breeding males.

For calculating the means in Table 23, SVL 500 mm was arbitrarily considered the lower limit for adult males and 600 mm for adult females. Adult females average about 115% of male SVL and about 132% of male weight. The table shows that mean adult size varied widely from year to year. Probably weather and food supply were major sources of variation over time. Also, changing age composition of the population was involved. In 1949 and 1950 the first 2 years of sampling, racers averaged smaller than in most other years because successional changes associated with removal of livestock and development of lush grasses and herbaceous growth permitted successful reproduction resulting in a high percentage of racers in the younger age classes. Similarly in the years 1962 through 1965 and in 1985, mean size in both sexes was relatively small. In contrast there were years when average size was greater than usual, with high percentages of the older age classes, e.g., 1962 through 1965, 1986, and 1990.

In most years sampling extended over the entire season of activity but trapping was most successful in May (the breeding season) and in October when racers were concentrated at hilltop outcrops preparing to hibernate. Within each season the ratio of spring-to-fall catches varied. Fall samples had relatively large numbers of adolescents and averaged smaller than spring samples.

Sexual behavior in racers has been reported by many observers and described in some detail. Ordinarily it is limited to the months of May and June. A female may be courted by two or several males simultaneously. Courting males may sometimes behave aggressively toward humans. In a typical courtship the male aligns himself atop the female with his chin pressed against her neck and makes writhing movements, but from time to time he separates and crawls about rapidly in the immediate vicinity, then returns. After intromission is accomplished the female moves forward slowly, dragging the passive male behind her (Fitch, 1963a). Evidently males find mates by following their scent trails. Lillywhite (1985) observed, within a short period of time, three racers in succession moving over the same course across a lawn. A little later two that had met were behaving aggressively. Later still Lillywhite observed a male approach a smaller female, following her trail. He initiated vigorous courtship, with tongue flicking and body alignment and soon accomplished intromission. Within 2 minutes the male began to move slowly forward, dragging the female in this instance. He moved to a bush, climbed to its top and from there into a pine tree to a height of 5 m, dragging the female. After 15 minutes a second large male appeared, following the same trail; he climbed through the bush and into the tree, to the place where the pair were resting. After 5 minutes all three snakes moved to a different part of the tree and were there for at least an hour. This remarkable sequence of observations emphasizes the important role of olfaction in mating, even though racers are more visually oriented than most snakes. The larger size of the male and dragging of the attached female by the male reverses the usual relationship, and raises the possibility that the sexes were confused at some point in the sequence of observation.

Racers were sometimes found in pairs, both in wire traps and beneath artificial shelters. Over the decade 1986 through 1995 27 pair captures were recorded. In two of these instances there was an additional male with the pair. One pair was caught on 21 October, 1992; all others were within the period 3 May to 12 June with the mean date 24 May and with most captures concentrated in the period 18 May to 1 June. In each of two pairs the male was larger than the female; in all other pairs the female was larger than the male, and males averaged 88.36±2.8% of female SVL. On the basis of size 50% of 28 males were believed to be of the newly matured second-year cohort.

In 118 clutches there was a total of 1393 eggs, mean 11.8 (5–26) per clutch. As shown in Table 28 and Figure 16, the average and maximum number of eggs increases with the age and size of the female. However, some large, and presumably old females produce small or medium-size clutches. As the size of the female increases the variance in clutch size becomes greater. Year-to-year changes in clutch size correlated with such factors as weather and food supply could not be shown with the small annual samples available. Most females are growing rapidly at the time when they are producing eggs; the portion of their food allotted to growth must be at least as large as the amount used to produce eggs. In 14 different years when intensive live trapping of racers was carried on throughout June, females that appeared to have recently laid their clutches (their abdominal areas were thin and wrinkled) were first seen on the 13th to 27th (average 22 June). Ovigerous females, almost ready to lay their clutches were seen as late as 3 July (in 1961), but in most years were last seen in the third or fourth week of June. Evidently egg laying is concentrated in the second half of June, with only slight variation from year to year. Yolking of follicles is rapid and occurs mainly within the period mid-May to mid-June. Ovigerous females are consider-

TABLE 28. Egg Production in Eight Size-Age Classes of Racers

Probable Year-Class of Female	N	Eggs per Clutch		
		Mean	Range	σ
Second	16	8.31±0.39	6–12	1.54
Third	13	10.85±0.82	6–14	2.94
Fourth	12	12.33±0.73	9–17	2.53
Fifth	6	12.67±1.03	8–17	4.88
Sixth	3	16.0	13–19	—
Seventh	2	13.5	11–16	—
Eighth	4	14.0±1.96	9–18	2.88
Older than Eight	4	14.25±2.28	11–21	4.57

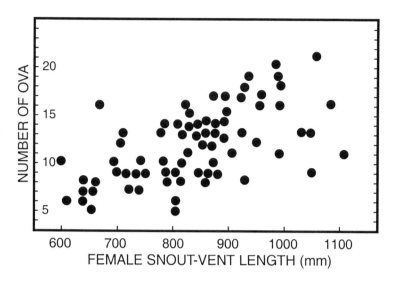

Figure 16. Size of clutch in the racer, correlated with size of female. Primiparous females average fewer eggs than larger and older females but clutch size is subject to wide variation in females of all sizes.

ably heavier than males and nongravid females of the same body length. Among 177 females captured within the period from May 15 to June 15, there were 13 that were below the weight range of any known gravid individuals and these were believed to be nonreproductive. The ratio varied from year to year; none of 39 in 1969 to 2 of 9 in 1983.

For clutches incubated in the laboratory (N=10) hatching dates ranged from 10 August to 22 September (average date 30 August). Hatchling racers (N=107) averaged 219.3 (178–250)mm SVL and 4.64 g (3.2–5.6) with no significant difference between the sexes. Females averaged slightly larger in 5 broods whereas males were slightly larger in 4 broods. The 107 young hatched included 71 males and 36 females; two broods had more females than males.

Evidently search for suitable nesting sites and deposition of eggs involves but little loss of time or interruption of normal activities, because females are captured as often as males during June, the egg-laying month. On several occasions racer nests were plowed up on NESA or a nearby farm, but nests are best known from the remains left by predators that had dug out the eggs and eaten them. Many such destroyed nests were found, but often evidence was largely obscured after a lapse of days or weeks. Typically eggs had been dug from a nest cavity that was part of a tunnel system of a small fossorial mammal (*Scalopus aquaticus, Microtus ochrogaster*) 10 to 15 cm deep, had been chewed, and the empty shells scattered over an area of a square meter or more. The striped skunk (*Mephitis mephitis*) was the suspected predator, but several carnivores such as coyotes, foxes, raccoons, and spotted skunks, or even opossums might have been involved. The eastern mole, suspected excavator of most of the next cavities is, of course, a predator of small vertebrates and their eggs, but its extensive tunneling, and abandonment of

tunnels after brief use, provides an abundance of reasonably secure nesting sites. The racer itself lacks the ability to dig and must find burrows that have been left open. Live-trap captures in July were slightly biased in favor of females, and it seems that they are especially active in feeding after egg laying.

Growth

As shown in Table 29, recently hatched young captured in August, averaged 23% longer (SVL) than those hatched in confinement. Presumably the difference is due to very rapid early growth. In the year after hatching, young more than doubled in average length, with most rapid gains in June, July, and August and somewhat slower growth in the cooler weather of spring and fall. In the second full growing season, females grow faster than males, and average 6.5% longer in the first half and 11.5% longer in the second half. The largest and oldest adult females average some 15% longer than the longest males. Table 30 is based on growth records of marked and recaptured racers and shows that growth continues in adults, slowing gradually with increasing age, and slowing more gradually in

TABLE 29. Sizes (SVL) of First-Year Racers

	Male			Female		
	N	Mean	Range	N	Mean	Range
Hatchlings*	72	218.1±2.0	178–250	46	223.1±2.5	186–250
August	5	254.8±22.0	203–333	2	226.0	247–285
September	16	288.1±7.0	242–332	17	269.1±19.6	221–355
October	35	308.7±5.6	220–372	26	311.4±8.4	213–361
November	14	319.7±10.3	249–380	9	320.3±10.8	291–380
April	31	309.5±15.0	238–382	10	305.5±16.2	227–365
May	13	331.0±8.5	275–368	15	344.3±6.0	304–376
June	16	355.1±9.4	288–395	16	391.8±12.1	295–488
July	13	438.3±9.4	387–490	10	424.0±9.5	362–462
August	16	514.1±11.6	432–580	12	524.8±9.4	432–574
September	16	536.0±9.1	466–598	28	551.0±6.7	488–591

*10 broods incubated and hatched in the laboratory.

TABLE 30. Growth in Individually Marked Racers

SVL (mm) and Weight	Dates of Capture	Age Span of Records
Males		
518 (43 g) to 840 (170 g)	10/19/56 to 5/9/61	2nd to 7th g.s.*
565 (53 g) to 896 (198 g)	5/26/55 to 6/26/61	2nd to 8th g.s.
508 (48 g) to 816 (163 g)	5/8/53 to 10/4/88	2nd to 7th g.s.
584 (60 g) to 828 (167 g)	5/15/80 to 5/1/83	2nd to 5th g.s.
603 (78 g) to 841 (170 g)	5/30/57 to 5/25/61	2nd to 6th g.s.
632 (78 g) to 813 (140 g)	5/19/56 to 5/23/60	2nd to 6th g.s.
714 (136 g) to 1110 (430 g)	10/17/50 to 10/4/58	3rd to 11th g.s.
770 (118 g) to 1005 (300 g)	5/27/83 to 9/28/87	4th to 8th g.s.
743 (118 g) to 900 (215 g)	5/10/77 to 10/6/81	4th to 8th g.s.
710 (117 g) to 865 (200 g)	5/25/55 to 5/15/59	3rd to 7th g.s.
Females		
436 (21 g) to 1106 (285 g)	7/3/77 to 7/18/85	1st to 9th g.s.
555 (43 g) to 1092 (385 g)	8/5/64 to 8/4/72	1st to 9th g.s.
603 (71 g) to 1047 (325 g)	5/20/54 to 5/24/60	2nd to 8th g.s.
680 (92 g) to 1034 (304 g)	10/14/56 to 6/30/63	2nd to 9th g.s.
678 (102 g) to 1080 (270 g)	9/24/77 to 6/16/83	2nd to 8th g.s.
728 (103 g) to 1138 (442 g)	5/5/78 to 4/9/81	2nd to 5th g.s.
680 (71 g) to 900 (210 g)	9/28/81 to 10/4/87	2nd to 8th g.s.
842 (195 g) to 1180 (410 g)	10/12/54 to 4/27/60	2nd to 8th g.s.
710 (78 g) to 1040 (370 g)	5/19/84 to 9/28/86	2nd to 4th g.s.
718 (112 g) to 1088 (310 g)	10/21/81 to 6/24/89	2nd to 10th g.s.

*g.s. = growing season

females than in males. Tables 31 and 32 showing sizes of racers of various age classes and their relative numbers is based on the growth rates shown in Tables 29 and 30.

Sex and Age Ratios

A population sample of 107 racers was obtained from BSA over the 10-year period 1986 through 1995. All these snakes were found resting beneath shelters and the sample was expected to show true ratios of the sexes and of young to adults. There were 40 males to 67 females, and females outnumbered males in nearly all age categories.

The sample was obviously biased in having too few first-year young—only 12.1% of the total. The small size of these first-year snakes enables them to find shelter more easily and they are therefore less inclined than adults to use the artificial shelters on BSA.

More than two-thirds of the racers marked and released were never recaptured. One female was recorded 16 times and was captured each year over a 6-year period. A male was captured 15 times—one or more times each year over an 8-year period. Many others were recaptured frequently over shorter periods. Although certain individuals were recaptured frequently, the majority were recorded only once. It seems that part of the population consists of drifters that are not permanent residents in the areas where they are captured, but are merely moving through. In Table 25 figures for the sexes are similar, indicating that males and females do not differ much in longevity or time and place of activity. The 49% males to 51% females captured may not show the true sex ratio. Greater activity of the males renders them more susceptible to trap capture. Of 658 unmarked racers caught in May over a period of years 60% were males, and evidently intensified activity, associated with sexual search, caused them to be caught more often than females. Over the same period of years a sample of 735

TABLE 31. SVL (mm) of Racers of 17 Age Cohorts

	Males			Females		
	N	Mean	Range	N	Mean	Range
Young in Fall*	89	304.0±3.6	233–361	64	294.7±6.7	206–388
1st FGS*						
Spring-Early Summer	134	346.8	238–390	101	369.2	227–458
Late Summer-Fall	68	473.7	387–588	35	510.8	362–553
2nd FGS						
Spring-Early Summer	17	597.2±255	525–174	12	628.9±9.3	581–733
Late Summer-Fall	15	658.5±7.0	608–690	13	743.3±18.7	600–860
3rd FGS						
Spring-Early Summer	48	701.5±11.7	538–778	33	790.1±14.9	690–903
Late Summer-Fall	32	726.8±11.7	676–872	12	838.8±23.4	683–980
4th FGS						
Spring-Early Summer	50	751.7±11.7	676–880	19	870.9±10.7	810–936
Late Summer-Fall	18	767.2±8.4	720–850	15	892.5±14.5	786–1040
5th FGS						
Spring-Early Summer	32	803.7±7.4	715–900	20	935.9±17.6	873–1111
Late Summer-Fall	5	811.8±12.6	773–840	11	940.5±10.8	883–1000
6th FGS						
Spring-Early Summer	21	829.0±7.9	770–880	14	949.4±10.0	866–1005
Late Summer-Fall	6	557.8±16.5	825–902	10	959.7±16.4	950–1000
7th FGS	16	857.6±9.5	813–900	4	1005.2±26.5	906–1030
8th FGS	6	861.8±12.1	845–902	5	1017 ±36.1	900–1080
9th FGS	3	906.0	900–912	5	1068.7±10.5	995–1180
10th or Older FGS	3	995.3	926–1110	6	1098.7±29.5	1052–1123

*First-year young recognized by size; others individually marked.
  FGS = Full growing season.

TABLE 32. Age Cohorts and Their Percentages over Five Decades in Racers

Decade	1950s	1960s	1970s	1980s	1990s	Combined samples
Number of racers	735	703	184	452	432	2506
Age cohorts	%	%	%	%	%	%
2nd year	32.2	37.4	39.7	38.6	33.9	36.4
3rd year	20.9	25.2	22.8	23.0	27.2	23.8
4th year	20.1	16.2	20.0	15.9	16.3	17.7
5th year	12.0	9.4	5.5	8.9	9.5	9.1
6th year	5.0	5.1	3.8	3.3	7.2	4.9
7th year	3.8	2.7	3.8	2.7	1.8	3.0
8th year	1.9	2.1	0	2.0	1.6	1.5
Older than 8	4.1	1.9	4.4	5.6	2.5	3.7

unmarked racers captured in October, consisted of only 49% males. Of the 1808 racers captured and marked 73.6% were recorded in only one year, 15.1% were recorded in 2 years, 5.5% were recorded in 3 years, 2.4% were recorded in 4 years, and 0.8% were recorded in 5 years. In racers that were captured in more than 1 year, the years of capture tended to be consecutive, but occasionally a snake was missing from the records for 1 or more years: 81 snakes missed 1 year, 28 missed 2 consecutive years, 12 missed 3 years, 6 missed 4 years, 2 missed 5 years, 1 missed 7 years and 1 missed 8 years. Trends were significantly different in the sexes. Of the racers that missed just 1 year in the records 34.6% were males, but of those missing more than 1 year 62.8% were males.

Most records were of racers captured in traps; there were 1588 male records and 1592 female records, seeming to indicate a 50–50 sex ratio. However, the number of individual snakes was somewhat less, because each was recorded separately for each year of capture, and many were caught in two or more years. Males were recaptured somewhat more consistently than females perhaps reflecting greater activity. Among immatures, both in fall after hatching, and in the first full growing season after hibernation, males were more numerous: 425 to 310 females (57 to 43%). However, among adults, females were more numerous. From 1977 to 1990 inclusive 306 males and 385 females were captured, a ratio of 44 to 56%.

Immature racers were not captured in their true ratio to adults. They were often able to escape from the traps. In 1965 and 1966 special traps for such small snakes were used, and many more were caught than in other years. Many racers that were well above average adult size were found to have continued growing when they were recaptured. Table 30 shows some of the most significant records of racers recaptured after periods of years. Only the first and last record for each snake is shown, but there was an average of more than six captures per snake. It is shown that racers occasionally survived to ages of 8 to 11 years. The largest male recorded was 1110 mm SVL and 430 g at an estimated age of a little more

than 11 years, the largest female was 1180 mm SVL and 410 grams at an estimated age of 11 years and 8 months.

Numbers

In an earlier report on the racer (Fitch, 1963a) I presented many census figures for areas on FNHR and RET. The figures were based on live-trap records over the years 1955 to 1962 and capture-recapture ratios (Petersen Index). Three separate areas were involved: (1) bottomland fields in the northwestern part of FNHR (15.5 ha), (2) hilltop fields of regenerated prairie in the northeastern quadrant of FNHR (19.8 ha), and (3) hilltop fields including recently regenerated prairie on RET with two small fields on the adjacent northern edge of FNHR (55.5 ha). Census figures for each area varied widely from year to year and also within each year, depending how sampling periods were arranged. Average population densities per hectare (Petersen Index) for the three areas were respectively 4.7, 6.9, and 5.8.

These figures are of interest for comparison with more recent data from the same areas. As succession proceeded the racers' habitat deteriorated and populations dwindled. By the 1990s, formerly cultivated fields of area 1 had grown up to a dense woodland with closed canopy and racers were no longer present. The remaining 60% of area 1, formerly brome-grass pasture, had become overgrown with trees and brush thickets, with patches of grass remaining in a mosaic pattern. Racers had become rare; 15 were recorded in 7 years of sampling (by artificial shelters) in the 1990s. Area 2 had become overgrown with groves, and thorny thickets of blackberry and wild rose; remaining open patches were small and scattered and racers had become scarce. The extensive regenerated prairie of area 3 was also in transition to woody vegetation, with racer habitat deteriorating, but by the 1990s grassland still predominated on much of it and racers were present in moderate numbers. Quarry Field was a triangular hilltop of former pasture on the north edge of FNHR; it was part of area 3, but its succession was more advanced, with woody vegetation replacing the pasture grasses. From 1990 through 1997 only 13 racers were taken in Quarry Field where formerly they had been abundant. Of the 34 racers recorded in the deteriorated habitat of House Field and Quarry Field during the 1990s, 23 were first-year young, suggesting that the young tend to disperse to various habitats.

Table 33 shows 22 census calculations in 8 different years for two areas: Quarry Field, 1977 to 1982, when it was still open enough for racers to thrive, and a hilltop grassland area in the northern part of NESA maintained by annual mowing. The figures fluctuate widely and

TABLE 33. Population Densities of Racers on Two Study Areas Derived from Petersen Index Ratios

	Area (1=Quarry Field 2=NESA)	Year	Period of First Sampling	Period of Resampling	Number in First Sampling	Ratio of Recaptures to Total in Resampling	Estimated Population	Density/ha
2 to 4 mo	1	1977	4/1–6/30	7/1–10/1	20	6 of 32	107	28
Sampling Periods	1	1980	4/1–6/30	7/1–10/1	27	3 of 15	135	35
	2	1990	5/1–6/30	7/1–10/30	48	6 of 20	160	16
	2	1991	5/1–6/30	7/1–10/30	78	2 of 7	273	27
	2	1992	5/1–6/30	7/1–10/30	42	5 of 21	176	18
1 and 5 mo	2	1990	May	June–Oct.	44	19 of 49	114	11.8
Sampling Periods	2	1991	May	June–Oct.	73	19 of 31	119	12.3
	2	1992	May	June–Oct.	41	17 of 41	130	13.4
	2	1993	May	June–Oct.	21	3 of 26	182	18.2
1 mo	1	1977	May	June	19	2 of 11	104	27.4
Sampling Periods	1	1980	May	June	20	2 of 8	80	21
	1	1982	May	June	24	1 of 2	48	12.6
	2	1990	May	June	45	13 of 24	88	8.3
	2	1991	May	June	67	15 of 21	94	9.4
	2	1992	May	June	59	7 of 19	160	16
	2	1993	May	June	21	2 of 11	116	11.6
0.5 mo	1	1977	May 1–15	May 16–31	17	6 of 13	37	9.7
Sampling Periods	1	1980	May 1–15	May 16–31	11	1 of 8	88	28
	2	1991	May 1–15	May 16–31	47	8 of 31	182	18.2
	2	1992	May 1–15	May 16–31	10	3 of 35	116	11.6
	2	1992	June 1–15	June 16–30	17	2 of 10	85	8.5
	2	1992	May 1–15	May 16–30	25	4 of 24	150	15.0
	2	1994	May 16–21	May 22–28	21	2 of 12	126	12.6

obviously are inexact for any one census. Year to year differences may reflect changes in the numbers of snakes, but also are influenced by the chances of sampling, especially when the sample included only one or two recaptures. With relatively long sampling periods, extending over the entire season of activity, relatively high figures were obtained than with 1-month or samplings with 0.5-month samples. No doubt this trend is due to population turnover with loss of marked individuals and their replacement by newcomers, so the shortest sampling periods should yield the most reliable figures. However, their samples are so small that their ratios are much influenced by chance. Seven censuses of Quarry Field with sampling periods of different lengths, in 2 years, averaged 23.1/ha (9.7–35.1) and 16 censuses of the NESA pens area in 5 years averaged 14.2/ha (8.3–27.0); see Table 33. Biomass would amount to 2.44 kg and 1.99 kg respectively. Both Quarry Field and the NESA sampling area were near to other areas that supported populations of racers with interchange occurring. However, each area was largely enclosed by partial barriers—a county road and blocks of woodland that tended to inhibit free interchange of snakes and Quarry Field was more nearly separated.

Geographic Differentiation

Several subspecies of racers are recognized with striking changes in size and color There are important but less obvious changes in habitat food habits, and reproduction. Literature records indicate that compared with local *C. c. flaviventris, C. c. constrictor* of the northeastern United States is more melanistic, is several percent larger, is more partial to woodland habitat, and takes larger prey, chiefly vertebrates. On the other hand, racers from west of the Continental Divide are markedly smaller than *C. c. flaviventris* and paler colored, prefer more open habitats with shortgrass cover, and prey mainly on insects (Fitch, 1963a).

In local *C. c. flaviventris* adult SVL averages 765 mm (male 707, female 822). In contrast, some populations are much smaller and some much larger: *C. mormon* (west coast) 563 (males 515, females 600); *C. c. anthicus* (northern Louisiana) 582; *C. c. oaxaca* (southern Texas) 664; *C. c. priapus* (Florida) 713 (Fitch, 1963A). In Virginia, Mitchell (1994) recorded an average SVL of 1036 mm and weight of 351 g for males, 1020 and 350 for females contrasting with the much smaller racers of my study. The black racers of Virginia are more than twice the bulk of their Kansas counterparts, and seem to have no sexual size dimorphism. Their hatchlings are only slightly larger (6.3 versus 4.6 g), but clutches average almost twice as large (21.0 versus 11.8). In Arkansas, Trauth et al. (1994) recorded 19 clutches of yolked follicles or oviductal eggs of *C. c. priapus* that averaged 16.9±2.0 (8–26).

Crotalus horridus

Traits of the Species

The timber rattlesnake's geographic range corresponds with the Deciduous Forest Biome of the eastern United States. Preferred habitat is open, rocky woodland or woodland edge, but with some geographic differences; in the northern states open sunny places are necessary, but in the south the snakes may frequent dense woods or thickets along streams. (See Plates 9 & 10). There is geographic variation in body size (largest in the south), in color pattern, and in various ecological traits. In the north (and at high altitudes) hibernation may extend over more than half the year, with dozens or (formerly) hundreds of snakes gathering at traditional hibernacula such as talus slopes having southern exposure. In milder southern climates the snakes hibernate singly or in small aggregations. In northern populations females may require as much as 9 years to reach sexual maturity and subsequently, may reproduce only at 3-year intervals. In the local population males mature in their third year, females in their third or fourth, and annual or biennial reproduction is most frequent. Females palpated were found to have an average of 8.9 eggs or embryos, and the average number of viable young per litter is believed to be between seven and eight. In their first year, young snakes most often add two rattle segments to the natal button, and adult males also most often gain two segments per year but females may have only a single annual ecdysis. Timber rattlesnakes are sit-and-wait predators, preying almost entirely on mammals. Runways of prey animals are detected by scent, and the snake positioning itself beside the trail may wait for hours or days for a victim to pass within striking range. Most often the snake strikes its prey at close range, and venom injected into the body cavity causes rapid collapse. There is no struggle. The snake follows the victim's scent trail and finds it dead or dying. Woodrats, tree squirrels, young cottontails, and voles make up most of the adults' food; first-year young eat shrews and various kinds of mice. In adults an annual mortality rate near 25% is indicated. Locally, adult males average 1045 mm SVL and 0.9 kg; females average 927 mm and 0.53 kg (Table 34).

In contrasting environments, such as montane Appalachian forests and New Jersey pine barrens, timber rattlesnakes tend to select habitats that are similar with respect to canopy structure, logs, and surface vegetation (Reinert, 1993). However, adult males, gravid females, and nongravid females all differ from each other in the habitats that they prefer. Adult males choose deep forests with abundant shade and relatively low temperatures, whereas gravid females choose more open sites with abundant sunshine, permitting them to bask and maintain a high body temperature. Nongravid females choose habitats most like those of adult males but measurably more open (Reinert, 1993).

Behavior

Timber rattlesnakes tend to be nocturnal in hot weather but are diurnal when daytime air temperatures are near their preferendum. Normal locomotion is by rectilinear crawling dependent on rib movements and is so slow that the movement is likely to be unnoticed. The snakes are usually associated with dense cover, and the bold pattern is so effectively cryptic that the snake may not be seen by a person passing nearby or even stepping over it. The snake tends to rely on crypsis rather than aggression and is reluctant to sound its rattles. On several occasions, trailing individuals that were carrying transmitters, I actually stepped on a rattlesnake before

TABLE 34. Sizes of Timber Rattlesnakes in a Local Population of Northeastern Kansas

	N	Mean SVL (mm)	Mean Weight (g)
Adult			
Male	45	1050±6.6 (825–1360)	868±92(260–2084)
Female	37	927±14.2 (803–1082)	530±39.5(340–1100)
Neonate	19	324.7± (298–345)	26.5±0.84(19.2–29.1)
Yearling			
(Fall)			
Male	7	620±9.0 (606–670)	156±6.5(134–188)
Female	5	574±8.5 (548–600)	122±5.6(103–137)
2-year-old			
(Fall)			
Male	8	730±32.4 (658–915)	237±48.6(150–518)
Female	5	698±64.5(504–814)	290 (71–313)

seeing it. Even then it did not always rattle, but uncoiled and slithered away silently and rapidly. A timber rattler that is threatened rattles vigorously, with its forebody raised in an S-shaped striking coil, its tongue extended, waving slowly, its coils shifting in a writhing mass. A snake that is grasped and restrained struggles to free itself with violent lateral thrashing, tries to bite and releases jets of musk in a spray of fine droplets that may distract the handler by striking his eyes. Prey is obtained by ambush (Reinert, Cundall, & Bushar, 1984). Even in darkness the snake can detect approach and position of the prey by its heat sensitive pit. The close range strike results in deep penetration and a lethal bite. The snake recoils from the stroke and lies immobile for periods of minutes before setting out on olfactory search for the dead or dying victim.

Responses to Succession

During the span of this study numbers of timber rattlesnakes declined sharply, as indicated by numbers recorded per decade on FNHR and immediately adjacent areas including the county road: 1950s: 67; 1960s: 19; 1970s: 0; 1980s: 2; 1990s: 2. Ecological succession caused habitat deterioration; although the timber rattlesnake is known as a forest inhabitant the spread and development of forest in an area free from fire and grazing has produced conditions unfavorable to the snakes. Dense undergrowth and an unbroken leaf canopy eliminates the open sunny places favorable for basking that seem to be a prime requirement for the snakes. NESA, adjoining FNHR on the north, retains extensive open areas of prairie and mowed fields, and continues to support a population of rattlesnakes. This suggests that habitat deterioration on the adjoining FNHR was the cause of their decline there.

Other changes affecting the local rattlesnake population were: (1) Steady increase in the human population, with a dozen new residences on the periphery of the combined FNHR-NESA and increased volume of traffic on the county roads and private driveways, with many snakes becoming traffic casualties and others killed when found in fields, gardens, and the vicinity of buildings, (2) Drastic decline in the population of woodrats (*Neotoma floridana*) during the early 1950s, with slow recovery through the 1980s.

Of 118 captures, 62 were at limestone outcrops and 36 were away from the outcrops mostly in relatively open situations; 27 were in fields (often at woodland edge), 14 were on roads or driveways, and 12 were beside buildings. Of the 62 snakes at hilltop outcrops 39 were in places that had southward exposure, 13 had eastward exposure, 10 had westward exposure, but none faced north.

Replacement of Fangs

Thirty-six of the timber rattlesnakes captured were checked for accessory fangs. Normally the fang on each side is solidly fused with the maxillary bone but is replaced from time to time. A replacement fang that has completed its growth moves forward to a second socket on the maxillary beside the older fang. For a short time both may be functional, but soon the older fang loosens, its base is eroded so that it breaks away from the maxillary, and eventually is swallowed. Of 16 first-year timber rattlesnakes eight had an accessory fang in some stage of replacement on one side or the other (but not solidly attached to the maxillary). Of 13 second- or third-year snakes three had an accessory fang. Of 25 adults and adolescents from NESA and neighboring areas in the 1990s, 17 lacked accessory fangs, 4 had an extra fang about to be shed on the right side, and 4 others had an extra fang on the left.

Spatial Relationships

Spatial relationships in timber rattlesnakes were studied from the records of those marked and recaptured after intervals of from 1 day up to more than 6 years, and from those equipped with radio transmitters and monitored once or twice daily over periods of days or weeks (Table 35). Neonates recaptured after periods of 1 to 9 days ($\bar{x}$ = 5) had made movements up to 95 m ($\bar{x}$ = 31.2 m), but another neonate shifted 318 m in 19 days, a 2-year-old female moved 18 m in 25 days and an adult female moved 12.8 m in 9 days. An adult male moved 174 m in 15 days. All 10 of these records were in fall and were near rock outcrops where the snakes may have been orienting to hibernacula. Three immature males each recaptured after about 1 year had moved an average of 243 m (177–336). From 25 April 1952 to 19 October 1955 a large adult female had moved 85 m. Three adult male movements averaged 555 m (153–896) over intervals that averaged 45 months (16–58).

Table 35 summarizes the records of six snakes trailed by radiotelemetry including three adult males, two adult females (one gravid), and one half grown (2-year old) female. It is noteworthy that on 30% of the occasions when snakes were checked they were found to have made no movement since the previous day. Most often the snake would be found in a tight coil, and often it appeared to be in exactly the same position as on the day before. Perhaps such snakes were in ambush positions and had oriented themselves with respect to scent trails left by rodents as found by Reinert, Cundall, and Bushar (1984), but trails were not visible. Maximum daily movements for the six snakes trailed were 510, 431, 418, 418, 256, and 35 m.

TABLE 35. Movements of Timber Rattlesnakes Trailed by Radiotelemetry

	Dates of Trailing	Days Followed	Days of No Movement	Mean Daily Movement (m)	Mean Daily Movement (m) Including Days of No Movement	Span of Movements (m)
Adult Male	9–29 July 1966	21	11	136	124	501
Adult Male	6 June to 30 July 1966	40	23	17.4	11.9	219
Adult Male	11 September to 22 October 1987	41	11	57.1	37.6	683
Adult Female (gravid)	15–22 June 1966	7	2	156	117	841
Adult Female (nongravid)	11–24 September 1987	13	7	86.5	31.4	484
2-year-old Female	6–12 September 1989	7	2	412	247	1003
Combined Sample		129	56	94.5	57.5	576

Ordinarily the snakes trailed did not move or rattle when they were approached and since they were usually in dense, concealing vegetation there was risk of stepping on them before they were seen. In 53% of the cases the snake was in grass or other ground vegetation, in 31% it was in woodland, and in 11% in brush thickets. In 63% of the cases the snake was not seen even after it was located because it was sheltered in a hollow or beneath a flat rock or dense ground vegetation. Active snakes that were found comprised only 4.6% of the total. The timber rattlesnakes trailed tended to move consistently in one direction for days or even weeks, but then, presumably, reaching its range limits, the snake would change to a new direction. Features that influenced behavior and resulted in linear travel routes were: rock wall (2 instances), county road (1 instance), and the forest-field border (3 instances). In keeping with the habits of a sit-and-wait predator, each snake spent relatively little time in moving and was usually inactive but in potential ambush position. Activity was highly erratic and seemed to lack any rhythm. A snake might sojourn for 2 days or more before moving on. There were seven 2-day sojourns, three of 3-days each and one each of 5, 7, 9, 12, and 18 days. The 18-day sojourn was at the end of the season of activity and the snake was underground preparing to hibernate, but it then made a final shift of 76 m to the actual hibernaculum.

Spatial relations of timber rattlesnakes are best known from the telemetric studies of Brown, Pyle, Greene, and Friedlander (1982) in northern New York, and Reinert and Zappalorti (1988) in the New Jersey pine barrens. Brown et al. tracked the snakes from their winter dens to summer habitat — distances averaging 1400 m for males and 280 m for females. They found that mobility was greatly increased immediately after ecdysis. Snakes seemed to use the same migratory routes that they had followed in spring when returning to dens in autumn. The snakes controlled their body temperatures by moving in and out of rock crevices or making slight shifts between shade and sunlight in grass and shrub habitats. Mean body temperature was 26.9 °C for 157 readings; in clear weather it averaged some-what higher, 30.1 °C. Reinert and Zappalorti (1988) followed 20 snakes equipped with transmitters and found mean movement per day of 18.9±2.33 m, range length of 1036±139 m, convex home range polygon 27.4±4.47 ha, 45.17±13.577 ha for 95% isopleth and 4.52±1.509 ha for the 50% isopleth. There was no difference among males, nongravid females, and gravid females in total distance moved, mean movement per day, nor in 50% or 95% isopleths. However, males had significantly longer ranges, mean 1463.1 m vs. 995.0 m for nongravid females and 644.6 m for gravid females. Habitat partitioning was noticeable; gravid females stayed in relatively open habitat, typically along sand roads. In Wisconsin, Keenlyne (1972) found that gravid females stayed on south-facing, grassy slopes, with large flat rocks which were used for thermoregulation, and they did not take food.

Most of the timber rattlesnakes caught at hilltop outcrops were found in October, with smaller numbers in September, November, and April, but few during the summer months. The snakes come to these outcrops in search of hibernacula, and evidently they hibernate singly or in small groups, as no concentrations have been found, although in the northeastern states and in the Appalachians farther south the species is notorious for its denning aggregations (Martin, 1992). Of the snakes found at hilltop outcrops, half (37) were neonates. Evidently the outcrops provide birthing shelters as well as hibernacula. Only eight first-year young were found away from the hilltop outcrops and these encounters were in May (1), June (2), July (1), September (1), and October (3).

In their radiotelemetric studies of timber rattlesnakes in the New Jersey pine barrens, Reinert and Zappalorti (1988) obtained evidence that young of the year were guided to secure hibernacula by following the scent trails of adults. In the barrens adults hibernate singly in burrows along streams in the lowland habitat of white cedar swamps. On various occasions in October, when adults of either sex were travelling from summer ranges to the cedar swamps, or had arrived and were near their hibernation burrows, young of the year were seen to follow their trails, or were found coiled beside or actually on top of the adult.

Kinds of Prey

Only 14 of the timber rattlesnakes examined had prey in their stomachs, as follows: three each of *Sylvilagus floridanus, Microtus ochrogaster,* and *Peromyscus leucopus;* and one each of *Sciurus niger, S. carolinensis, Neotoma floridana,* and *Cryptotis parva.* The larger animals including the rabbits, squirrels, and woodrat were eaten by fully adult snakes (1073–1270 mm SVL). Both squirrels and the woodrat were adults, the three rabbits were immatures, partly grown and large enough to have left the nest and become independent. One of the voles was eaten by an adult snake. The shrew and one of the white-footed mice were eaten by first-year young. Other items including two voles, two white-footed mice, and a cottonrat, were eaten by well-grown young ranging from 646 to 883 mm SVL. Thus it appears that cottontails, tree squirrels, and woodrats are the mainstay of the diet for adults and make up most of the biomass eaten locally. White-footed mice are eaten by snakes of all sizes but are important chiefly as food for immatures, and shrews are probably important for neonates that are too small to ingest other kinds of prey.

Reproduction

It is known, from studies in other parts of the range, that August is the main breeding season for the timber rattlesnake. On 25 August a pair was found beneath a metal shelter on BSA, the only time adults were found together. It seems that ovulation takes place soon after emergence from hibernation, in spring. Those females that are reproductive in the current season emerge from hibernation with large yolked follicles. Pregnancy lasts through most of the season of activity. Most young are born in September.

In October 1950 an adult female was captured soon after giving birth. Subsequently, over a period of 15 days seven neonates were observed at the site within a radius of a few meters. One was found on 30 September, three on 7 October, five on 13 October, one on 15 October, and one on 17 October. On each occasion the young snakes were found tightly coiled, separated from supposed siblings by a meter or more, and it seemed that their continued proximity and slow dispersal involved mutual affinity. Those recaptured had moved 1.5 m in 4 days, 1.8 m in 6 days, 1.8 m in 6 days, 0 in 7 days and 6.1 m in 7 days.

Eggs were palpated in 13 females and numbered 14, 14, 14, 11, 11, 11, 8, 8, 6, 5, 5, 5, and 4, mean 8.9±0.88.

Three counts of 14 were from females of 1050, 1050, and 1038 mm SVL—near maximum for the local population, and these females had incomplete rattle strings of 9, 10, and 10 segments hence were relatively old. The lowest counts 6, 5, 5, 5, and 4 were from relatively small females 803 to 902 mm SVL. They had rattle strings of seven or eight segments and all were probably primiparous 3-year olds. In his population study of *C. horridus* in Warren County, New York, William S. Brown (personal communication, 1984) found that 186 eggs ovulated by 20 females produced 149 viable young, with 12 stillborn and 25 infertile. If similar ratios apply in Kansas, the mean litter size of 8.9 found by palpation would be reduced by 20% to about 7.2 live young per litter. Of 18 adult females in spring and early summer 10 were gravid but eight others were nongravid, suggesting a biennial cycle in the local population. However, five of the eight nongravid females were within the size range of primiparae and perhaps merely indicate postponement of maturity until the fourth year in more than half of adolescent females. For fully mature females (over 900 mm SVL) the ratio is seven gravid to three nongravid, suggesting that the majority may reproduce annually. The ratios of three-year-olds, four-year-olds and old adults that are fecund annually cannot be determined without larger samples but it is evident that the Kansas population has a high reproductive potential contrasting with that in the northern part of the range (e.g., northern New York) where Brown (1991) found that maturity may be postponed until at least the seventh year and a triennial cycle prevails.

Size, Age, and the Rattles

With each successive ecdysis a rattlesnake acquires a new rattle segment—the thickened corneous tissue at the end of the tail, adaptively altered in shape with grooves for interlocking of the previous slough. The diameter of the rattle segment reflects the size of the snake at the time of shedding, but there is allometric growth. Nineteen neonates averaged 323.7 mm SVL; and the button width averaged 1.77% of SVL. In adults that percentage is decreased; 23 females 800 to 1082 mm SVL had basal segments averaging 1.35% SVL and in 12 males of 825 to 1195 mm SVL the corresponding figure was 1.30%.

Compared with other snakes, rattlesnakes have tails that are short, thick, and muscular. The locomotory function is lost. The main function of the tail is to vibrate the rattle. Also, in males the tail houses the paired hemipenes. Males have longer tails than females. In 44 first-year males tails averaged 8.23±0.1(7.1-10.0)% of SVL, whereas in 43 first-year females tails averaged 7.12%±0.01(5.8-8.4) of SVL. In 29 adult

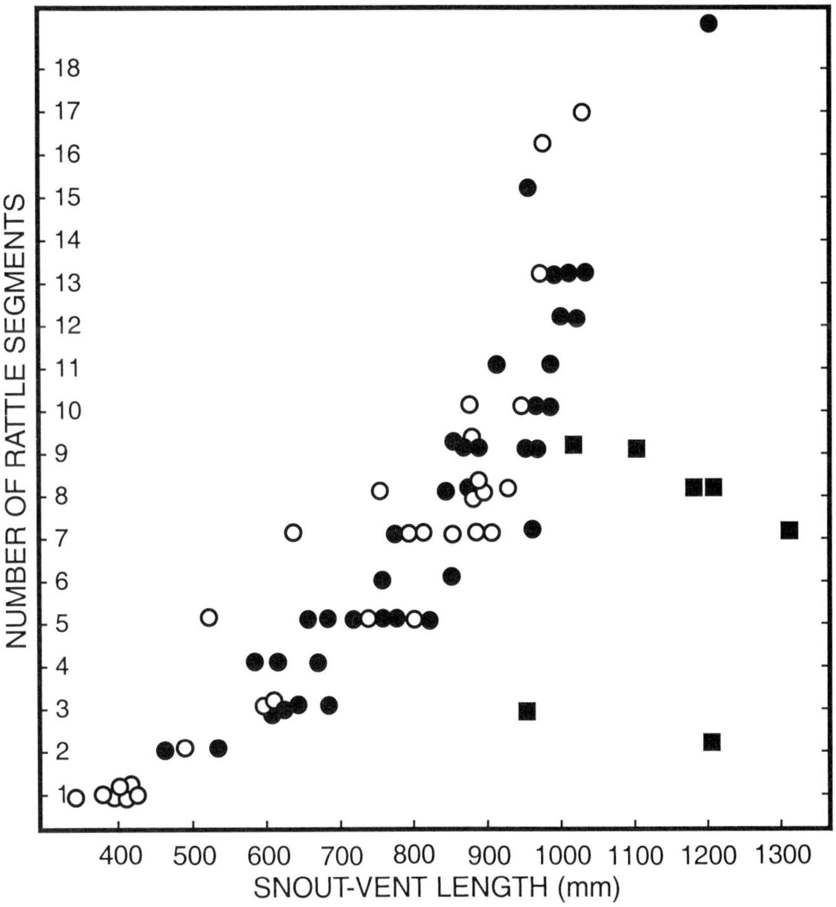

Figure 17. Snout-vent lengths of timber rattlesnakes vs. number of rattle segments in intact or projected strings, 1980s and 1990s. Dots show males; open circles show females; squares show large adults (all males) in which rattle strings lacked discernible taper, and hence the number lost (and total number produced) could not be estimated. In snakes of more than 850 mm SVL, one or more distal segments were almost always lacking, but the number lost could usually be estimated from the size and taper of those still attached.

males tails averaged 8.60%±0.10(7.6-9.9) of SVL and in 18 adult females tails averaged 6.64%±0.10(5.8-7.7). It seems that males' tails increased slightly in relative length during ontogeny whereas female tails underwent slight decreases.

The terminal rattle segment or button averaged 5.7 mm (5.2-6.7) in width in 29 snakes, and successive segments were: 7.21, 8.51, 9.56, 10.41, 11.21, 11.71, and 12.2 with no significant difference between the sexes (Fitch, 1985). By the time the eighth segment is acquired the snakes are young adults and subsequently annual gains in SVL and rattle diameter are relatively small, with males growing faster than females. The largest rattle segments measured were 16.0, 15.6, 15.2 and 14.9 mm in snakes that were 1195 to 1318 mm in SVL. Figure 17 shows correlation between SVL of snake and number of rattle segments. The largest male (1318 mm SVL) was 22% longer than the largest female (1082) and 17 of 41 adult males were longer than that female.

The number, size, and taper of segments in an individual rattle string provide an important clue to a snake's age and growth rate. In young and newly matured adults each rattle segment is markedly larger than the one distal to it. In adults it is fairly common to find a rattle segment slightly smaller than those

adjoining it distally indicating a period of suboptimum conditions. Adult males, being more active and more capable of sustained growth, shed more frequently than adult females. It might be expected that the interval between sheds would be affected by pregnancy or by food scarcity, but these relationships have not been demonstrated.

For 23 young in fall (average date 15 October) mean SVL was 386 mm, 19% more than average length at birth. For eight young captured in spring (average date 27 May) mean SVL was 398 mm. Table 36 shows that young with no rattle segments other than the natal button have been found mainly in fall in the weeks after birth, but also have been found in April and May, and

TABLE 36. Seasonal Incidence of Rattle Strings in Immature Timber Rattlesnakes

Number of Rattle Segments	April	May	June	July	Aug.	Sept.	Oct.
Button only	2	2	2			3	26
Button+1			1	1			1
Button+2		1	1	1	1	2	4
Button+3			3			1	3
Button+4		2	2	1			5
Button+5		3		1		1	1
Button+6	1	1	1	1	1	2	1

as late as 4 June. Young with a second rattle segment are present in June and July. One juvenile of 495 mm SVL, having a button and one additional segment when captured on 10 October 1955, had gained more than 50% in length (if it was of average size at birth) and may have been either an accelerated first-year individual or a second-year individual retarded in its rattle development.

One-year-old snakes in fall normally have two segments plus the natal button. The fourth segment is acquired in the second summer — as early as 30 May. Two-year-olds typically have five rattles (four segments plus the button) but may have four or six. Three-year-olds typically have six segments plus the button and this group includes primiparous gravid females, the smallest a little more than 800 mm in SVL. Sexual maturity is attained early in males. On 23 May 1965 a male of 682 mm SVL, early in his third year with a string of five rattle segments including the button, was found to have abundant motile sperm.

Table 37 shows a tentative correlation of age, SVL and number of rattle segments for the timber rattlesnakes of

my sample. It represents an attempt to show survivorship in a sample of 146 snakes, with the assumption that 1-year-olds have three rattle segments including the natal button, and that thereafter males add two segments annually; females only one. Snakes that had lost rattle segments were assumed to have had the same number as similar sized individuals of the same sex. On this basis 93.5% of those in the sample were believed to be 7 years old or younger. Eight males having SVL of 1175, 1195, 1196, 1197, 1230, 1248, 1270, and 1270 mm and rattle strings of 15 to 11 segments of uniform width were of indeterminate ages. Obviously each had lost many segments — at least six acquired during growth from birth to maturity, and perhaps others after attaining adult size. From known rates of attrition, and growth of rattles it seems that most were within the age range 8 to 10 years.

Table 38 shows growth in length and gains in rattle segments in the marked rattlesnakes recaptured, indicating that both young snakes and adult males gain about two segments per year. For immatures that supposition is supported by the concentrations in fall of

TABLE 37. Tentative Correlation of Age, Size (SVL), and Number of Rattle Segments* in a Sample of Timber Rattlesnakes

	N			
	Male	Female	SVL (mm)	Rattle Segments
Fall of Birth	9	17	377.9±7.5 (310–345)	button only in 25
				Button+1 in 1
Following Spring	5	3	406.9±22.4 (324–591)	Button only in 7
				Button+1 in 1
1-Year-Old	14	6	615.9±38.3 (548–712)	Button+2 in 10
				Button+3 in 3
2-Year-Old	18	9	717.8±19.3 (504–834)	Button+3 in 2
				Button+4 in 13
				Button+5 in 3
3-Year-Old	9	5	849.1±24.8 (644–999)	Button+5 in 2
				Button+6 in 9
				Button+7 in 3
4-Year-Old	11		925.5±20.0 (875–1003)	Button+8 in 9 B+9 in 1
		6	856.4±37.4 (760–900)	Button+8 in 3
5-Year-Old	5		1028±8.4 (1003–1080)	Button+9 in 1, B+10 in 1,
		4	904±7.7 (885–922)	B+11 in 2 ♂, B+8 in 3 ♀
6-Year-Old	6		1127±7.8 (1110–1147)	Button+12 in 1**
		4	965±16.4 (933–1010)	Button+13 in 2**
7-Year-Old	4		1177±8.6 (1150–1196)	Button+11 in 1**
		2	1016(1000–1031)	
8-Year-Old	3		1239(1230–1248)	Button+15 in 1**
		4	1044	
9-Year-Old		1	1082	5 many missing **
15-Year-Old	1	—	1270	26 many missing***

*Rattle strings missing in several. Incomplete strings were projected on the basis of size of the terminal segment.

**All segments of uniform diameter, indicating that those gained before maturity have been lost in snakes that are relatively old but of indeterminate age.

***When first captured on 2 June 1953 this male was near maximum size, SVL 1270 mm, and had 5 rattle segments of uniform width. He was estimated to be at least 9 years old then — at least 7 years to grow to that length while producing a string of 8 to 11 tapered segments and 2 more years to produce the 5 equal-sized segments. At a later capture on 16 October 1954 he had added 4 new segments bringing his total to around 20, and at a final capture on 13 October 1959 he had added another 6 segments, bringing his total to a possible 23 to 26 segments at a probable age of about 15 years.

TABLE 38. Growth and Addition of Rattle Segments in Individually Marked Timber Rattlesnakes

Age & sex	Dates of Capture		SVL (mm)		Rattle Segments	
	1st	2nd	1st	2nd	1st	2nd
Adult Male	2 June 1953	26 October 1954	1270	1270	5	9
Adult Female	9 May 1983	22 April 1986	966	1050	7	10
1-Year-Old Male	26 September 1961	15 October 1962	610	647	button+2	button+4
First-Year-Male	17 October 1960	9 September 1961	373	613	button only	button+2
First-Year-Male	9 November 1954	23 October 1955	423	632	button only	button+2

snakes with button only, button plus two and button plus four segments. The single adult female recaptured long after marking had gained three segments in approximately 3 years, supporting the finding in California *C. viridis* that ecdysis is less frequent and rattle development less rapid in females (Fitch, 1949).

Geographic Differentiation

The timber rattlesnakes of my study were much smaller than those measured by Gibbons (1972) in South Carolina. The SVL ratios of Kansas to South Carolina snakes were, for adult males, adult females, and neonates, respectively, 80%, 82%, and 86%; for weights the same three groups were 51.7%, 42.8%, and 85.5%. In the South Carolina study, evidence indicated that females matured and reproduced in their sixth year, males in their fourth year. In northern New York near the species northeastern range limit Brown (1991) recorded mean sizes only slightly larger than in Kansas timber rattlesnakes, but he found that female reproduction was delayed, usually first occurring in the ninth or tenth year (mean 9.3, range 7–11). In contrast, the Kansas snakes may mature much earlier, males in their second year, females in their third. Some mature females may reproduce in successive years, others biennially. Because of early maturity and relatively frequent reproduction, the reproductive potential in Kansas is much higher than in the eastern part of the range. In Pennsylvania, Galligan and Dunson (1979) found relatively small adult size (mean SVL 912 in males, 840 in females) with bulk only about two-thirds of Kansas snakes. Of 173 captured snakes, 111 (64%) were males; of adult females 38% were gravid indicating a breeding cycle of 2 or 3 years. The smallest gravid female had SVL of 770 mm and was estimated to be 5 years old. Litters averaged seven young with one undeveloped egg. Neonates from 220 to 280 mm SVL, had grown to from 400 to 500 mm in their third summer, 640 to 740 in their fourth summer and 700 to 900 mm in their fifth. At the northwestern extreme of the range in Wisconsin, Keenlyne (1972) found a biennial breeding cycle in females.

Diadophis punctatus

Traits of the Species

The ringneck is a small xenodontine having a slender, elongated body, tiny head, and smooth scales. It is a polytypic transcontinental species that occurs in many habitats including boreal coniferous forest, southern swamps, prairie, and chaparral. It is subject to striking geographic variation in body size and ecological traits, but less variation in color and pattern. Except for a narrow, pale orange neck ring the dorsum is uniformly dark, brown, or almost black, or most typically, dark bluish-gray. The venter is orange-yellow, gradually brightening posteriorly to coral red on the underside of the tail. (See Plate 11.) When attacked or frightened, a ringneck generally responds with an aposematic display; it coils the tail in a tight spiral with the underside turned upward showing its bright color — ostensibly a warning of distastefulness to avian predators, supported by the foul-smelling musk, which oozes from the vent and is rapidly smeared over the body surface by squirming movements.

Ringnecks are secretive. Rarely venturing into the open, they stay under shelter of flat rocks, or the surface mat of vegetation. Major food sources for ringnecks in other parts of the range are certain insects, salamanders, anurans, and small snakes (other than conspecifics), but the local population feeds upon earthworms almost to the exclusion of other kinds of prey.

The Kansas subspecies *Diadophis punctatus arnyi* extends south into central Texas, but with striking changes in habits. In Texas both *D. p. arnyi* and its much larger neighbor *D. p. regalis* prey on small snakes (Gehlbach, 1974). Attacking ringnecks were observed to seize their prey and cling persistently to it for 40 to 375 minutes, until the attacked snake was dead or paralyzed, apparently from the effects of venom injected by enlarged, recurved, fanglike teeth at the rear end of the maxillary bone.

For local ringnecks the preferred habitat is the forest-grassland border, and phenomenally high densities are attained, often more than 1000 per ha, exceeding in number and biomass all associated species of snakes combined. Body temperatures between 25° and 29.5 °C are preferred. Eggs average 3.9 (1–10) per clutch, are elongate and sausage-shaped, and are laid in late June or early July, often in communal underground nests. Clutch size is proportional to female size. Females attain sexual maturity in their third year at SVL ca. 235 mm, males in their second year. Average adult SVL is 254 mm in males, 288 mm in females; growth continues (at reduced rate) after attainment of sexual maturity, with an annual mortality rate of approximately 20%. Some snakes survive to an age of 20 years or more. Successive capture points for individual snakes were usually within 130 m suggesting home ranges of perhaps 0.65 ha. Females are more vagile than males and adults are more vagile than immatures. Some ringnecks hibernate within their summer ranges, in tunnels made by burrowing animals; others migrate to crevices in hilltop limestone outcrops.

Variation in Pattern

In the local population there is much individual variation in the dorsal color and in the amount and distribution of ventral pigmentation. Ventral markings may take the form of spots, blotches, dots, or transverse bars. Regardless of size or shape, markings may be perfectly symmetrical or they may be irregular. The pattern may change from one part of the venter to another. It is of interest that several of the pattern types occurring locally have been used to characterize subspecies in other parts of the range. In an earlier publication (Fitch, 1975) I described and figured six types of ventral pattern in the local population. Table 39 shows the relative frequency of these types and indicates slight differences between the sexes. Types A and D are slightly more frequent in females than in males, whereas type B is more frequent in males.

Determinants of Size

Table 40 compares lengths (SVL) and weights of adult *Diadophis* in 38 different years over a 46-year period.

49

TABLE 39. Relative Frequency of Six Types of Ventral Patterns in 523 Ringneck Snakes from Northeastern Kansas (Fitch, 1975)

Pattern Type	N	Percentages		
		Male	Female	Combined
A	128	21.6	30.0	24.5
B	170	37.3	23.3	32.5
C	6	1.1	1.1	1.1
D	193	34.4	41.6	37.0
E	6	1.5	0.6	1.2
F	20	4.1	3.3	3.7

A: A median black spot on each ventral scute
B: A pair of spots on each ventral
C: A pair of widened blotches on each ventral
D: Irregular ventral spotting with no clear-cut pattern
E: Ventral surface nearly immaculate with only occasional spots
F: A black bar along posterior edge of each ventral scute

The small year-to-year differences are due to chance sampling, to minor changes in the age structure of the population, and to the food supply. The variance in weight is much greater than the variance in SVL, as an individual snake may undergo substantial losses or gains in weight while maintaining the same SVL or making only slight gains.

Females are consistently heavier than males but less so than might be expected since they exceed male SVL by 11%. In early May ovarian follicles rapidly acquire yolk and are ovulated before the end of the month. In May and June females carrying their eggs exceed their nongravid weights by about 23%. Weights change rapidly in both sexes throughout the season of activity and the trends are somewhat different in the sexes. Female weights are more variable, and despite their greater length, females average only a little heavier than males in spring and fall; at those seasons some appear thin, not having fully recovered the energy invested in their egg clutches at the end of June. Eggs are retained in the oviducts for approximately a month

TABLE 40. Yearly Variation in Size in Ringneck Snakes on FNHR

	Male			Female		
Year	N	SVL ($\bar{x}$)	Weight (g)	N	SVL ($\bar{x}$)	Weight (g)
1950	20	251 ±4.8 (220–281)	6.34±0.37	22	271.5±4.7 (228–325)	7.17±0.53
1951	42	242.1±10.7 (220–315)		24	272.8±6.6 (227–320)	
1953	25	247.9±11.8 (223–307)		16	278.1±7.0 (228–340)	
1954	24	256.4±4.2 (224–296)		21	268.6±5.8 (223–313)	
1955	51	245.5±2.7 (220–291)	5.49±0.23	29	269.4±5.2 (223–337)	6.4 ±0.66
1956	28	253.9±2.9 (220–290)		18	283.9±6.8 (222–328)	
1957	42	245.3±2.2 (220–270)	4.94±0.16	50	280.0±3.2 (220–356)	7.35±0.34
1958	50	254.7±2.4 (224–299)		50	265.1±11.2 (222–338)	
1959	50	257.7±2.8 (223–310)	5.05±0.73	49	266.2±3.8 (230–322)	5.15±0.43
1960	56	248.7±2.6 (220–305)	5.41±0.17	50	273.2±13.1 (235–340)	7.65±0.49
1961	50	254.5±2.5 (220–287)	5.39±0.13	50	279.3±4.9 (221–368)	6.84±0.69
1962	60	243.3±2.2 (220–289)		60	266.2±7.2 (223–320)	8.30±0.46
1963	50	248.2±3.1 (220–285)	5.65±0.17	50	275.2±4.2 (220–342)	7.11±0.51
1964	50	246.4±2.0 (222–284)	5.80±0.17	50	267.7±3.6 (220–339)	5.53±0.35
1965	50	248.2±2.4 (220–281)	5.14±0.14	50	266.0±4.2 (220–324)	5.36±0.28
1966	50	248.3±2.6 (220–307)	5.26±0.16	50	270.7±3.2 (228–309)	5.95±0.20
1967	50	241.3±1.8 (220–268)	4.66±1.02	50	272.0±3.5 (229–342)	5.18±0.26
1968	50	250.7±10.5 (221–300)		50	272.0±4.1 (220–328)	6.70±0.20
1969	50	249.9±2.4 (220–292)	5.54±0.27	50	272.6±6.4 (222–324)	9.83±1.03
1970	50	251.1±2.6 (220–280)	5.51±0.17	50	269.2±3.7 (220–323)	5.45±0.22
1979	29	250.7±2.6 (222–280)	5.94±0.19	15	258.9±3.8 (221–293)	5.56±0.20
1980	121	252.0±1.5 (220–303)	5.58±0.14	67	269.8±3.5 (223–336)	6.34±0.36
1981	153	251.3±1.4 (220–304)	5.95±0.34	63	278.9±2.8 (228–325)	
1982	71	237.4±8.8 (220–293)	5.69±0.28	26	275.4±5.5 (221–333)	6.41±0.42
1983	113	253.1±1.5 (220–299)	5.89±0.13	47	264.0±3.8 (222–318)	6.08±0.32
1984	62	245.3±1.8 (220–275)	6.44±1.40	22	278.3±4.7 (237–323)	6.02±0.34
1985	121	248.9±4.4 (220–300)	6.13±0.20	42	275.5±4.7 (226–343)	7.35±0.41
1986	107	244.5±5.1 (220–305)	5.86±0.14	76	267.9±4.3 (224–364)	7.34±0.17
1987	104	243.3±5.9 (226–312)	6.40±0.15	59	272.2±7.7 (228–353)	7.94±0.89
1988	60	253.2±3.6 (220–296)	5.81±0.22	18	281.1±8.9 (233–382)	6.59±0.53
1989	48	252.6±2.8 (220–293)	5.78±0.17	23	268.7±4.6 (231–322)	6.11±0.31
1990	50	253.2±0.20 (220–334)	5.92±0.24	40	291.1±5.4 (234–376)	9.37±0.41
1991	50	254.9±0.30 (230–295)	5.76±0.18	50	272.3±4.4 (220–352)	6.63±0.31
1992	50	256.1±10.6 (220–302)	6.05±0.18	50	277.3±7.4 (226–340)	7.17±0.28
1993	50	243.7±10.4 (229–287)	5.96±0.17	50	260.17±4.1 (220–302)	7.28±0.51
1994	81	253.3±7.0 (220–293)	6.12±0.13	88	291.6±2.7 (228–362)	8.57±0.24
1995	106	262.0±2.3 (223–315)	6.13±0.12	73	290.2±2.3 (223–363)	8.55±0.36
1996	59	261.6±2.8 (222–305)	6.62±0.18	46	300.8±5.3 (235–374)	10.59±0.55
1997	104	259.5±2.0 (220–305)	5.81±0.11	69	291.6±3.8 (236–346)	8.38±0.31

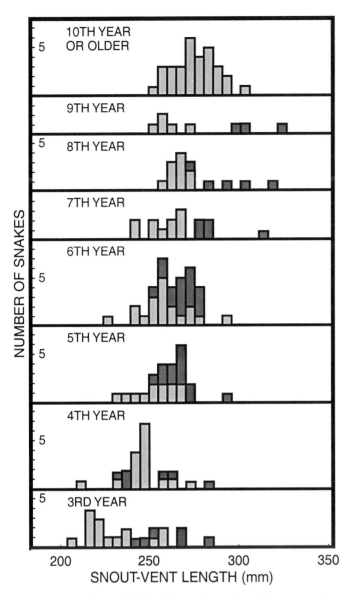

Figure 18. Sizes (SVL) of ringneck snakes where approximate ages were known because they were individually marked early in life. Male records are lightly shaded. Females are heavily shaded. Females grow to be larger, but males tend to survive longer, or at least are more subject to recapture after relatively long intervals.

and are laid at the end of June or early July. The wide range of SVL for each age class of recaptured individuals (ages 3 to 11 years) is shown in Figure 18.

Males attain their maximum weight in spring, the season of maximum activity and food abundance. By June male activity is waning and that is the only time of year when females are more in evidence than males.

Behavior

Ringneck snakes are highly secretive and spend most of their time underground or beneath surface litter.

Rarely do they cross open places such as roads, and when this occurs, movement is so slow that it easily escapes notice. If the snake is approached while it is in the open, it generally "freezes" and avoids moving until it is actually touched, then it heads for shelter at top speed. Most of the ringnecks that were seen were exposed when rocks or other shelters were lifted. They usually froze for a few seconds, then started to glide away. However, response depended partly on the temperature. Snakes that were fully warmed might dart away the instant that they were exposed, at the same time elevating the tail and coiling it in a spiral, with the red undersurface exposed. A snake that was grasped nearly always spiralled its tail, and the spiralling was accompanied by an exudation from the musk glands.

The tail-spiralling response to disturbance is a sematic display that is strongly developed in some geographic populations, including the one that I studied. In some other populations it is relatively weak, and in these the brightening of ventral color posteriorly is also less developed. The flash of bright color involved in tail spiralling is obviously adapted to deter visually oriented predators (birds), but would not be useful in darkness, beneath shelters, in burrows, nor against predators that lack color perception (including moles, opossums, skunks, and larger snakes). Birds including various passerines are probably important predators in some parts of the range.

Tail length averages 21.0% of SVL in male hatchlings, but as a result of allometric growth, increases to 22.8% in adult males. In second-year males, already sexually mature, but only about half the bulk of average adults, the tail proportions are those of adults. In females undamaged tails average 17.4% of SVL with no statistical difference in those of different ages or sizes. Partly because of its prominence in the spiralling display, the tail is exposed to attack by predators, and often bears injuries. Scars that might have resulted from bites by sharp-toothed predators such as shrews and moles sometimes resembled the marks made by scale-clipping for individual recognition. Also, many of the snakes examined had incomplete tails, perhaps having had the ends bitten or torn off in encounters with predators, in fact 6.5% of a large sample (N=13,927) were missing part of the tail. As might be expected, the smallest and youngest snakes had relatively few injuries whereas the largest and oldest had a much higher incidence (Table 41). In the first-year snakes (mostly from spring samples after one hibernation and perhaps 3 months of activity), slightly more than 1% were missing part of the tail, whereas in those judged to be more than 12 years old (males exceeding 280 mm SVL, and females exceeding 320 mm) the incidence had risen to more than 20%.

The incidence of missing tails in different age-size groups has implications concerning longevity in the

TABLE 41. Ratio of Damaged and Incomplete Tails in Ringneck Snakes, Increasing with Age

Probable Age in Years (Based on SVL)	N	Damaged Tails N	Percent with Damaged Tails
1st	1925	25	1.3
2nd	2362	60	2.5
3rd	2480	117	4.7
4th	1926	126	6.5
5th & 6th	2351	196	8.3
7th & 8th	1213	109	9.0
9th & 10th	724	84	11.6
11th & 12th	460	70	15.2
13th or Older	418	85	20.4

local population; it seems that on the average about 1.3% lose their tail tips each year. In presumed 9-year-olds (268–271 SVL in males and 301–305 in females) about 10% have lost part of the tail, and in the largest 3% that incidence has approximately doubled, suggesting that this group averages about 18 years old, with the maximum age considerably more than that.

Rarely snakes retained only a stump of the tail base, but only 13% of those lacking part of the original tail had more than half of the tail missing. Often only the tip was missing. In 40% of those with incomplete tails the remaining part was still within the length range of undamaged tails, and tail functions such as the spiralling display would not have been impaired. In males damaged tails averaged 18.2% of SVL (2 to 24%), and in females averaged 13.9% (2 to 19%).

Ordinarily a ringneck snake moves only a few meters at most in the course of a day. Movement is extremely slow with many long pauses. In contrast, those startled as by being exposed when a sheltering object is raised, may dart away rapidly, wriggling with violent lateral undulations and spiralling the tail. If the snake is restrained, musk exudes from the vent and squirming of the tail spreads the offensive secretion over the snake's body and that of its attacker. Trailing of conspecifics by olfaction and Jacobson's organ is a prominent aspect of behavior. In early spring when the snakes are most active, two or more may often be found beneath the same shelter, and Dundee and Miller (1968) have shown that such aggregations result from scent trailing. Aggregations may include both sexes of young as well as adults, but adult males are especially prominent and it is evident that male-male trailing occurs. Often two or more hatchlings are found together under the same rock. When such gatherings occur soon after the time of hatching, in late summer or fall, it may be assumed that the young came from a nest in the immediate vicinity and had not had time to disperse, but such associations have also been found in spring and early summer, suggesting mutual affinity. On numerous occasions when large numbers of ringnecks have been captured

and bagged together, it has been found that pairs have interlocked jaws, seemingly in combat. The adversaries are usually about the same size, but may be of either sex. Anderson (1965) noted similar behavior and concluded that prey odor (earthworm) on the head and jaws triggered attack by conspecifics.

Responses to Succession

Over the 50 years of my observations the abundance of *Diadophis* changed drastically but the changes could not be measured with precision. During the first few years the greatest concentration was found to be in Rat Woods, a rocky, sparsely wooded south-facing slope that had been heavily used by livestock as it connected hilltop and bottomland pastures. Low vegetation was sparse, eaten back by grazing and browsing animals, and soil was heavily trampled, but the many flat rocks and crevices provided shelter for the snakes. Skink Woods was likewise used by livestock and relatively open, but its exposure was partly to the north and its *Diadophis* population was less concentrated. Removal of livestock in 1948 promoted growth of low herbaceous vegetation and brush on both areas. After a 20-year interval they had become heavily shaded, and the snakes were rarely found on either area. Meanwhile former pastures, both on hilltops (Quarry Field) and bottomland (House Field), were transformed into habitat favorable to the snakes. From relatively barren terrain, with soil trampled and compacted, and sparse weedy vegetation, they had developed a dense cover of herbaceous plants with trees invading and brush clumps expanding. This vegetation provided food and cover for burgeoning populations of small mammals and the soil became riddled with their burrows providing ample shelter for the snakes. By 1968 after 20 years of succession these fields may have reached the stage of optimum habitat for snakes. Subsequently the shade of expanding brush clumps and trees rendered it less favorable.

Ringneck snakes were occasionally found alive or as recent traffic casualties on the county road adjacent to FNHR or the driveway on the area. However, in view of the great abundance of ringnecks such occurrences were remarkably rare demonstrating that the snakes tend to stay under cover and are disinclined to expose themselves in open areas. This tendency was further emphasized by experience on the BSA (NESA) where islands of natural vegetation were maintained in a large field that was mowed frequently maintaining a shortgrass cover between islands. Many artificial shelters consisting of metal or wooden strips were placed in the islands of vegetation, and a second series was set out at intervals around the margin of the field. These marginal shelters were often used by the snakes, which, however were rarely found beneath a shelter on any of the islands.

Spatial Relationships

In the course of a 3-year field study concentrated at the north edge of FNHR (Quarry Field), Richard M. Lattis, using radioactive tantalum implanted in ringneck snakes, and using a scintillator to monitor movements, accumulated much information concerning the day-to-day activities of the snakes. Pieces of the radioactive wire 2–3 mm in length were inserted hypodermically. The snakes were found to have no definite "homes" but were constantly shifting from one location to another. Daily movements were variable, but were remarkably short — often less than 1 m, typically from 1–3 m. Because of the scintillator's short detection range, occasional snakes that made unusually long movements were liable to be lost. In some instances snakes made such long movements in October, shifting 100 m or more from the grassy field summer habitat to hibernacula in crevices of south-facing limestone outcrops.

Because of their abundance ringneck snakes were collected in batches, often dozens at a time, and the provenances of individuals were known in terms of general areas rather than precise spots. However, in 1966 and 1967, and to a lesser extent in the years immediately preceding or following, effort was made to keep accurate locality records for individuals and two or more capture points were obtained for 151 ringnecks over periods ranging from a few days to more than 6 years. Mean distance between capture points was 82.9 m. Table 42 shows figures for subgroups according to sex, age, and elapsed time. Females move farther than males and first-year young move farther than adults. Distances are not significantly greater with elapsed time; evidently ranges are relatively permanent. In 29 instances (19.2%) snakes had returned to approximately the same spot. The longest movement recorded was 380 m.

The distances recorded were rather evenly distributed up to 130 m, but tapered off from 130 to 380 m. This suggests that individual snakes have activity ranges with diameters up to 130 m, but occasionally wander for greater distances. For 118 records less than 130 m the mean was 45.33 m, and if this mean movement is equated with the radius of an activity range, the area represented (πr^2) would be approximately 0.65 ha.

Nearly all recorded movements were from one or the other of two study areas. One of them, Quarry Field, was a triangular upland area of 3.36 ha including an abandoned limestone quarry at its southern end. The other was a small valley with arbitrary units House Field, Horse Field, Vole Field, Picnic Field, nearly surrounded by woodland. The valley extended from the western edge of FNHR near its center ENE approximately 610 m, and was up to 215 m across. A wooded slope approximately 215 m across separated Quarry Field from House Field. At the upper edge of the wooded slope where exposure was to the southwest, a massive slab of the Toronto limestone served as a landmark "Tomb Rock," and many snakes, especially ringnecks, hibernated in the immediate vicinity. Each year at the time of spring emergence they were abundant there, and typically were found singly or in small groups, sheltered beneath flat rocks within a 10 m radius. In all, 41 of the Tomb Rock ringnecks were recaptured at other places and/or times; 27 of them (66%) were from the lowland House Field area and thus had made migratory movements across intervening terrain including the 300 m of wooded slope, to reach their hibernacula. Nine others (22%) were recorded also in Quarry Field. It is remarkable that the Quarry Field contingent was only one-third of the House Field contingent although Tomb Rock was much nearer to Quarry Field and the snakes were more abundant in Quarry Field. Five of the marked and recaptured snakes from Tomb Rock were not found elsewhere; two were recaptured after 2 years and one each after 3, 4, and 5-year intervals. The Tomb Rock area is believed to be just one of many hibernacula used by the hundreds of ringnecks in Quarry Field and House Field. Some of the snakes equipped with radioactive wires were trailed to other hibernacula scattered along hilltop outcrops near the edges of Quarry Field. Still other ringnecks were believed to have hibernated in fields within their summer ranges, in the tunnels of small mammals or large insects, because they were found there beneath shelters in early spring.

Of 325 recaptured ringnecks from the combined House Field-Quarry Field areas 62.0% were captured just twice, 25.8% three times, 8.3% four times, 1.8% five times, 0.6% six times, 0.6% seven times, 0.3% nine times, and 0.6% ten times. Individual time spans for these snakes were : 2 years 22.0%, 3 years 21.3%, 4 years 14.1%, 5 years 15.5%, 6 years 11.9%, 7 years 11.2%, 8 years 3.3%, and 9 years 0.7%. Thirty-three snakes that were first captured in House Field were recaptured in Quarry Field, or were captured in Quarry

TABLE 42. Mean Distances Moved by Marked Ringneck Snakes That Were Recaptured

Category	N	Mean Distance from Previous Capture Point (m)
Combined Sample	151	82.9
Males	126	78.9
Females	25	102.8
First-Year Young	16	92.3
Recaptured Same Season	43	62.9
Recaptured after 1 Hibernation	46	94.8
Recaptured after 2 or 3 Hibernations	30	76.5
Recaptured after 4 to 6 Hibernations	32	84.3

TABLE 43. Annual Variation in Egg Production in Ringneck Snakes

Year	N	Mean Number of Eggs per Clutch	Spring Precipitation (mm)	Number of Spring Rains
1965	33	3.30±0.22	196	15
1966	48	3.60±0.21	120	21
1969	47	3.55±0.18	266	16
1970	53	3.48±0.15	289	20
1973	14	4.00±0.28	509	23
1974	62	3.73±0.15	238	20
1982	19	4.68±0.27	358	20
1983	17	4.17±0.28	404	21
1985	43	3.71±0.18	306	18
1986	18	3.89±0.25	299	19
1987	12	4.33±0.36	224	17
1990	13	4.54±0.45	340	31
1991	19	4.11±0.33	283	25
1992	37	3.76±0.20	202	17
1993	15	4.86±0.51	430	33
1994	33	4.30±0.23	217	19
1995	31	5.23±0.36	336	36
1996	37	5.70±0.28	309	31
1997	29	4.66±0.27	264	29

Field and recaptured in House Field after 1 to 7 years; four of them later reversed the trip and were last captured in the field where they were found originally.

Reproduction

In local *Diadophis* mating may occur in fall or spring, but is concentrated in early May. Yolking of ovarian follicles proceeds rapidly in May and ovulation occurs in June. Egg laying is concentrated in the first week of July. Number of eggs per clutch averages from 2.7 in primiparous (third year) females to more than five in the largest and oldest females. Eggs (N=251) averaged 25.2 mm in length and 7.11 mm in width and 0.89 g, and usually were slightly bent (sausage-shaped) with one end a little wider than the other. Clutch size varied from year to year depending on weather and food supply. Frequent heavy rains promoted the abundance and availability of earthworms and resulted in larger average clutch size, whereas in drought years clutch size was reduced (Table 43). Clutch size averaged 3.96 for unlaid eggs palped (N=267 clutches), but averaged 3.36 for 50 clutches laid. Gravid females tend to aggregate and often lay their eggs in communal nests. Embryos are already partly developed at the time eggs are laid.

Clutches incubated in the laboratory hatched in 42 days, 50 days, and 50 days. During incubation eggs gradually increase in size by absorption of moisture. Thirteen eggs of three clutches observed in 1969 gained, on the average, 2.7% in length, 7.7% in width, and 66.0% in weight during the interval from 19 July to 8 August — less than half of the entire incubation period.

Growth

Table 44 compares mean SVL measurements for hatchlings and for first year young in 10 different years in which substantial series were obtained in early spring (late March and the first half of April). Presumably these young had not grown appreciably since emerging from hibernation, and their increase over hatchling size shows the extent of early growth in late summer and fall, varying from year to year according to weather conditions. In most years the emergent young averaged between 122 and 127 mm SVL having gained about 14 mm in about 70 days of activity, but in 1962 they averaged only 117.6 mm having made less than half the average gain and in 1965 they averaged 131.5 with a gain of 43% greater than usual. At hatching the largest young averaged 19% longer than the shortest, but by spring they averaged 63.8% (56–86%) longer as the differential increased, with rapid growth in some young and stunting in others.

In an earlier study of growth it was found that as hatchlings, at the end of August or early September, females are already larger (SVL 114.1±1.22 mm, N=33) than males (SVL 109.3±91 mm, N=50) and subsequently they grow faster. Hatchlings of each sex are variable in size and the variance increases with age. In spring after emerging from their first hibernation these young have grown to a little more than 120 mm SVL, with the average for different years differing by as much as 13 mm, and with females averaging 5 mm longer than males. Table 44 shows the wide size range in the first- year young in spring — from a minimum of 98 mm to a maximum of 158. In samples of second-year young in early April males averaged 183 mm (N=187), and females averaged 194 mm (N=117). Growth in the adolescent and adult snakes up to the 14th year is

TABLE 44. Comparison of SVL in Ringneck Snakes in a Composite Sample of Hatchlings and in Newly Emerged First-year Young in Spring, Showing Varying Amounts of Growth Before Hibernation

	Hatchlings	1960	1962	1964	1965	1966	1968	1970	1974	1985	1986	Mean of 10-Year Combined Sample
Mean	111.3	126.8	117.6	124.0	131.5	124.5	126.9	122.4	124.0	125.5	129.6	125.3
Minimum	98	113	98	116	115	110	110	101	101	117	118	109.9
Maximum	121	142	141	158	158	158	151	140	153	149	151	150.1
Apparent Gain		15.5	6.3	12.7	20.2	13.2	15.6	11.1	12.7	14.2	18.3	14.0
Percentage gain from hatching		12.1	5.4	10.2	15.3	10.6	12.3	9.1	11.2	11.3	14.1	11.2
N	29	87	241	123	131	176	27	107	63	26	62	1043

TABLE 45. Mean SVL of Adult Ringneck Snakes of Various Ages as Shown by Recapture of Marked Individuals

Age (in Years)	Males	N ♂	Females	N ♀
3rd	228.6 ±1.93	31	250.4 ±4.00	15
4th	243.56±1.86	39	262.55±4.10	11
5th	250.5 ±1.59	38	268.5 ±2.30	18
6th	251.80±1.43	55	281.67	3
7th	259.6 ±1.58	45	291.14±4.37	7
8th	261.5 ±1.51	37	297.43±7.63	7
9th	263.19±1.95	27	307.25±4.13	4
10th	265.09±2.09	33	307.6 ±4.05	5
11th	266.53±2.52	15	306.0 ±2.28	6
12th	274.74±2.64	19	308.5	2
13th	279.92±2.44	17	328	1
14th	281.85±3.62	13		
or more				

TABLE 46. Growth in Individually Marked Ringneck Snakes (All Males) Recaptured as Large Adults

Growth in SVL	Elapsed Time (Years)	Mean Gain per Year SVL (mm)
120–295	13	13.5
148–296	12	12.3
216–293	12	5.9
283–296	1	13.0
272–298	3	8.6
292–298	3	2.0
289–295	1	6.0
291–296	3	1.7
248–293	18	2.5

shown in Table 45 from 447 records of marked individuals that were recaptured. These figures show the general trend of growth, but the means are obviously inexact for some of the older age groups, especially the females, whose samples are small. For example, 9th-, 10th-, and 11th-year females are shown as averaging approximately the same size; 5th- and 6th-year males, 10th- and 11th-year males also are too close to the same size. Yearly averages should show consistently slowing growth and steadily increasing size differential between the sexes.

Although growth was tentatively traced to snakes as old as 12 years, some of those caught were much larger and presumably older. There were 379 records (253 of males, 126 of females) of snakes larger than average 12-year-old size, and these were 4.6% of the total. The largest male (396 mm SVL) was 44% longer than a

TABLE 47. Survivorship in Individual Ringneck Snakes Marked and Recaptured

	Original Capture			Last Capture			
Sex	Date	SVL (mm)	Probable Age (year)	Date	SVL (mm)	Probable Age (year)	Other Captures
♂	9/20/72	286	13th	3/17/86	301	27th	3 in 1978
♂	5/12/67	270	9th	4/2/81	298	23rd	
♂	5/2/67	248	5th	4/27/85	293	23rd	5, '67 to '70
♂	10/3/65	278	12th	10/8/75	281	22nd	5, '68 to '70
♂	4/13/66	286	13th	10/3/72	300	17th	
♂	4/25/66	267	8th	4/17/74	281	16th	
♂	4/13/68	273	10th	4/17/74	283	16th	
♂	5/27/66	216	3rd	4/2/78	293	15th	
♂	4/13/68	280	12th	4/27/70	283	14th	
♂	3/30/68	265	8th	4/20/73	269	13th	
♂	5/14/65	208	2nd	5/4/76	286	13th	
♂	9/23/66	243	4th	4/17/74	278	12th	
♂	5/12/66	246	4th	4/22/73	268	11th	2, '68, '70
♂	5/10/67	252	5th	10/14/73	273	11th	2, '68, '70
♂	5/10/67	261	7th	10/4/70	273	10th	
♂	5/9/66	235	4th	10/2/72	284	10th	4, '69, '72
♀	3/26/68	282	8th	4/25/73	301	13th	
♀	4/12/67	260	4th	4/24/74	298	11th	
♀	7/9/66	283	6th	4/24/74	298	14th	1 in 1968

typical 12th-year male, and the largest female was 382 mm, 18% longer than a typical 12th-year female. Table 46 shows records of the largest *Diadophis* recaptured after making substantial growth. Records of the first three marked early in life demonstrate that SVL near 300 mm can be attained by an age of 13 years. The last five were already large adults when marked, and they show highly variable growth rates with annual gains in SVL of 1.7 to 13.0 mm.

Females average substantially larger than males, but it is remarkable that in this large series the largest snake was a male of 396 mm SVL. The second largest male was 321 mm. By 1994, after more than a decade of low reproductive success, the ratio of such large adults (exceeding average 12-year-old size) had increased, with 58 of 174 (33%) in this category. Table 47 shows survivorship in 19 marked ringnecks that were recaptured as large adults after intervals of 2 to 18 years.

Sex and Age Ratios

Sex ratios in samples were highly variable but followed definite seasonal patterns (Table 48). In March, April,

TABLE 48. Seasonal Sex Ratios in Ringneck Snakes, 1964 to 1969

	Spring		Summer		Fall					
					September		Early October		Late October	
	N	%Female	N	%Female	N	%Female	N	%Female	N	%Female
First-Year Young	1169	49.0	175	40.0	407	52.1	431	45.8	270	47.7
Second-Year Young	450	23.1	149	43.4	373	27.6	204	31.3	126	38.9
Adults	2602	22.0	503	55.5	504	27.2	470	24.4	268	50.0

and May, the time of year when the snakes were most in evidence, males consistently outnumbered females in samples of adults, usually by a little more than three to one. Collected samples at that season might give the impression of much biased sex ratios. However, the imbalance is presumably correlated with greater activity of males in the breeding season.

Nearly all the ringneck snakes found were beneath sheltering objects and often were in groups, which might include both sexes or might be of only one sex (usually males). In warm weather of early summer the snakes are much less in evidence, tending to use deeper shelters, and the sex ratio in samples changed; in fact, females outnumbered males. Nearly all these females were gravid and tended to maintain slightly higher body temperatures as a strategy for hastening embryonic development by resting in contact with the undersurfaces of sun-warmed objects.

Both first-year and second-year males definitely outnumbered their female counterparts in summer samples. In July and August, especially in extended periods of dry weather, the snakes virtually disappear from the places where they are abundant earlier in the season. They retreat to deeper shelters. In early autumn, when surface soil is moistened by rains, the *Diadophis* population reappears in force, and in samples of adults the sex ratio returns to approximately three to one in favor of males. However, late in the season females increased in relative abundance, and by the latter half of October the sexes were found in approximately equal numbers. In first-year young males and females were found in approximately equal numbers also, but with males slightly more numerous. In spring these first-year young are still not much above hatching size in some instances, and males (51%) outnumber females only slightly. However, by June the sex ratio of samples changes with males increased to 60%, suggesting that the sexes have begun to diverge in behavior. In samples of second-year young in spring males occur in about the same three-to-one ratio as in adults, indicating that in these half-grown snakes adult behavior patterns already prevail. Males of this age class are already sexually mature after two hibernations and about 10 months of active life, but females require another year to attain sexual maturity.

Although the trends of changing sex ratios follow the pattern described above and shown in Table 48, each year is somewhat different. Weather affects the activities of the snakes, and unusual drought or precipitation or heat or cold changes the seasonal timing. True sex ratios are obscured by differences in behavior of the sexes. Evidence suggests that the highly unbalanced sex ratios in samples result from differences in behavior and catchability of the sexes, that males are slightly more

numerous than females at the time of hatching, and that this natal ratio remains little altered in older age classes. In first-year young sexes are alike in behavior and are found in approximately their true ratios, but in second-year young the males attain sexual maturity and predominate in samples. Perhaps true sex ratios and ratios of adults and first- and second-year young are best shown by population samples taken near the end of the season of activity in late October. Table 49 shows ratios of age-size cohorts and sexes in a large sample. Figure 19 compares annual population structure (ratios of adults, second-year young, and first-year young) over 2 decades. These ratios are shown to fluctuate drastically with first-year young ranging from less than 10% to more than 50% of the total in different years. Doubtless these fluctuations are due to variations in the weather, affecting the success of reproduction. With all adult females contributing an annual clutch of 3 to 5 eggs, the population could be more than doubled, but unfavorable weather such as drought might eliminate most of the annual crop before hatching.

Also, the data suggests a trend of worsening reproduction during the latter decades of the study. Throughout the entire study the ratio of adults to immatures was most often 60% to 70%, but during the first three decades adults were always less than 70% and often they were less than 60%. In contrast, during the 1980s and 90s, as the population shrank to much lower levels, adults exceeded 70% of the total in nearly half of years sampled, and were less than 60% only once. During the last 5 years especially, young were few, with adults making up more than 70% of the snakes recorded. In these years hatchlings appeared relatively late in the season. Shading over of favorite nesting areas by invading arborescent vegetation may have caused both a delay in hatching and a reduction in hatching success.

TABLE 49. Age-Size Correlation in Ringneck Snakes and Composition of a Population Sample*

Age (in Years)	Males		Females	
	Typical SVL (mm)	% of Sample	Typical SVL (mm)	% of Sample
1st	110–146	10.9	110–159	23.3
2nd	147–214	17.2	160–223	8.8
3rd	215–233	15.7	224–256	17.0
4th	234–245	13.1	257–265	14.7
5th	246–252	11.6	266–278	8.8
6th	253–258	7.1	279–288	6.3
7th	259–263	5.4	289–296	5.6
8th	264–267	4.4	297–303	5.6
9th	268–271	4.1	304–309	2.7
10th	272–274	2.7	310–314	1.9
11th	275–277	2.2	315–319	1.7
12th	278–280	2.1	320–324	1.5
13th or Older	281–321	3.5	325–382	2.1

*Composite sample of 1469 records for the decade of the 1980s in March, April, and May

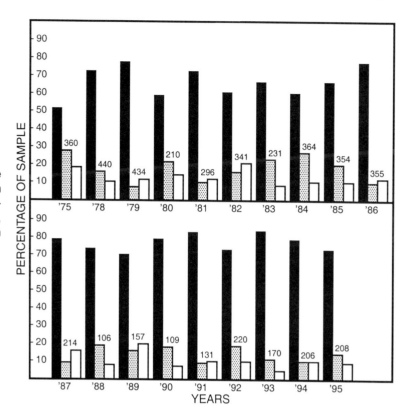

Figure 19. Age composition of ringneck snake populations, comparing 19 different years from 1975 to 1995. Each annual sample shows percentages of adults (solid), second-year young (stippled), and first-year young (open). Number of snakes in each annual sample is indicated.

Numbers

Many of the ringnecks captured and marked were recaptured after periods of years but their ratio showed progressive decrease. Doubtless both mortality and migration were involved in this progressive decrease over time. Those captured as first-year young were more likely to be recaptured only after short intervals — less than a month in 41% of the cases (vs. 12.3% in adults), young certainly are more subject to mortality and also may be more likely to shift to new areas. Because of their concentrated activity in spring, snakes were more at risk of capture then. For many, both the original record and the recapture were made in April (or May) hence recaptures were often at intervals of even years, 12, 24, 36, or 48 months. Only 12.2% were recaptured after periods of more than 49 months, and only 6 of these 45 were females.

Over a period of years from 1965 to 1970 several censuses of ringneck snakes were attempted in the Quarry Field and House Field areas on the basis of mark-capture-recapture samples (Fitch, 1975). Four censuses of Quarry Field for 1966, 1967, 1969, and 1970 respectively, averaged 4743 (1374 per ha), and three censuses for House Field 1965, 1966, and 1967 averaged 7242 (923 per ha) (Table 50). More recent trends on these areas are indicated by the figures in Table 51 showing number of captures per day in different years. The number of captures obviously is influenced by the

abundance of the snakes, but also is affected by collecting effort and by weather. The data suggests that the population was relatively high from 1977 to 1979 and in 1984–1985 when the catch averaged 49.5 to 70.2 per day, but was relatively low in the years 1971 through 1973 and 1987 through 1989 when the numbers captured ranged from 12 to 22.2 per day.

Table 52 shows the cumulative numbers captured and marked on the combined House Field and Quarry Field study areas, and the percentage of recaptures, which increased through 1965 and 1966 until more than 2800 snakes were marked, and recaptures slightly exceeded 20% of those taken. Subsequently, the ratio of recaptures ceased to increase, and declined slightly, probably indicating that marked snakes were being eliminated through natural causes faster than new ones were being added. At known replacement rates (Fitch, 1975), it is estimated that by the end of the 3-year study period covered by Table 52 approximately half of the snakes marked there would have been eliminated. The approximately 2000 snakes estimated to remain were about one-fifth of the total population, if the ratios of already marked to newly caught individuals are to be credited. Hence it is estimated that the population amounted to some 10,000 snakes (1040 per ha).

To judge the validity of census figures obtained from mark-and-recapture samples, the numerous records accumulated during the 1966 season were reexamined, with comparison of relatively long or short sampling

TABLE 50. Population Densities of Ringneck Snakes on Two Study Areas, Derived from Petersen Index Ratios

Area	Year	Period of First Sampling	Period of Resampling	Number in First Sampling	Ratio of Recaptures to Total in Resampling	Estimated Population	Density/ha
2 or 3 Month Sampling Periods							
1	1969	3/1–4/30	5/1–6/30	346	12 to 187	5398	1565
1	1970	3/1–4/30	5/1–6/30	57	6 to 442	4199	1217
2	1965	7/1–9/30	10/1–11/30	386	23 to 267	4481	773
1 ½ Month Sampling Periods							
1	1966	3/1–4/15	4/16–5/31	253	10 to 278	7033	2039
1	1967	3/1–4/15	4/16–5/31	182	6 to 90	2730	791
2	1966	3/1–4/15	4/16–5/31	332	17 to 532	10,392	1792
2	1967	3/1–4/15	4/16–5/31	238	8 to 230	6854	1181
1 Month Sampling Periods							
1	1966	3/1–3/31	4/1–4/30	179	3 to 231	13,800	4000
1	1966	4/1–4/30	5/1–5/31	231	9 to 136	3490	1011
2	1966	3/1–3/31	4/1–4/30	28	1 to 253	7100	1221
2	1966	4/1–4/30	5/1–5/31	253	11 to 383	8809	1518
2	1966	5/1–5/31	6/1–6/30	383	3 to 80	10,213	1761
½ Month Sampling Periods							
1	1966	4/1–4/15	4/16–4/30	84	6 to 147	2058	597
2	1966	4/1–4/15	4/16–4/30	59	7 to 180	1517	262
2	1966	5/1–5/15	5/16–5/31	166	7 to 217	5146	887

1. Quarry Field, 3.45 ha
2. House Field, 5.8 ha

periods. The census figures originally published were based on sampling intervals of 1.5 months, 2 months, or 3 months. To test the possibility that within these relatively long sampling periods some population interchange occurred, with occasional marked snakes leaving the study area, and occasional unmarked individuals replacing them, the data was rearranged, with 1-month and 0.5-month sampling intervals (Table 50). With such

replacement of marked snakes occurring, the ratio of marked to unmarked in samples would be erroneously low resulting in a census estimate higher than the actual population, and the longer the sampling period the more inflated the census figure. However, the data does not indicate such a trend. With sampling intervals of 2

TABLE 51. Daily Catches of Ringneck Snakes in March–April–May Over a 26-Year Period

Year	Days of Sampling	Number Captured	Mean Captures per Day of Sampling
1970	44	1132	25.8
1971	30	362	12.0
1972	26	576	22.2
1973	23	316	13.8
1974	17	576	33.9
1975	1	38	38.0
1976	1	41	41.0
1977	2	99	49.5
1978	10	616	61.6
1979	6	421	70.2
1980	11	243	22.1
1981	11	249	22.6
1982	11	269	24.4
1983	14	270	19.3
1984	7	361	51.6
1985	6	327	54.5
1986	17	492	28.9
1987	14	222	15.9
1988	8	97	12.1
1989	7	103	15.0
1990	4	118	29.5
1991	13	182	14.0
1992	15	179	11.9
1993	10	124	12.4
1994	18	184	10.4
1995	19	237	12.5

TABLE 52. Numbers of Ringneck Snakes Marked and Recaptured in Combined Study Areas of Quarry Field (3.45 ha) and House Field (5.8 ha)

Month	Number Captured and Marked	Number of Recaptures	Cumulative Number Captured	Percentage of Recaptures
1965				
April	183	9	183	4.9
May	154	11	337	7.2
June	52	7	389	13.5
July–Aug.	76	1	465	1.3
Sept.	347	26	812	7.3
Oct.	328	41	1140	12.5
1966				
March	199	20	1339	10.0
April	505	50	1844	9.9
May	518	113	2362	21.8
June	123	15	2485	12.2
July-Aug.	47	8	2532	17.0
Sept.	135	24	2667	17.7
Oct.	111	19	2778	17.1
1967				
March	94	24	2872	25.6
April	294	61	3166	20.7
May	234	53	3400	22.6
June	98	26	3498	26.7
July-Aug.	80	19	3578	23.8
Sept.	45	11	3623	24.5
1968				
March	63	10	3686	15.9
April	359	82	4045	22.8
May	65	13	4110	20.0

or 3 months, 1.5 months, 1 month, and 0.5 month, mean densities calculated by hectare were 1100, 1390, 1785, and 550. In *Diadophis* populations turnover is relatively gradual, and marked individuals persist in the same general area where they were originally captured after many months or years.

It seems that these minute snakes move over the habitual ranges so gradually that after a 2-week interval one would be in the same vicinity and at greater risk of recapture (perhaps from beneath the same shelter) than if it had shifted to another part of its range.

Geographic Differentiation

The ringneck snakes of this study are demonstrably different from those in various other parts of the extensive range in pattern, color, size, and certain ecological traits. *Diadophis punctatus regalis,* occurring to the southwest of the range of *D. p. arnyi,* and preying on small snakes instead of earthworms, provide an especially striking contrast in its greater size. Vitt (1973) mentioned a female *D. p. regalis* from Santa Cruz County Arizona, which was 600 mm SVL; it laid a clutch of eggs on 25 July 1972. The eggs averaged 44 × 11.3 mm and 3.4 g. Compared with these dimensions the average for local Kansas snakes was 47% SVL, (estimated 10.4% in bulk), 57.2% in egg length, 63% in egg width, and 26.2% in egg mass, 62% of hatchling SVL. The egg-laying date for the Arizona female was about a month later than the average for Kansas, doubtless timed to the summer rainy season of the Sonoran Desert.

Mitchell's (1994) account of ringnecks in Virginia (*D. p. edwardsii*) indicates that they are approximately the same size (averaging slightly larger), but vertebrates, especially salamanders (*Eurycea bislineata, Plethodon cinereus, P. cylindraceus, P. glutinosus*), and also lizards (*Scincella lateralis*) are eaten as well as earthworms.

Elaphe emoryi

Traits of the Species

The Great Plains rat snake is a medium-sized colubrid of constricting habits, with weakly keeled dorsal scales, and dark brown mid-dorsal blotches on a gray ground color for the length of the body and tail, with pairs of alternating smaller lateral blotches. The ventral surface is pale with scattered, small, squarish black or dark brown marks. A pair of short brown neck stripes meet on top of the head, extending to a point anteriorly between the eyes. A pair of slanting temporal bands extend through the eyes and meet in the frontal region. (See Plates 12 & 13.) The species is found in rocky, arid terrain from southern Nebraska to central Mexico. Collins (1993) summarized literature records concerning the habitat as "rocky hillsides, canyons—frequent inhabitants of caves—open woods or along woodland edge." Often it is associated with short-grass habitats. The corn snake, *E. guttata,* having an Austroriparian distribution in the southeastern United States is alleged to be conspecific, but it differs from the Great Plains rat snake in many respects, including habitat, size, and reproduction. Great Plains rat snakes tend to be nocturnal, and prey mainly on small rodents, but also on birds and bats. They are mainly terrestrial, may climb trees, but spend much time underground or beneath shelter.

Size Relationships

The 31 Great Plains rat snakes captured included two young of the year, two that may have been second or third-year young and 27 adults, of which 14 were males and 13 were females. The adults were remarkably large. Males averaged 1184±27.4 mm SVL (993–1340) and females averaged 1040.2±15.7 (952–1230). According to Collins (1993) the largest recorded specimen and the largest from Kansas were, respectively, 60 ¼ inches (= 1530 mm total and 1290 SVL) and 51 inches (= 1295 mm total and 1090 SVL) The largest male in my study totalled 1545 mm (with the tail tip missing) exceeding the record 1530 mm, and the male average of 1185 mm SVL exceeded the previous maximum length for

Kansas (1295 total minus an estimated 206 mm for the tail). The largest *emoryi* in my study grew from 1310 mm SVL and 445 g in 1986 to 1340 mm and 530 g in 1991, but gained only 1 mm in total length because of the loss of his tail tip. Judging from his record size this snake must have already been relatively old when he was first captured in 1986. Year-to-year growth made by the adults recaptured was remarkably little, perhaps reflecting deteriorating habitat and food supply. The average annual gain in SVL was 1.1% (N=17), with average weight gain of 5.1% (N=15). The smallest *emoryi* recorded was a female, no doubt hatched recently, captured 5 September, 1991; SVL 295 m, tail 49 mm, 8.8 g. Another juvenile female was 343 mm SVL, 55 mm tail, and weighed 10.1 g. Three males thought to be second- year young had SVL of 708 mm (30 March 1986), 770 mm (8 May 1988), and 792 mm (2 May 1988). This last snake was captured three times over a 10-day interval, but the other four immatures were not recaptured, suggesting that young are more inclined to wander and less inclined to utilize habitual shelters than adults are.

Responses to Succession

In 1985 a 4 ha farmstead (CWF) 0.8 km west of FNHR was purchased by a family member. Subsequently, it was used as an ancillary source of snakes for my study, and was found to be inhabited by a colony of Great Plains rat snakes. Over a 10-year period 31 Great Plains rat snakes were recorded a total of 109 times. At the eastern end, the CWF area had a two-story residence, a dilapidated barn, and a series of outbuildings (including pigpen, chickenhouse, privy, and several sheds) enclosing a yard and barnyard area. In the early spring of 1986, 20 artificial shelters of corrugated sheet metal 0.6 x 1.2 m were distributed over the area, and most of the rat snakes recorded were found under them.

Of the 20 artificial shelters 12 were never used insofar as known, but eight others were used, some regularly. One shelter yielded 22 records, two others each 16, and another 14; 78% of snakes recorded beneath artificial shelters were in a 30 m radius within the old barnyard area. One snake was recorded 15 times in four different years, spanning the interval from 1986 through 1991, but missing in 1989 and 1990. Two others were each caught 11 times, one spanning 6 years and the other 3 years. However, eight of the 14 snakes that had two or more records were each recorded in the barnyard, and were also found at the far end of the area under at least one of three favorite shelters there. It is suspected that each snake ranged over an area more extensive than that encompassed by all the shelters combined. A snake might be found several times under the same shelter at consecutive checks, then it would leave. Obviously most of the time the snakes were using shelters that were unknown or inaccessible. On several occasions a snake was found on or in the nest of a cottonrat.

The data suggest a declining population of rat snakes and deteriorating habitat during the course of the study (Table 53). Number of individual snakes and number of records for each year were as follows: 1986, 14 and 44; 1987, 10 and 29; 1988, 7 and 21; 1989, 3 and 3; 1990, 4 and 5; 1991, 4 and 14; 1995, 2 and 4.

Obviously, after the land was purchased in 1985 there were major habitat changes that were detrimental to the snakes. Before the purchase the pasture had been grazed by both cattle and horses. Pigs and chickens were also raised. The rations distributed to these domestic animals also supported commensals, notably thriving colonies of house sparrows and house mice, and doubtless both were major food sources for the rat snakes. When the area was purchased in 1985 livestock were removed. The abundant food supply that had been available for commensals was lacking, and both sparrows and mice underwent drastic reduction. Meanwhile the pasture underwent rapid succession, with three-awm grass and lespedeza giving way to more luxuriant vegetation. Sweet clover and various weedy forbs were abundant at first, gradually losing ground to pasture grass. In 1989 horses were kept in the pasture for part of the summer and invading clumps of honey

locust and Osage orange were cut. In 1990 the pasture was mowed. These treatments seemed to favor the rat snakes, which ceased to decline and made small gains in 1990–91, but none was found in 1993 or 1994. Two were found in 1995, both adult females, one new and the other from the original group marked in 1986. In early spring, 1996 a first-year rat snake was found that evidently had hibernated in the basement of the residence at CWF.

Great Plains rat snakes inhabit various types of grassland including tallgrass prairie, as well as the short grass dominating on the High Plains farther west. Like other animals of tallgrass prairie, the snakes must cope with the annual burning of this fire-type association. Doubtless their chances of survival are improved where the stand of grass is broken by barriers such as streams or rock outcrops. On the Konza Prairie near Manhattan, Kansas, Heinrich and Kaufman (1985) found these snakes to be common. After a controlled burn on 26 April they found 11 dead rat snakes killed by the fire.

Rat snakes of the colony that I studied were subject to skin infections taking the form of raised and hardened nodules, sometimes distributed over much of the body. Some of these snakes seemed emaciated and debilitated, and perhaps the infections were a major cause of mortality. Similar skin infections have been noted in various other species on the study areas and were most conspicuous in the first few weeks after emergence from hibernation, but no other species had such severe infections as the Great Plains rat snakes.

Spatial Relationships

In 34 instances the distance between successive capture points averaged 109.6 m. In 32 instances successive captures were recorded beneath the same shelter, after intervals varying from two days to 12 months, and if these nonmovements are included, the average distance between captures is 56.5 m. More than any other species studied, this one showed fidelity to specific sites and shelters. Of the rat snakes marked and recaptured, two were each found repeatedly at three different sites, two others were found repeatedly at two sites, and four others were each found more than once at a single site. In 10 instances snakes were found together under the same shelter. In six of these cases the association involved an adult male and female and was presumed to be sexual: 21 March 1987; 31 March 1986; 16 April 1986; 7 May 1986; 24 May 1986; 31 May 1986. Male-with-male associations were recorded on 27 April 1990 and 24 May 1986. The other two cases both involved adult females thought to be gravid, on 30 May 1987 and 5 June 1986. The associations of gravid females beneath

TABLE 53. Changing Population of Great Plains Rat Snakes

Year	Adults Captured	Immatures Captured	Losses from Previous Year	Gains from Previous Year
1986	6♂, 7♀	1♂**		
1987	6♂, 4♀		4♀, 1♂**	3♂
1988	6♂, 2♀	2♂**	2♂, 2♀	1♂, 2♂**
1989	1♂		1♂, 1♀, 1♂**	2♂
1990	1♂, 2♀	1♀*		1♀*
1991	2♂, 1♀	1♀*	1♀*	1♂, 1♀*
1992				
1993				
1994				
1995	2♀			2♀

*First Year Young
**Second Year Young

the same shelter suggests the possibility of communal egg laying. At the five most favored locations, over a 3-year period, there were respectively, 19 captures of 10 individuals, 14 of 11, 13 of 7, 6 of 4, and 2 of 2. Three other sites yielded only one capture apiece, and 12 other sites having similar shelters and situated in the same habitat yielded no captures. In three instances snakes were known to have used the same shelters in 4 different years and in another instance shelters were used by the same snakes in 3 years. There were six more instances of a snake using the same shelter in 2 years.

Spatial relations of the closely related *E. guttata* are best known from a New Jersey field study by Zappalorti and Rocco (1992). A key part of their study involved daily monitoring of snakes (N=6) that were carrying radio transmitters—over periods of months, and for one snake, over consecutive seasons. It was found that corn snake movements averaged 26 m/day in linear distance, and that home ranges measured as convex polygons (Dixon & Chapman, 1980) averaged 13.8 ha (10.5 to 21.3). These polygons were based on six to nine peripheral points. However, the pattern of movements indicated that convex polygons as mapped were not used uniformly; "harmonic mean activity ranges" (Dixon & Chapman, 1980) of 95% isopleths were mapped and measured as 18.4 (11.9 to 30.9) ha; core areas from 50% isopleths were 1.46 (0.68 to 2.67) ha. One snake had three core areas, two snakes had two and one had only one. Corn snakes were found to make unusually long movements to shelters that were used as hibernacula, or as egg-laying sites or for shedding. Such shelters often were provided by the cavities left from decaying pine roots. The same shelter was likely to be used for successive hibernations, ovipositions or ecdyses. Also, in many instances individual corn snakes returned to the same shelters, beneath boards or trash.

Kinds of Prey

Four snakes at CWF contained recent meals, and in each instance the prey, palpated into the gullet for identification, proved to be *Microtus ochrogaster*. One had eaten an adult, two had each eaten three small young voles, and one had eaten three half grown voles and an adult female. These few records suggest a feeding strategy of active search and nest robbing. Other potential prey species present in the pasture or the vicinity of the barn and outbuildings where the snake occurred include *Peromyscus maniculatus, Reithrodontomys megalotis, R. montanus, Sigmodon hispidus, Blarina hylophaga, Cryptotis parva, Mus musculus,* and as eggs and nestlings, *Passer domesticus, Hirundo rustica* and *Columba livia.*

TABLE 54. Productivity in Great Plains Rat Snakes on CWF

Number of Eggs in Clutch	Female SVL (mm)	Female Weight (g)	Date
9	1050	374	5-29-86
11	1080	370	6-3-86
4	972	320	6-5-86
8	1013	255	5-23-97
4	1010	230 (after laying)	7-27-93

Reproduction

Presumably breeding occurs in spring within the time span 21 March to 31 May (mean date 26 April) when heterosexual pairs were found together under shelters (on six occasions). Gravid females were found on 7, 20, 22, 23 and 29 May and 3 and 5 June, and in two instances were found in pairs. In both cases the pairs were beneath shelters that were used on many other occasions. Five females that were palpated contained 4, 4, 8, 9, and 11 eggs ($\bar{x}$ = 7.2 ± 1.39). Their lengths (SVL) were, respectively 972, 1010, 1013, 1050 and 1080 mm indicating that production is correlated with size and probably with age of the female (Table 54). Clark (1953) recorded clutches of 4 and 5 eggs from females collected near Manhattan, Kansas, SVL 945 and 975 mm, weights 190 and 213 g. The larger female laid the larger clutch. Egg-laying extended over approximately 5 hours. Clutches were laid on 4 and 8 July, and clutch weight averaged 32.5% (31.6 and 33.4%) of female weight.

Geographic Differentiation

Relationships within the *Elaphe emoryi-guttata* complex are somewhat clarified by a recent study in Texas (Vaughan, Dixon & Thomas, 1996). On the basis of numbers of dorsal body and tail blotches, numbers of ventrals and subcaudals, and ventral pigmentation, three subspecies were recognized within the state: *Elaphe guttata emoryi* over, roughly, the northern two-thirds, and the recently described *E. g. meahllmorum* Smith Chiszar, Staley and Tepedelen, in the southern part, with *E. g. guttata* only in the extreme southeastern part not contacting either *emoryi* or *meahllmorum,* which integrade in a 100-mile-wide strip extending from east of San Antonio to the El Paso region. Collins (1997) allocated *Elaphe emoryi* with its subspecies *meallmorum,* as a species distinct from *Elaphe guttata. Elaphe guttata* occurs only in the Austroriparian region of extreme eastern Texas and does not contact either *E. e. emoryi* or *E. e. meahllmorum.* Furthermore, these Texas corn snakes differ from typical *E. guttata* (east of the Mississippi River) in being darker colored with a grayish ground color and reddish brown blotches, but lacking the yellow and red characteristic of eastern corn snakes. Recent taxonomic studies, including Vaughan et al. (1996), show that the currently recognized subspecies of *Elaphe guttata* conform with zoogeographic regions in their range limits, but there is no mention of demographic or ecological traits of subspecies that may be significant: body size, sexual dimorphism, number of eggs per clutch. Zappalorti & Rocco (1992) in their New Jersey study found that adult male corn snakes (N = 25) averaged 809.6±2.24mm (660–1110) SVL and females averaged 793.2±1.60mm (660–1000), whereas the Great Plains rat snakes in my study were markedly larger and had much more size dimorphism. Male weight averaged 398.0±31.4 (152 to 625) grams and female weight averaged 327.9±19.8 (186 to 540) grams.

Compared with the Great Plains rat snake, which is gray with brown blotches, the corn snake is more colorful, having red dorsal blotches on a yellow or yellowish-gray background. The corn snake typically is found in woodland or woodland edge habitat; the rat snake inhabits more open and rugged terrain. Mitchell's data (1994) on corn snakes in Virginia provides striking contrasts with my data for local rat snakes. In the Virginia sample mean SVL was 870 in males (N=12) and 868 in females (N=17) and weights averaged 159 g in both sexes, whereas in Kansas SVL averaged 1184 and 1040, weights 398 g and 328 g. Thus the Kansas snakes were more than twice the bulk of their Virginia counterparts and had marked size difference between the sexes which was not found in the Virginia snakes. The clutch size of 11.3±0.51 in Virginia was well above the 6.43±1.09 average for the larger Kansas snakes.

Wright and Wright (1957) mentioned remarkably large clutches of 14 and 15 eggs laid by female *Elaphe emoryi* from San Antonio and Brownsville, Texas, but these localities fall within the range of the recently described *E. e. meahllmorum,* and its ecology and demography are virtually unknown.

Seigel and Ford (1991) reported on the productivity of 29 female corn snakes in a captive colony kept under experimental conditions. Fourteen that were fed maximum amounts (30% of snake's body mass weekly) produced clutches averaging 12.6±1.15 eggs, whereas 15 fed minimum amounts (10% of body mass weekly) produced clutches averaging 9.4±0.84. The purpose of their experiment was to demonstrate that life history parameters such as number of eggs per clutch are highly plastic, and subject to changing environmental conditions such as food supply. In demonstrating this fact they suggested that apparent geographic differences are often caused by such temporary environmental changes: ". . . much of the observed intraspecific variation in life history traits of squamate reptiles may be the result of phenotypic plasticity." The 29 females used by Seigel and Ford were from South Carolina, and had SVLs from 750 to 1000 mm.

It is no doubt significant that the five *E. emoryi* clutches from northeastern Kansas recorded (Table 54) in my study, plus two recorded by Clark (from Manhattan) averaged only 6.43±1.09 eggs—well below the 9.4±0.84 found by Seigel and Ford for those fed minimum quantities, although the Kansas females averaged larger than the maximum for South Carolina females, and therefore should have had larger clutches. Bechtel and Bechtel (1962) recorded six corn snake clutches that averaged 12.63 (7 to 21) eggs; they also (1958) recorded four clutches of 2-year old females that averaged 5.5 (3 to 8) eggs. Allowing for age and amount of food taken, it seems evident that Kansas *Elaphe emoryi* grows to substantially larger size and produces significantly smaller clutches compared with the eastern *E. guttata.*

Elaphe obsoleta

Traits of the Species

The black rat snake is a large, active, partly arboreal colubrid that subdues its prey by constriction. The geographic range corresponds with the Deciduous Forest Biome of the eastern United States, except that it extends farther west into the Great Plains in Kansas, Oklahoma, and Texas. There are striking differences in color and pattern in populations of the Florida Peninsula. Elsewhere in the range geographic differences in color and pattern depend on loss or retention of juvenile markings. There may be important geographic differences in size and ecological traits but these have not been documented. In the local population adult males average 1232 (900 to 1723) mm SVL (N=241) and females average 1081 (900 to 1385) mm SVL (N=187). Males average 511 g, females 334 g. The pattern is shiny black dorsally, with chin white and belly slatey. (See Plates 14, 15, & 16.) In contrast immatures have a pattern of dark brown angular mid-dorsal blotches and smaller lateral spots on a gray background. (See Plates 17 & 18.) A dark facial marking crosses the frontal region, and on each side extends through the eye and along the posterior supralabials. Adolescents and young adults may retain traces of the juvenile patterns. In adults there are colored flecks between the scales on loose skin of the sides; these flecks may be red, pale yellow, or dull white. Rarely, red markings may be more extensive. One half-grown snake had a small mid-dorsal red blotch behind each brown blotch. Black rat snakes have been found in a wide range of local habitats, but seem to prefer an open, rocky type of woodland. The name pilot black snake, commonly used in the Northeast, is based upon its frequent association with the timber rattlesnake and the myth that it pilots the rattlesnake to safety when danger threatens. Birds and their eggs and nestlings constitute a major part of the diet, especially in spring. Young chicks and hens' eggs are commonly taken by large rat snakes. The roles of vision and airborne odors in locating nests and prey are still poorly understood. Small mammals of various kinds (cottontail, woodrat, cottonrat, vole, white-footed mouse, jumping mouse, harvest mouse, house mouse) are preyed upon, espe-

cially young in the nest. Densities of 0.9 to 3.6 per ha have been calculated for local rat snakes. Individuals may wander widely or may stay within a small area where food and other resources are abundant. When climbing in trees they are often harrassed by birds, even pecked (blue jays). The snakes seem to ignore such harrassment, but may gain clues as to the locations of nests from the birds' behavior. When alarmed black rat snakes sometimes vibrate their tails producing a buzzing sound, and may escape into a thicket, hole, or crevice with rapid undulatory movements, or may climb out of reach. One that is restrained is usually quick to strike, with little or no preliminary threat.

Interactions with Birds

Scansorial activity is the most notable aspect of the black rat snake's behavior. Climbing is facilitated by the slender but muscular body, and the ventral scutes, each having a 90° angle on both sides so that the free posterior edge is enabled to cling effectively to roughened surfaces. The snake can ascend a vertical tree trunk even if the bark is almost smooth, or it can move through outer twigs of treetops. Because of its slow, gliding movements and its resemblance to a branch, the climbing snake is well concealed. However, many of the rat snakes captured in my study were discovered because birds were scolding them (Fitch, 1963b). The kinds of birds that harass rat snakes are frequent victims of their predation. On FNHR a dozen species have been found participating in the heckling aggregations. A typical group may have 10 to 15 birds of four to six species. The species most often observed in these aggregations were: blue jay, tufted titmouse, black-capped chickadee, downy woodpecker, red-bellied woodpecker, eastern bluebird, crested flycatcher, eastern phoebe, summer tanager, eastern wood pewee, red-eyed vireo, and myrtle warbler, in about that order of importance. The blue jay was by far the most commonly observed heckler because of its raucous calls heard from a greater distance than the scolding of other species. The tufted titmouse also was usually represented. The jay, titmouse, and chickadee seemed to disregard territorial boundaries in joining a heckling group, so that several neighboring pairs united against the common enemy, whereas other species were typically represented by a pair or only a lone bird in a heckling group. Most of the hecklers maintained a safe distance between themselves and the snake, but jays were seen to attack, pecking the snake's tail or the posterior part of its body. Probably in most instances the birds that were hecklers had active nests in the vicinity. Most of the snakes heckled were climbing trees but some were on the ground. Heckling might continue intermittently over periods of days; the amount and intensity of heckling waxed and waned, evidently controlled by the amount of activity by the snake. Although heckling groups often dispersed after brief periods of scolding, individual birds may have kept informed concerning the snake's locale and movements, with the possibility of reassembling a group whenever the threat became severe.

The adaptive value of heckling behavior is evident. Many rat snakes had their prowling interrupted when heckling birds led me to them, and natural enemies of snakes must likewise benefit from observing such behavior. The red-tailed hawk, especially, is a major predator on the black rat snake, and the relative abundance of *Elaphe* remains in its pellets suggest that it may find the snakes in trees by observing the heckling behavior of birds from a distant lookout perch. My own attempts to find rat snakes by observing heckling were relatively inefficient; as I approached the scene of disturbance the birds would rapidly disperse, usually leaving me with only a general idea of the snake's location. Usually it was necessary for me to come within 15 to 20 m and to observe where the lines of vision of two or more scolding birds converged to have much chance of finding the snake. A hawk, having much more acute vision, might often be able to see the snake while watching quietly from a remote perch.

Spatial Relationships

Individual rat snakes were captured as many as 10 times over periods of years and the locations of these successive capture records yielded impressions concerning the extent, shape, and permanency of supposed home ranges, but records were too few to plot the complete home range of any individual. Most of the movements recorded (93%) were shorter than 500 m; 81% were shorter than 300 m. Movements longer than 500 m are considered to be shifts beyond the limits of a home range, and those from 300 to 500 m may represent unusually large ranges or those of elongate shape. Excluding movements longer than 500 m, mean distance for 120 movements within supposed home

ranges was 177 m, and was the same for 62 movements by males and 58 by females. Assuming home ranges tend toward circular shape, a mean area of about 9.84 ha is suggested. For movements within a single season (N=49), those extending into a second season (N=34), or into a third season (N=26), or into a fourth season (N=10), or into a fifth season (N=9), means were, respectively, 166.4 m, 189.7 m, 176.6 m, 103.4 m, and 201.7 m. These figures seem to indicate that home ranges are fairly stable in size over periods of years.

Like several other local snake species, black rat snakes make seasonal movements to hibernacula at hilltop limestone outcrops with exposures at least partly to the south, and with deep fissures and clefts that allow snakes to retreat below the frost line. Many rat snakes were caught at such locations in late September and October, and occasionally they were found emerging in spring. Many of these snakes found at hibernacula are believed to have been outside their regular home ranges, and their records were not included in calculation of home range sizes discussed in the previous paragraph. In 18 instances rat snakes that were captured at hibernation outcrops were also recorded on summer ranges, with mean intervening distance of 383 m (30.5 to 966). In six instances distance was greater than the 500 m considered to be about the maximum diameter of a home range. In their preferred rocky, open-woodland habitat the snakes can often find hibernacula without leaving their usual ranges. On FNHR rat snakes shared hibernation outcrops with racers, timber rattlesnakes, copperheads and garter snakes, and may have actually intertwined with them in mixed hibernating aggregations. Unlike these other species, rat snakes were not found to return to the same site or even to the same outcrop for successive hibernations. Nine rat snakes were found beside supposed hibernacula more than once; the same season in one, after a lapse of a year in five, after 2 years in one and after 3 years in two. The distance shifted per snake averaged 410 m (27 to 1174), and there was no evidence that any snake returned to a hibernaculum it had used in an earlier year.

Weatherhead and Haysack (1989) studied spatial relations in a population of *E. obsoleta* at the northern edge of the range, Lake Opinicon, eastern Ontario. Individual ranges, derived from radiotelemetric records, were plotted as convex polygons. Areas of water surface in the lake that fell within the polygons were subtracted. Many locations were recorded for each individual. For eight males average range was 3.90 ha ±1.68 (S D), and six females averaged 1.22 ha ±0.70. Range lengths averaged 420.7 m for males and 178.9 m for females. All rat snakes on the area used one or the other of two nearby hibernacula. These hibernacula averaged 247 m from the nearest points of the home ranges that were plotted. Ranges of individuals overlapped; population density was estimated at 3.9 to 4.2 per ha.

Kinds of Prey

The black rat snake preys chiefly on small birds and mammals which are found by active search, following visual and olfactory cues. A total of 122 separate prey items were palpated from the stomachs of snakes or were found before swallowing was completed, as follows: 43 *Microtus ochrogaster,* 17 *Peromyscus leucopus,* 12 *Colinus virginianus* (eggs and young), 7 *Cardinalis cardinalis* (eggs and young), 6 *Sylvilagus floridanus* (young), 6 *Sialia sialis* (eggs and young), 5 *Cyanocitta cristata* (eggs and young), 4 *Peromyscus maniculatus,* 4 *Sigmodon hispidus,* 2 *Microtus pinetorum,* 2 *Zapus hudsonius,* 2 *Gallus domesticus* (chicks), 2 *Zenaida macroura* (eggs), one each of *Mus musculus, Neotoma floridana, Reithrodontomys megalotis, Agelaius phoeniceus, Coccyzus americanus, Corvus brachyrhynchos, Molothrus ater, Sayornis phoebe,* snake egg, and *Hyla chrysoscelis.* These 122 items represent 81 predation episodes, as many of the snakes had eaten more than one item in each such instance the two or more prey animals were apparently from the same nest—eggs of the same clutch or littermates of the same size. In three instances the snake had eaten a female prairie vole and one or more of her young of matching sizes, and in three other instances two or more young of matching sizes, evidently littermates, had been eaten. More than half of the total of prey items were from nests of birds or mammals.

Allowing for the relative bulk of different kinds of prey (many of which were taken only or partly as young) the following estimates of relative biomass were made: *Microtus ochrogaster* 32%, *Sylvilagus floridanus* 19%, *Peromyscus leucopus* 12%, *Sigmodon hispidus* 8%, *Cyanocitta cristata* 6%, *Gallus domesticus* 6%, *Colinus virginianus* 6%, *Neotoma floridana* 3%, *Corvus brachyrhynchos* 2%, *Microtus pinetorum* 2%, *Cardinalis cardinalis* 2% and all others each less than 1%. Presumably in a larger sample many other species would be represented. Weighing on average 18 g. *P. leucopus* was estimated to be third in biomass with 12% of the total—allowing 2% collectively for the 11 species which each made up less than 1% of the total. The local fauna includes 27 passerines, 4 woodpeckers, 2 goatsuckers, a cuckoo, a mole, 2 shrews, 2 tree squirrels, 2 bats, and five kinds of rodents that are potential prey but were not found in my sample.

Immature rat snakes, especially first-year young, are seen less often than would be expected from the numbers of adults; they are cryptically colored and may be more secretive. Of five first-year young that contained prey, one had eaten an immature tree frog and three had each eaten a mouse (*Mus* and *Peromyscus*). The fifth had robbed a cardinal's nest. Seven second-year young contained prey (*Peromyscus leucopus* in three, *Zapus hudsonius* in two, *Microtus ochrogaster,* and *M. pinetorum* each in one) while the seventh contained remains of bird eggs. The predominance of terrestrial mammals in this sample suggests that young rat snakes may be less arboreal than adults.

The seasonal distribution of feeding records suggested that birds are most important in early summer. The bird-to-mammal ratio by month was: March 0 to 1, April 1 to 3, May 3 to 32 June 20 to 8 July 6 to 11, August 0 to 7, September 0 to 7, October 0 to 5, and November 0 to 1. All but one of the food items recorded were birds or mammals.

Black rat snakes have potential to exploit colony-nesting birds, and the abundant and continuous food supply within a small area permits them to thrive and grow to a larger size than they would otherwise. The most striking example was provided by Plummer's (1977) study in 1974 at a bank swallow colony along the Kaw River 6.8 km south of my study area. Ten of the snakes were captured and individually marked at a swallow colony that had about 370 nest holes extending for about 60 m along the vertical cutbank on the south side of the river. All 10 were unusually large adults, the largest (1850 mm SVL) of record size for Kansas. The snakes seemed to be living in the swallow colony, were frequently seen moving from one hole to another, and were feeding on eggs, nestlings, and adults (the latter apparently trapped on their nests when the snakes entered their burrows). Unlike other small passerines, swallows did not harass marauding snakes. In early June heavy rains caused the river level to rise, with undercutting of the banks and sloughing that destroyed all the nests in the colony exploited by the snakes and also in three larger colonies nearby that had not been exploited, perhaps because they were farther from woodland. Within a few days renesting had begun in the three larger colonies, but the exploited colony was abandoned. Two of six snakes recaptured subsequently in the colonies were from the colony that had disappeared.

Three other instances of rat snakes attaining both unusually large size and high concentration while preying on bird colonies were at farmsteads near, or adjacent to, the FNHR-NESA (Table 55). In each

TABLE 55. Contrasting Sizes of Black Rat Snakes on FNHR and Nearby Farmsteads

Area	Male		Female	
	SVL (mm)	N	SVL (mm)	N
FNHR	1214.5 (915–1550)	222	1063.25 (900–1290)	171
CWF	1401±65.4 (1224–1670)	7	1180±30.3 (1108–1300)	6
RC–KB	1530±94.0 (1224–1723)	4	1249±94.0 (1130–1480)	7

instance the feeding of domestic animals and poultry and the presence of a barn, sheds and other outbuildings, and a residence with vine-covered walls had created conditions favorable for the house sparrows, feral pigeons, and barn swallows on which the snakes preyed (taking also commensal rodents, and occasionally young chicks or chicken eggs).

At JFM near the SW corner of FNHR, I was called upon to remove a dozen rat snakes over a 20-year period. Most of these had already been killed when I retrieved them. Most were large adults but none was outstanding, and no doubt the long-continued policy of killing the snakes on sight prevented any from growing to near maximum size. Rat snakes found at CWF were not killed. At RC-KB those found were killed occasionally, when they were preying upon eggs or poultry. The farmyard environment with its concentration of bird and mammal commensals provided a better food supply than did the more natural environments of woodland and edge. The surfeit of food at the farmsteads seemed to cause the snakes to reduce their ranges and remain within relatively small areas. As shown in Table 55 the farmyard snakes were 14–22% larger than were those from FNHR. However, greater average and maximum (1850 mm SVL) were attained by the rat snakes that Plummer found in bank swallow colonies.

The adaptive and exploitive aspects of rat snake predation were emphasized by actual or attempted attacks on caged animals. Once when a colony of harvest mice was maintained in an outdoor cage, a rat snake was found lying across the top of the cage apparently trying to gain entry. In 1985 chipmunks were reintroduced to FNHR, and temporarily were confined in small individual cages inside a larger cage of quarter-inch wire, a rat snake entered the cage through a small opening, ate a chipmunk, and then, distended with its prey, was unable to leave. From time to time I was called upon to remove rat snakes which had entered a henhouse or chicken yard at RC-KB. On six occasions such snakes had swallowed objects from the hens' nests, presumably because they had the odor of chickens — glass egg, golf balls, and in one instance, a rock which had sharp angles and edges. One large rat snake had constricted and killed a hen on her nest, but she was much too large to be swallowed by the snake.

The prey eaten consisted of birds and mammals, except for a single tree frog palped from a first-year rat snake. However, further evidence of frog eating was the occurrence of lung flukes in many of the rat snakes examined — since lung flukes passing through early stages of the life cycle require a snail and then a frog as hosts. The snake host can only acquire the adult fluke by eating a frog, that has acquired its infestation in its aquatic larval stage. The adult flukes, normally found in the snakes' lung cavity, migrate up the trachea to the gullet and mouth in the breeding season, and the eggs pass through the snakes' digestive tract.

The flukes found in rat snakes were markedly larger than those found in other snakes (*Coluber, Thamnophis, Nerodia*) and seem to be a different species that is limited to *Elaphe*. The intermediate hosts may be *Hyla chrysoscelis* and an aquatic snail such as *Heliosoma trivolvis*. All the infestations observed involved few flukes; in fact eight of the 24 infested snakes had only one fluke each. Infestations were seasonal, as follows: 44% of 48 snakes in May; 12.5% of 40 snakes in June; 8% of 36 snakes in July, but none of the snakes checked in late summer, fall, or early spring was infested. Infestations are evident only in May and early summer and the 44% snakes having flukes at that season indicate that frog-eating must be fairly common.

Reproduction

Rat snakes have been found in closely associated pairs or actually copulating 18 April, 7, 9, 13, 15, 26, 27, 28, 30 May, and 7 July. Many encounters at other times of year all involved lone individuals, but a female checked on 14 October had abundant sperm in her cloaca indicating recent mating. These records indicate that the main breeding season is late April and May with occasional mating at other times of year.

The smallest females having large ova were 960 and 983 mm SVL, and others having thickened cloacal capsules (indicating sexual maturity) were 942, 957 and 990 mm, and each was probably in its fourth year. The smallest males having motile sperm were 825 (May), 845 (May), and 860 (October) mm SVL. Judging from their sizes, these males were still in their third year; it seems that males attain sexual maturity a year earlier than females.

In rat snakes greater size of the male is correlated with male combat, and probably with competition for mates. Rigley (1971) described a hostile encounter between males under natural conditions, 15 June 1969, in West Virginia. Both males were about 1.2 m long. They were observed on a lawn struggling for 18 minutes. Tails were tightly intertwined, heads were close together with S-curves of about 50 mm in the neck. From time to time, with its front and rear ends against the ground, one would raise its midbody about 0.3 m high. Each attempted to cover his rival with loops and coils. Separation occurred after one pinned down the other's head for several seconds, holding it in place beneath body coils.

Gillingham (1979) described a triphasic mating pattern in rat snakes and compared *Elaphe obsoleta* with *E. guttata* and *E. vulpina*. The main phases were characterized as: tactile chase, tactile alignment, and intromission and coitus. "Motor patterns" that were recognized include: touch, mount, chase, chase-mount, dorsal-advance movement, forward jerking, writhe, caudocephalic waves, writhe-bump, tail-search copulatory attempt, intromission, and biting. The three species differed only in minor details. The duration of coitus averaged 20.7 minutes in *Elaphe obsoleta*.

Discovery of ovipositing females and emerging hatchlings has revealed that eggs usually are laid in crumbling decaying wood of old stumps or logs. Egg-laying dates include 21 June 1994, 27 June 1952, 29 June 1977, 4 July 1992, 11 July 1959, and 13 July 1956 signifying the end of June and early July as the season of ovipositing. As in most reptiles, small females producing their first clutches lay few eggs, whereas females near maximum size produce the most. In 19 clutches eggs ranged from 5 to 28, mean 9.68 ± 1.19. The clutch of 28 eggs was laid by a female of 1041 mm, and had many more eggs than those of other females including those that were larger. Hence factors other than size of female must influence clutch size. No doubt the food supply and the female's nutritional state affect size of clutch.

Females that are gravid are markedly heavier than nongravid individuals of similar length. During the entire period of the study a total of 11 gravid females was captured in June versus 22 that seemed to be nongravid suggesting that on the average only one-third produce clutches in any given year. However, there may be differences in activity patterns between females that are gravid and those that are not. Handicapped in locomotion and especially in climbing by their burden of eggs, gravid individuals are probably much less active and spend much time in hidden oviposition sites before laying occurs. In any case an attempt to distinguish reproductive and nonreproductive females from July samples yielded contrasting figures. Thirty had low weights within the range of those known to have recently oviposited and therefore were assumed to have produced clutches, whereas only 12 were within the weight range between those that were gravid and those that had recently oviposited. Presumably the true ratio of repro-

ductive females to nonreproductive varies from year to year but lies somewhere between the 33% indicated by the June samples and the 72% suggested by the July samples. The sample's larger females (1100 mm or more in SVL) had an incidence of 66% reproductives (N=29) whereas the smaller females (less than 1100 SVL) had an incidence of 47% reproductives.

A clutch of eggs hatched on 28 August 1952 after 58 days of incubation. Another clutch incubated in the laboratory hatched on 27 October 1960. A clutch of 10 laid 4 July 1992 were found to have hatched on 8 November. The 2-month span of hatching dates suggests the possibility of occasional second clutches but variable weather, differences in incubation sites and asynchrony in the breeding cycles of different females may account for much of the difference in time of hatching. On 25 September 1952 and 9 October 1969 broods of hatchlings were found emerging from a decaying black oak log and from the root cavities of a decaying elm stump. The hatchlings from eggs incubated in the laboratory tended to burrow more deeply into the incubation medium to the bottom of their container, remaining concealed there for periods of days.

The eggs are cylindrical, 1.6 to 3.0 times longer than wide, with neither end noticeably more pointed. Shells are white and flexible. Eggs that are in contact when they are extruded become glued together as their mucous film dries and there may be several clusters within a clutch, rigidly attached in pairs or groups. However, most eggs are free of others, because the female moves about actively during oviposition. Size and shape of eggs is highly variable, between clutches and also within each clutch (Table 56). During incubation the eggshells become stained and mottled with reddish brown.

In the course of normal incubation, the eggs gradually absorb moisture from the surrounding medium, changing shape to become less elongate, since there is more latitudinal than longitudinal stretching. Average gain per egg in a clutch measured on 27 June and 25 August amounted to 13.7% in length, 29.3% in width and 42.2% in weight. A clutch laid on 21 June 1994 was remeasured on 24 August. There was no gain in length

TABLE 56. Varying Sizes and Shapes of Eggs in Six Clutches of Black Rat Snakes

Date of Laying	N	Length (mm)	Width (mm)	Weight (g)
June 7, 1952	26	39.6 ± 1.19 (25–49)	23.9 ± 0.27 (21.0–27.5)	15.7 ± 0.42 (11.5–17.6)
July 13, 1956	6	57.3 ± 1.43 (53–65)	18.9 ± 0.30 (18–20)	12.9 ± 0.35 (11.6–13.9)
July 7, 1965	11	40.6 ± 0.56 (38–43)	28.8 ± 0.38 (23.5–26.5)	15.5 ± 0.24 (14.5–17.0)
July 7, 1965	6	49.4 ± 1.82 (46–57)	22.7 ± 0.44 (21.3–24.0)	16.4 ± 0.33 (15.5–17.5)
June 29, 1977	10	40.7 ± 0.83 (37–46)	21.6 ± 0.22 (21.0–23.0)	12.1 ± 0.29 (11.4–14.4)
June 21, 1994	13	41.8 ± 0.53 (39–45)	24.0 ± 0.24 (22.5–25.3)	15.7 ± 0.17 (14.9–16.8)

TABLE 57. Sizes of Young Black Rat Snakes, Showing Monthly Growth in SVL and Weight

Month	N	SVL (mm)		N	Weight (g)	
(Hatchling)	81	316.6±0.36	(276–368)	81	11.7±0.36	(9.0–15.0)
Sept.	7	361.0±6.96	(334–377)	7	14.4±1.10	(12.1–17.3)
Oct.	23	355.7±3.69	(303–409)	23	13.6±0.80	(9.0–23.7)
May	4	377.0±17.2	(336–420)	4	13.5±1.63	(9.1–16.0)
June	13	418.9±13.9	(313–498)	12	18.7±1.86	(7.7–29.5)
July	8	476.8±17.9	(375–543)	5	27.3±3.29	(21.6–38.0)
Aug.	4	529.0±63.9	(340–608)	4	45.6±2.47	(39–63)
Sept.	4	554.0±6.34	(517–571)	4	37.5±3.30	(30–44)
Oct.	24	579.6±8.34	(503–630)	18	45.1±2.42	(30–67)
May	5	613.8±13.8	(560–633)	4	49.5±6.35	(33–64)
June	11	654.7±8.0	(618–715)	11	73.1±5.36	(43–101)
July	9	693.9±17.2	(630–773)	9	70.2±3.00	(55–106)
Aug.	7	733.3±17.2	(668–789)	7	83.2±8.64	(51–113)
Sept.	12	762.7±26.4	(706–829)	12	91.3±5.91	(60–123)
Oct.	43	782.2±5.2	(503–848)	28	111.9±5.29	(30–165)

Growth

For 22 hatchlings captured in September and October the average date was 16 October, and these snakes had a mean length (SVL) of 353 mm and a mean weight of 13.3 g. If at hatching these averaged the same size as 81 young hatched in the laboratory, and hatched at the same time, they averaged an 11.7% gain in length and a 14.6% gain in weight in 16 days. This implied growth rate would translate to an average increase of 40 mm in length and 7.52 grams for each snake in its first month of life. Only three of the 22 fall hatchlings were captured in September (24th, 26th, 29th); 18 were captured in October and one in November.

During their first year the young constitute a discrete size group fairly well set off from older snakes, and their average size increase from month to month provides an index to their growth rate (Table 57). There are some discrepancies in the table due to the small size of some of the samples. For instance, the September sample of young averaged slightly larger than the October sample. This is because most clutches hatch in October and young caught in that month included many that were recently hatched. At the end of their first year some young, stunted by lack of success in obtaining food, have grown little whereas others have overtaken the most retarded 2-year-olds, and the size overlap between age groups increases in older snakes. Nevertheless, most second-year snakes are recognizable as such and an attempt was made to sort them and trace their growth up to an age of 2 years. In Table 57 1-year-old snakes in October average 580 mm and 45 g; 2-year-olds in September average 763 mm and 91 g. During 2 years of growth the average monthly gain per snake was 37 mm and 7 g.

but a mean gain of 24.6% in width and 38% in weight. These eggs hatched on 12 and 13 September after 83 and 84 days of incubation. The hatchlings shed their skins from 28 September to 1 October. Other eggs that were experimentally incubated in relatively dry media changed little in size and shape, but nevertheless produced normal hatchlings. Average hatching date for 10 clutches was 2 October (28 August to 8 November). Of the 87 hatchlings, 55 were males and 32 were females. The 63% males in this small sample is remarkably similar to the 64.3% males in the total sample of 846 black rat snakes, including young and adults. In the laboratory, eggs developed successfully in various incubation media (sand, loam, crushed rock, decaying wood), with varying moisture content, over a temperature range from near 0° to 40°C.

In a sample of 81 hatchlings from nine clutches artificially incubated, mean SVL was 316.6±2.68 (276–368) mm and mean weight was 11.7±0.36 (9.0-15.0) g, with no significant difference between the sexes.

TABLE 58. Growth in Young Black Rat Snakes Individually Marked and Recaptured

Original Record				Recapture Record			
Date	SVL (mm)	Weight (g)	Probable Age (mo)	Date	SVL (mm)	Weight (g)	Probable Age (mo)
Males							
9/22/52	338	15	0	6/7/53	413	16	9
9/27/52	351	13	0	7/13/53	483	222	10
10/15/59	372	15	1	9/28/62	922	142	36
10/25/54	409	24	1	10/28/55	604	146	13
9/1/56	570	34	12	7/15/58	683	92	34
6/29/59	750	93	21	9/6/59	896	173	24
7/11/58	758	104	22	5/3/59	845	156	32
Females							
10/22/54	354	10	1	6/11/57	850	139	33
5/30/59	560	33	8	7/30/59	664	62	10
				5/9/61	900	196	32
5/29/57	633	64	20	7/9/57	688	79	22
6/11/56	664	89	10	7/15/58	955	212	35
5/26/82	728	63	20	6/22/83	830	121	33
10/16/56	757	134		9/12/58	960	215	49
7/31/78	830	120	10	7/16/80	928	200	34

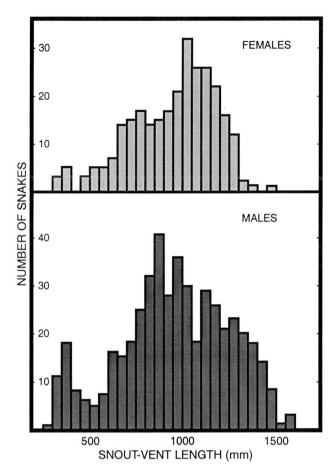

Figure 20. Size (SVL) groups in black rat snakes, with the sexes shown separately. Average and maximum adult size is greater in males.

TABLE 59. Rates of Gain in Length (mm per Month) in Recaptured Adult Black Rat Snakes

Size Range in Sample at Beginning and End of Growth Period	Sex	Mean Growth Rate, mm per Month SVL	N	Total Snake Months Excluding Hibernations
From 800–899 to	♂	19.3 (11.5–27.5)	6	110.0
Adult Size Range	♀	17.5 (4.1–41.3)	6	91.5
From 900–999 to	♂	18.7 (12.0–26.6)	4	31.5
1000–1099	♀	12.5 (4.0–28.0)	5	46.0
From 1000–1099 to	♂	7.5 (3.2–13.6)	4	64.0
1200–1299	♀	5.4 (5.3–5.6)	2	62.0
From 1200–1299 to	♂	6.6 (3.0–12.8)	6	95.0
1300–1399	♀	0.75 (0.0–1.5)	2	23.0
From 1300–1399 to	♂	5.3 (2.2–10.5)	3	46.0
1400–1499				
From 1400–1499 to	♂	1.9 (1.7–2.2)	2	65.5
1500–1599				

after 6 years, four after 5 years, eight after 4 years, 14 after 3 years, 20 after 2 years, and 29 after 1 year. Some of these snakes were already large adults when they were marked. For example, a male first captured 16 July 1950 had a SVL of 1373 from which a probable age of 13 years was estimated. He was recaptured in 5 subsequent years with the final capture on 25 April 1958 (SVL 1448) and would then have been in his 21st year if the original age estimate of 13 years was correct. It is obvious that the more successful individuals survive for many years, but there is fairly rapid population turnover, with newly matured young making up a substantial part of the adult population each year. Table 60 shows average gains made by recaptured snakes.

Table 61 presents a tentative age-length correlation, based on all available records, recognizing that adults continue to grow, and that the rate of growth decreases as the individual's age increases and that this rate decreases faster in females. In my sample 16 annual age groups are recognized, with the smallest sexually mature male (825 mm SVL) probably in his 3rd year, and the smallest mature female (960 mm SVL) proba-

Table 58 shows records of 14 black rat snakes that were individually marked early in life (hatching size to probable 3rd year size) and recaptured after intervals of 2 to 35 months. All snakes made substantial gains in length but growth rates were extremely variable. Eleven recaptured snakes averaged 904±14.9 mm SVL at an average age of a little more than 3 years having made average gains of about 17 mm per month. Some males mature in the third year. Most snakes of both sexes reach small adult size by the time they are 4 years old, and during the third year the growth rate declines to somewhat less than half of that maintained during the first 2 years. Figure 20 shows SVL for both adults and young measured in the course of my study.

Adults grow also, and most of those recaptured after months or years had made substantial gains in length and weight, but a few lost weight and several failed to make measurable gain in length. Table 59 shows rates in adults, males growing faster, especially in the larger size classes.

Of the 658 rat snakes individually marked, two were recaptured after 8 years, one after 7 years, four

TABLE 60. Age and SVL in Individually Marked Black Rat Snakes That Were Recaptured

Age (in Years)	N	Males SVL (mm)	N	Females SVL (mm)
Hatchling	54	319.6±0.33 (261–368)	27	310±0.47 (276–343)
1	3	652 (604–688)	1	664
2	3	854 (822–896)	3	838 (830–850)
3	5	906.8±25.8 (845–968)	2	950 (940–960)
4	5	927±26.8 (894–1035)	6	964.7±31.0 (893–1076)
5	10	1092.9±29.5 (944–1182)	10	1082.4±30.2 (928–1220)
6	5	1171.6±20.1 (1095–1213)	3	1025±49.0 (953–1120)
7	3	1194.0±35.3 (1135–1257)	4	1171±33.2 (1127–1270)
8	4	1186.7±40.8 (1110–1300)		
9			6	1179±23.0 (1110–1274)
10	3	1346±30.4 (1290–1408)	3	1260±20.7 (1177–1247)
12	5	1345.6±17.1 (1300–1405)		

TABLE 61. Tentative Correlation of SVL and Age in Black Rat Snakes

Years After Hatching	Males		Females		Both Sexes	
	N	Typical Range in SVL (mm)	N	Typical Range in SVL (mm)	N	Percentage of Adult Population
1st	47	316–554	31	316–554	78*	—
2nd	59	555–762	32	555–762	91*	—
3rd	42	763–877	30	763–866	72*	—
4th	59	878–965	40	867–957	99	18.4
5th	40	966–1039	34	958–1009	74	13.8
6th	31	1040–1085	30	1010–1057	61	11.4
7th	30	1086–1131	21	1058–1100	51	9.5
8th	26	1132–1176	21	1101–1140	47	8.8
9th	33	1177–1220	19	1141–1179	52	9.6
10th	24	1221–1263	14	1180–1217	38	7.1
11th	21	1264–1306	17	1218–1254	38	7.1
12th	15	1307–1349	13	1255–1290	28	5.2
13th	16	1350–1391	4	1291–1320	20	3.7
14th	11	1392–1432	3	1321–1350	14	2.6
15th	8	1433–1472	0	—	8	1.5
16th	6	1473–1511	0	—	5	1.1

*Young underrepresented in samples

bly in her 4th or 5th year. Each successively older group is represented by fewer individuals, up to the oldest group with less than one percent of the total. Females are fewer than males in nearly all samples and make up 39% of the total. Immature snakes (first- second- and third-year) are not represented in their true numbers in relation to adults; they are less noticeable in the field, and some of those caught in traps may have escaped by squeezing through small openings.

Geographic Differentiation

Mitchell (1994) found a mean SVL of 1182 and 1136 mm respectively for adult males and females in Virginia—contrasting with my data, 1226 (male) and 1081 (female) for Kansas, where sexual dimorphism is more pronounced. Also, Virginia hatchlings (285 mm SVL) were smaller than Kansas hatchlings (317 mm SVL). Clutch size was 19.4 in a series from northern Virginia (N=21) but 11.3 in 24 other clutches from the state, whereas in my northeastern Kansas sample, mean was 9.7 (N=19). Literature records indicate clutch size to be relatively high in the eastern states: 13.9 ± 1.3 (N=29) for NY, PA, OH, IN, MD, KY, DC, WV; 14.1 ± 2.3 for SC, GA, OK, LA, FL, TX. In Arkansas Trauth et al. (1994) recorded a mean of 24.0 ± 3.1 (16–33, N=10) for previtellogenic follicles and 11.6 ± 2.7 (7–17) for nine females having either yolked follicles or oviductal eggs.

Lampropeltis calligaster

Traits of the Species

The prairie kingsnake is a medium-size, smooth-scaled, constricting colubrid. The species' range includes the southern Great Plains (south from Iowa and Nebraska) and east to the Atlantic, from Maryland to northern Florida, but excluding the Florida Peninsula. Eastern populations are assigned to a separate subspecies, *rhombomaculata,* the "mole kingsnake." Prairie king-snakes have a pale, grayish-brown ground color with dark brown mid-dorsal rhombs, and on each side two series of large spots alternating with the dorsal rhombs. The markings are vivid in juveniles but may become obscure or indiscernible in old adults, which become uniformly dark brown, or may show four faint dusky longitudinal stripes. (See Plates 19 & 20.) The mole kingsnake differs from its western subspecies in having fewer, smaller, and more widely spaced mid-dorsal rhombs and lateral spots, and ontogenetically it loses its spotted pattern sooner. The food consists mainly of small mammals, but includes also lizards, snakes, and the eggs of birds and reptiles. Prairie kingsnakes are secretive and spend much of their time underground. Their preferred habitat is tallgrass prairie. The tail is relatively short (14.9% of SVL in 142 males, 13.6% in 99 females) with no perceptible ontogenetic change in proportions. Of a total of 275 prairie kingsnakes, 34 (12.3%) had incomplete tails; in approximately half of these only the tip was missing. Incidence of damaged tails was positively correlated with the age cohort of the snake (deduced from SVL) as follows: first year, 4.5%; second year, 12.0%, third year, 10.9%; fourth year, 14.8%, fifth year, 13.0%; sixth year, 13.0%; seventh year, 13.0% eighth year and older, 17.9%.

Behavior

Prairie kingsnakes move slowly, depending on cryptic coloration for protection. A characteristic response to disturbance is to coil, flattening the head, vibrating the tail, and making short, jabbing strikes at a potential attacker. The head is jerked or twitched, sometimes at intervals as short as a second. The movement may be a sideways wagging, or may be in a vertical plane.

The gray and brown markings are effectively cryptic, especially against a background of dead ground vegetation beneath grass. Also the color and pattern are remarkably similar to those of the venomous massasauga. The defensive coiling, vibrating the tail, and head twitching all resemble behavior patterns of the massasauga. Evidently Batesian mimicry is involved and the two snakes overlap extensively in their geographic ranges and local habitats.

Like other species of kingsnakes this one has sexual size dimorphism with males larger than females, and with male rivalry and combat. Male prairie kingsnakes confined together in spring (with no females present) fought, biting each other viciously. In such combats the larger male had a decided advantage and was almost certain to be the winner if there was much size difference.

Spatial Relationships

The prairie kingsnake was a relatively uncommon species, and over 50 years of fieldwork captures averaged only 7.6 (0 to 19) annually. In the successive decades of the 1950s, 1960s, 1970s, 1980s, and 1990s the annual catch averaged 5.3, 11.0, 6.4, 6.4, and 11.1. Fieldwork on RET in the 1960s and NESA in the 1990s increased the catch substantially as numbers dwindled on FNHR because of deteriorating habitat.

In general these snakes were found only in open grassland, except that in fall and spring some were found at wooded hilltop rock outcrops where they had come to hibernate. Like most other local snakes they seem to depend on the hilltop limestone outcrops for hibernacula; 15 snakes, all adults or adolescents, were found there. Perhaps juveniles hibernate away from the outcrops wherever they may happen to be, and some adults also may hibernate away from the outcrops. On 2 April 1981 a large adult male was found as a traffic casualty on a county road in the Kaw River floodplain more than a kilometer from any outcrops, but he must have emerged recently. In unusually warm weather in January 1975 a prematurely emerged male was found on a road in the Kaw Valley more than 2 km from hilltop outcrops.

Seventy-four movements were recorded in marked kingsnakes that were recaptured after intervals ranging from 3 days to 3 years. The longest movements were: 950, 763, 482, 430, and 408 m. In each instance the snake was believed to have shifted its range to a new area. The remaining 69 movements form a graded series up to 370 m. Thirty-three male movements averaged 150 m and 36 female movements averaged 123.8. The many movements rather evenly distributed up to 350 m suggest that home ranges may have about that diameter, and diameters of this size encompass areas of 9.86 ha. One kingsnake was caught six times, two were each caught five times, and six three times; 43 were each recorded only twice. Three were recorded in 3 different years and 26 each in 2 years. One female was found beneath the same shelter five times within a 1-month period, but there was only one other recapture (after 35 days) which showed no movement.

Kinds of Prey

The 35 food items palped from stomachs represent 27 feeding episodes (in five instances a snake had eaten more than one individual of the same kind of prey). Small mammals make up the greater part of the food, with snakes, lizards and bird eggs making up relatively minor components. The food consisted of 19 *Microtus ochrogaster*, 6 *Blarina hylophaga*, 2 each of *Cryptotis parva*, *Ophisaurus attenuatus*, *Colinus virginianus* (egg), and *Synaptomys cooperi* and one each of *Coluber constrictor* (juvenile) and *Eumeces fasciatus* (juvenile). In terms of biomass, mammals were calculated to comprise 81%, lizards 9%, snake eggs and bird eggs each 5%. First- year young had eaten 5 shrews (3 *Blarina hylophaga*, 2 *Cryptotis parva*) and a juvenile *Eumeces fasciatus*, whereas adults and well-grown young took larger prey: shrews (all of them *Blarina*), microtines, glass lizards, and quail eggs.

In addition to these 35 prey items from stomachs, 39 items were identified from scats of prairie kingsnakes from the years 1954 through 1962. There were 19 *Microtus ochrogaster*, 3 *Scalopus aquaticus*, 3 *Blarina hylophaga*, 3 *Peromyscus* (*maniculatus*?), 2 *Microtus pinetorum*, 2 *Cnemidophorus sexlineatus*, and 1 each of *Mus musculus*, *Sigmodon hispidus*, *Sylvilagus floridanus*, *Crotalus horridus*, *Diadophis punctatus*, *Eumeces* sp., and *Eumeces obsoletus*. Most of these scats were from adult snakes, but two lizards (*Eumeces* sp. and *Cnemidophorus sexlineatus*) and one vole were from first- or second-year young.

Reproduction

In the breeding season male prairie kingsnakes find females by following their scent trails. On several occasions pairs were found together in traps. The pair association may last for several days. Male confrontations probably occur most often when two meet as a result of following the same female. Males were mutually hostile when caged together, even without a female.

Females carrying oviductal eggs were captured on 16, 17, 20, 21, 26 and 29 May and 2, 4, 10, 12, 14, 16, 19, 22 and 24 June in different years. On 24 May the female of a pair found in a trap had active sperm in her cloaca. Another pair was found under a board on 10 May 1991. In 14 fecund females (clutches palpated in 11, laid in 3) the average number of eggs was 9.14±0.58 (6 to 13). Clutch size tended to be proportional to female size. On 19 June, 1959 a female captured 5 days earlier deposited her clutch of seven eggs. Five of the eggs were glued together when the clutch dried. The female weighed 215 g before laying and 138 after. A female captured on 13 June 1978 laid seven eggs on 24 June. Eggs averaged 43.2 × 19.6 mm and 10.2 g at laying. They hatched on 29 August. The female weighed 182 g before laying and her clutch weighed 70.2 g. A clutch of 10 eggs plowed up in a field (HB) on 25 June 1978 were all adherent with a total weight of 122.2 g. They hatched on 17 August. A female found dead as a traffic casualty on 20 May 1958 contained eight ova, all approximately 36 × 17 mm.

Some females may be nonbreeders. The sexes have similar proportions except that tails average about 10% longer in males, but females vary more in weight, especially in late May, June, and July, when oviductal eggs may increase body weight more than one-third. After laying, body weight may be reduced to about two-thirds of the average weight of a male of comparable length. During late spring and early summer three fairly distinct groups of females are recognizable: those that are heavy with eggs, those that are relatively thin after recent egg laying, and those that are neither plump nor emaciated, appearing to be nonbreeders. In my combined records there were 25 obviously gravid females, eight that appeared to be post-ovipositional (mostly in July) and 16 that did not fit either category and may have been nonbreeders. The figures suggest that in the local population about two-thirds of the adult females reproduce each year, but probably there is much year-to-year variation, according to weather and food supply.

Tryon and Carl (1980) reported on reproduction in a pair of mole kingsnakes from Clayton County, Georgia. The female, hatched in 1976 and reared in captivity, was introduced into the male's cage on 12 February

TABLE 62. Lengths and Weights of First-year Prairie Kingsnakes

	N	SVL (mm)	Weight (g)
Hatchlings	16	264.4±3.8 (234–290)	8.26±2.5 (6.0–9.8)
September	8	289.6±6.9 (264–317)	9.84±1.25 (6.4–18.0)
October	9	301.4±8.0 (281–352)	10.10±0.78 (8.0–16.0)
Spring (April, May)	9	323.7±4.5 (286–382)	13.30±1.49 (8.0–20.0)
Summer (June, July, August)	11	438.0±12.1 (338–482)	28.10±2.64 (10.0–43.0)

1978. Both snakes reacted to each other's presence with rapid tongue flicking and body jerking. The female underwent ecdysis on 18 April and twice during the next 7 days she was seen lying on the male seeming to take the initiative in courtship with her cloacal region pressed against his, with occasional jerking and tongue flicking. The pair was observed copulating on 26 and 27 April. The male's body was lying loosely on the female's and parallel to it, with his head resting initially on her nape. The same pair was observed copulating again on 21 April 1979. On this occasion the male was lying on the female with a biting hold dorsolaterally (on her 5th anterior body blotch). In 1978 the 5 eggs averaged 39.6 mm long, 16.0 mm wide, and weighed 6.4 g, in 1979 13 eggs averaged 29.7 × 18.3 mm and 5.7 g. The first egg was slit 48 days after oviposition. Incubation periods ranged from 49 to 54 days for 17 eggs laid in the 2 years. Hatchlings averaged approximately 200 mm SVL and 5.5 g (1978) or 5.8 g (1979). In these Georgia kingsnakes both the female and the hatchlings were smaller than any of the *L. c. calligaster* that I observed in Kansas.

TABLE 63. Selected Records of Individually Marked and Recaptured Prairie Kingsnakes

Sex	Capture Dates	SVL (mm)	Weight (g)
♂	7/31/78–9/16/78	425–524	29–50
	6/13/80	800	190
♂	10/16/65–7/30/66	546–740	65–122
♂	10/22/58–8/2/62	495–1018	
♂	5/25/91–10/24/93	600–940	52–228
♂	4/7/76–5/4/77	603–723	64–130
♂	6/7/77–7/16/78	695–732	120–123
♂	6/29/59–9/15/63	708–1035	123–
♂	6/28/61–5/29/62	455–524	147–192
♂	5/12/87–5/9/88	800–860	160–211
♂	5/8/90–5/3/91	818–951	193–290
♂	5/19/92–4/23/93	840–870	186–170
♂	4/13/93–6/12/94	940–1010	280–337
♀	5/26/55–6/10/56	315–618	14–96
♀	4/12/78–5/10/79	447–675	31–112
	10/11/80	848	224
♀	7/17/81–9/9/82	653–843	106–222
♀	5/22/60–5/24/61	672–719	80–144
♀	9/18/86–4/10/88	688–870	106–230
♀	6/26/77–7/9/79	670–878	90–192
♀	6/1/90–5/10/91	840–886	193–220
	6/19/92	914	188
♀	5/5/75–8/17/77	908–993	200–292

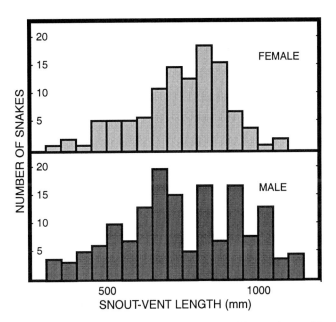

Figure 21. Size (SVL) groups in prairie kingsnakes, with the sexes shown separately. Average and maximum adult size is greater in males.

Growth

Early growth is deduced from the sizes of 1-year-old snakes; eight captured in August, September, and October averaged 557 (495–596) mm SVL and if they were of average size at hatching, they made average gains of 48 mm per month during their season of activity. Seven recaptured young had made average gains of 35 mm per month during their second year; a mean of 708 SVL is considered typical of 2-year-olds. Seven recaptured young had gained an average of 20.2 mm SVL in their third years, and SVL of 816 mm is considered typical for 3-year-olds. Adults that were recaptured had gained variable amounts, all less than 10 mm SVL per month (Tables 62 and 63).

Figure 21 and Table 64 show lengths (SVL) of all prairie kingsnakes recorded, bringing out size differ-

TABLE 64. A 50-year Sample of Prairie Kingsnakes Sorted According to Sex, Size and Probable Age

Probable Age (years)	Males		Females		Combined	
	N	SVL (mm)	N	SVL (mm)	N	% of Sample
1st	36	264–496	17	278–482	53	16.0
2nd	57	500–695	28	505–695	85	25.6
3rd	31	700–820	23	703–770	54	16.3
4th	17	832–892	13	780–830	30	9.1
5th	21	900–945	11	833–848	32	9.7
6th	14	950–1000	14	855–880	28	8.5
7th	11	1000–1042	11	881–938	22	6.6
8th	8	1050–1114	14	940–984	22	6.6
9th	2				2	0.6
10th			3	1050–1070	3	1.0

TABLE 65.   Numbers of Prairie Kingsnakes Captured on a 9.46 ha Area, and Their Ratio to Garter Snakes and Racers, Indicating Population Density

Year	Kingsnake to Garter Snake Ratio	Estimated No. of Kingsnakes from Garter Snake Petersen Index	Mean Density of Kingsnakes per ha (Estimated)	Kingsnake to Racer Ratio	Estimated No. of Kingsnakes from Racer Petersen Index	Mean Density of Kingsnake per ha (Estimated)
1990	9 to 81 (11.1%)	0.111 × 49.5 = 5.5	0.58	9 to 62 (14.5%)	0.145 × 83 = 12.0	1.27
1991	11 to 70 (15.7%)	0.157 × 84 = 13.2	1.40	11 to 83 (13.3%)	0.133 × 182 = 24.2	2.54
1992	10 to 33 (15.0%)	0.159 × 58 = 9.23	0.98	10 to 58 (17.2%)	0.172 × 114 = 19.6	2.07
1993	6 to 66 (9.1%)	0.091 × 135 = 12.3	1.30	7 to 30 (23.3%)	0.233 × 164 = 38.2	4.03
1994	5 to 44 (11.4%)	0.114 × 183 = 20.8	2.20	5 to 41 (12.2%)	0.122 × 153 = 18.6	1.87
1996	10 to 47 (21.3%)	0.213 × 104 =22.2	2.34	10 to 29 (34.5%)	0.345 × 221 = 76.5	8.06
1997	5 to 18 (27.8%)	0.278 × 84 = 23.4	2.47	5 to 13 (38.5%)	no racer recaptures	—

ences between the sexes. On the average adult females are 92.7% of male SVL and 81.9% of male weight. The largest female was 90.3% of the largest male's SVL and 73.4% of his weight. The smallest of 14 fecund females was 708 mm SVL, and the smallest male found to have active sperm was 629 mm. Probably these newly matured snakes were in their 3rd and 2nd years, respectively.

Sixteen hatchlings from three clutches incubated in the laboratory averaged 264.4±3.79 (234–290) mm SVL and 8.26±2.5 (6.0–9.4) g. Table 62 shows growth in first-year young. Recorded hatching dates were in August. Many of the juveniles captured in fall (September, October) and spring (April, May) were still in the size range of hatchlings, but in summer most young (10 of 11) had grown to more than 400 mm SVL (mean 438 by an average date of 28 July). At this rate of growth the snakes would exceed 500 mm by their second spring with males already reaching sexual maturity and by their 3rd spring females would be sexually mature, exceeding 700 mm.

Numbers

On every area where they were found prairie kingsnakes were less numerous than several other common species, and samples were too small to use for a Petersen Index. However, the ratio of kingsnake captures to captures of the commoner species provided a clue to their actual numbers. The NESA northwestern enclosure area, providing Petersen Index ratios for *Thamnophis* and *Coluber* over a period of years, also yielded several records of prairie kingsnakes each year. Table 65 shows the actual numbers of all three species

trapped there annually, 1990 to 1994 and 1996, and estimates of the actual numbers of kingsnakes derived from these ratios and from the census figures for the common species. The numbers derived from the kingsnake/racer ratios are consistently higher than those derived from the kingsnake/garter snake ratios — approximately 50% more. The data suggest that there were at most times from 9 to 38 kingsnakes on this 9.46 ha area, with population density in the range of 1.0 to 4.0/ha. These estimates assume comparable catchability in the three species. Actually, racers being more active and having greater site-fidelity, were, individually, the most likely to be caught (42.5% recaptures); kingsnakes less likely; and garter snakes, because of high vagility and tendency to shift, were probably the least at risk. Hence, kingsnake numbers may have been somewhat overestimated from comparison with garter snakes but possibly underestimated from comparison with racers.

Geographic Differentiation

Little information is available regarding population differences within *Lampropeltis calligaster*. Mitchell's (1994) figures for Virginia indicate that adults, both males and females, are several percent smaller than their Kansas counterparts. However, hatchlings evidently are much smaller — 176 to 210 mm SVL vs. a mean of 264.4 in Kansas. The eggs of Kansas females are relatively large, with compensatory reduction in the number per clutch, 9.2 vs. 13.5 in Virginia. In Arkansas, Trauth et al. (1994) noted clutches of 14.0±3.9 (9–20) in six females having yolked follicles or oviductal eggs.

Lampropeltis getula

Traits of the Species

The "common" kingsnake was one of the least common snake species encountered in the present study. However it is ubiquitous in the southern United States, occurring in a spectrum of habitats—marshes and swamps, open woodland, chaparral, grassland, and desert. There is much geographic variation in body size, color, pattern, and ecological traits. The color is mostly black and white; the paler color may be cream, yellow, or tinted with green. The dark and light colors may take the form of alternating transverse bands; there may be a white vertebral stripe, or there may be dark dorsal blotches; the pattern may be speckled, or the snake may be all black. In Kansas, kingsnakes are of the subspecies *L. g. holbrooki* and have a speckled pattern. (See Plate 21). The kingsnake is a slow-moving, powerful constrictor that is mainly terrestrial and may seek prey underground or climb in low trees or bushes. The prey includes small mammals, birds, lizards, and especially other snakes. Even venomous kinds are taken. The kingsnake has a high degree of immunity to the bites of pit vipers. The eggs of birds, turtles, lizards, and other snakes are also sometimes taken.

Reproduction

The courtship and mating of the kingsnake have been the subjects of detailed laboratory studies (Secor, 1987). Sexual activity is most prominent about 2 weeks after emergence from hibernation. Ten distinct motor patterns were recognized: touch, mount, chase, chase-mount, dorsal-advance movement, forward body jerk, writhe, biting, tail-search copulatory attempt, and intromission. Some of these were repeated many times during the course of a given mating sequence. Biting was directed at the neck and trunk of the female and occurred both before and during intromission. Most of the motor patterns observed by Secor are common to other kinds of snakes also, with details varying between species, genera, and families. Intromission was found to be remarkably lengthy (averaging nearly 1.5 hours) in the speckled kingsnake.

Geographic Differentiation

Over its extensive range the kingsnake is known to vary in size (from 635 to 1810 mm SVL in adults according to Wright and Wright, 1957) but this variation has not been studied in detail. Clutch size is relatively low (x=4.9, N=48) in the Southwest (Arizona, southern California, New Mexico, Sonora) higher in the Northeast (Ohio, Illinois, Kansas, Kentucky, 10.6±0.6; Fitch, 1985). In Arkansas Trauth et al. (1994) recorded a mean clutch size of 13.1±3.3 (7–23) in nine *L. g. holbrooki*. In Virginia Mitchell (1994) recorded a mean clutch size of 12.6±3.2 (9–17) in five *L. g. getula*. Only three kingsnakes were found during the course of my study, and these were well separated in time and space: 11 August 1949 (adult female), 6 July 1959 (adult male), 17 October 1980 (adult male). The two males were taken in funnel traps within 0.2 km of the northwestern corner of FNHR, the female was found on a county road 2 km farther south.

Lampropeltis triangulum

Traits of the Species

The milk snake is unique among New World reptiles in having a geographic range extending from the north temperate zone in New England south through the United States, Mexico, Central America, and far into tropical South America. Geographic variation developed in adaptation to different climates and ecosystems has produced many variants differing strikingly in size, color, pattern, and ecological traits. Throughout much of its range the species has assumed the role of a Batesian mimic of one or another of the venomous coral snakes (*Micrurus*) that occur sympatrically. The imitation in size, bodily proportions, markings, and behavior is so accurate that close scrutiny is necessary to discern whether a snake is harmless or venomous. For instance, in Guerrero, Mexico, *Lampropeltis triangulum blanchardi* and *Micrurus browni* both have red rings that are heavily spotted with black. In Nayarit, Sinaloa, and southern Sonora, *L. t. nelsoni* is like *M. d. distans,* both having red rings that are broad and immaculate. In Costa Rica and NW Panama the tricolor pattern of *L. t. gaigeae* matches that of *M. alleni* (Pough, 1988). Over most of the milk snake's range, the basic pattern is a tricolor of black, red, and yellow (or ivory) in recurring transverse series, with the black marks more numerous, separating the red and yellow. These color areas may take the form of rings encircling the body, or may be dorsal blotches or saddles. In the northeastern states, farthest from the range of *Micrurus*, the color and pattern are much altered losing any similarity to that of the ringed coral snakes, with reddish-brown mid-dorsal blotches on a gray ground color creating some resemblance to the related prairie kingsnake. The tropical representatives of the species *L. triangulum* are relatively large, usually more than a meter SVL, and like their model *Micrurus* species they are snake eaters. The name "milk snake" is based on frequent association with pastured cattle and the myth that the snake steals milk from the cows' udders — a myth extending far back in time and originally based on snake-and-cow associations in the Old World.

Milk snakes of the local population are relatively dwarfed; they are less than half the length of the species' largest tropical representatives, and perhaps 10% of their bulk, but the subspecies *amaura* and *elapsoides* of the southern and southeastern United States are even smaller. The tricolor pattern of local *L. t. syspila* has some resemblance to the ringed coral snake pattern, but the dorsal colors do not extend across the ventral surface as rings. (See Plates 22 & 23.) In terms of food habits, the five-lined skink outnumbered all other prey items but the food also included shrews (*Cryptotis*), ringneck snakes, worm snakes, and young moles. Clutches of five eggs were most typical for local milk snakes. Optimum habitat is open woodland or woodland edge, with flat rocks providing shelter. Milk snake density was estimated at 0.13 to 0.70 per hectare on the basis of relative numbers, compared with the much commoner *Thamnophis sirtalis* and *Coluber constrictor*. Small size in *Lampropeltis triangulum syspila* (Table 66) is presumably an adaptation to utilize most efficiently the main prey species. The local population preying on five-lined skinks thus averages smaller than conspecifics elsewhere that feed upon rodents or snakes. Although males average larger than females, the sexual size difference is slight and male combat or rivalry has not been observed.

Spatial Relationships

Forty-one movements were recorded in milk snakes that were recaptured. Three unusually long movements

TABLE 66. Mean Sizes of Milk Snakes in a Local Population

Stage and Sex	N	SVL (mm)	Weight (g)
Adult Male	81	630.5±8.13 508–768	69.5±3.0 30–153
Adult Female	42	600.7±8.90 514–800	68.2±3.6 38–143
Hatchling	15	201±24.0 188–223	3.01±0.01 2.3–4.1

of 504, 457, and 337 m were thought to indicate shifts in home range. Other movements were rather evenly distributed up to 300 m and these were believed to be mostly within the ranges of the individual snakes. Not including the three unusually long movements, mean distance between captures was 118 m (127 m for 22 male movements and 106 m for 16 female). If 300 m is considered an average home range diameter, the area represented ($\pi\ r^2$) is 7.07 ha. One milk snake was captured 10 times, one 8 times, one 7 times, and one 5 times; four were captured 3 times, three 6 times, and nine were captured twice. Records spanned 10 years in one, 9 years in one, 6 years in one, 5 years in one, 4 years in three, 3 years in six, 2 years in six, and were limited to a single year in 10. In many instances snakes returned to the same shelters where they had been on previous occasions. A female was found beneath a shelter 27 April, 7 May, 10 October, and 24 October in 1990 and was found at seven other locations within 75 m over a 6-year period. A male recorded only in 1986 was beneath the same shelter on 12, 14, 17, and 22 May. A female caught six times in three summers was beneath the same shelter on 1 June 1984, 5 June 1985, and 1 October 1985. A male caught seven times in 4 years was using the same shelter on 26 and 28 May 1987 and 1 May 1988. Thus milk snakes tend to return to specific shelters more consistently than most other kinds of snakes, but most often those recaptured were at new locations and obviously each snake had a plethora of unknown hiding places.

Kinds of Prey

Food habits of the local population of milk snakes were revealed by items palpated from stomachs of 19 snakes from 1955 to 1997 and prey residues in 8 scats collected in 1953, 1954, 1958, 1960, 1961, and 1962. The 36 prey items identified were: 11 *Eumeces fasciatus*, 9 *Microtus ochrogaster*, 4 *Eumeces obsoletus*, 4 *Cryptotis parva*, 3 eggs of *Diadophis punctatus,* and 2 snakes of this species, 2 *Blarina hylophaga*, and 1 *Carphophis vermis*. All mammals recorded were prey of adult milk snakes, whereas four first-year young had eaten an adult and 2 juvenile *Eumeces fasciatus* and a juvenile *Diadophis punctatus*. The evidence indicates that milk snakes obtain much of their food by raiding nests (Fitch & Fleet, 1970). One snake had eaten a litter of 4 nestling voles and each of two others had eaten two nestling voles; one had eaten a clutch of three *Diadophis* eggs; another had eaten a female *Eumeces fasciatus* and five skink eggs (presumably all from the same nest burrow) and two other snakes had each eaten a female five-lined skink distended with eggs ready to be laid. These gravid female skinks must have been caught in their nest burrows. Other prey not actually found in nests are

probably most often taken while inactive, hiding or resting, beneath flat rocks or in burrows in places where the snakes themselves are generally found. One snake contained a skink having a freshly broken tail and another contained the detached tail of a skink. In both instances the tail evidently was broken by the attacking snake.

Reproduction

Milk snakes were found together in pairs, under flat rocks or in funnel traps on 2 April 1981, 27 April 1960, 9 May 1965, 15 May 1988, 15 May 1990, 16 May 1986, 22 May 1982, 23 May 1962, and 26 May 1990. One pair (9 May) was actually mating. Another pair found in April 1985 mated soon after they were placed together in a cage. A large male caught in mid-October 1995 vigorously courted a female when they were placed together, indicating that mating may occur in fall. Vitellogenesis occurs mostly in late May and June. Natural nests have not been found, but probably eggs are laid in abandoned burrows of small mammals such as moles and voles. In one clutch of five eggs, average length was 33 mm, width 13 mm, weight 3.8 g; in another the corresponding measurements were 32.5 mm, 15 mm, and 5.3 g, respectively. Clutch size, determined from eggs laid in confinement or from palpation of oviductal eggs in May, averaged 6.89±0.36 (5–9, N=18). The number of eggs is proportional to female SVL. There were 4 clutches with five eggs, 3 with six, 4 with seven, none with eight, and 5 with nine. A female of 534 mm SVL laid five eggs in an adherent cluster on 2 July 1966. She weighed 62 g before laying and 33 g afterward. After evaporation of surface moisture, the egg cluster weighed 19 g. The eggs were 30 to 35 mm long and 13.0 to 13.5 mm wide. They had hatched on 15 September. A clutch of six laid on 1 July 1990 had hatched on 9 September. A clutch laid on 18 June 1962 hatched on 15 September. Incubations of 70, 76, and 99 days are indicated.

Growth

Like most other kinds of local snakes *Lampropeltis triangulum* ovulates in spring and lays its eggs in early summer, with hatching usually in late August or early September. However, young the size of hatchlings have been found many months after the time of hatching, e.g., SVL 199 mm 25 May 1993, 200 mm 29 May 1981, 198 mm 11 June 1951, 202 mm 18 June 1966. These may have been undersized at hatching and obviously had been unsuccessful in securing prey. They were somewhat emaciated and probably were destined for early elimination. Tryon and Murphy (1982) indicated that females of *Lampropeltis triangulum* may produce sec-

TABLE 67. Correlation of Age, Size, and Numbers in Milk Snakes of a 50-Year Sample

		Males			Females		Combined Sexes	
Annual Cohort (Year)	N	SVL (mm)	Weight (g)	N	SVL (mm)	Weight (g)	N	% of Total
1st	22	237.2±5.6 198–273	4.6±1.6 2.5–7.8	13	230.1±5.5 199–268	4.4±2.5 3.2–6.0	35*	14.0*
2nd	17	343.4±7.8 261–397	12.8±3.2 7.0–21.0	11	342.9±9.5 280–380	12.2±1.6 8.3–21.0	28*	11.3*
3rd	13	433.2±7.1 383–474	21.8±1.8 11–29	18	452.1±6.6 413–478	27.0±1.5 16–40	31	12.4
4th	17	523.3±5.4 480–550	39.4±1.7 24–48	13	520.1±6.2 484–553	43.3±2.5 24–62	30	12.0
5th	17	608.3±4.7 563–624	62.6±2.2 48–76	15	567.3±2.9 568–588	56.6±2.2 45–70	32	12.9
6th	13	634.1±1.9 624–645	74.0±4.0 59–95	14	600.6±2.4 592–615	65.8±4.3 54–90	27	10.8
7th	16	664.9±1.8 658–673	77.0±3.2 63–98	9	630.0±3.1 618–640	75.2±2.9 65–86	25	10.1
8th	11	693.5±4.6 690–720	117.2±6.2 88–134	6	654.0±1.4 650–662	74.5±6.7 62–98	17	6.8
9th	8	735.5±1.2 730–740	116.4±6.8 88–138	5	677.8±4.1 670–692	89.4±5.8 75–104	13	5.3
10th or older	8	766.4±7.0 747–800	122.8±4.3 110–143	3	753.8 740–800	154.0 130–172	11	4.4

*First- and second-year young were not caught in representative numbers because they could pass through the quarter-inch wire mesh of the funnel traps and escape. However, of the snakes obtained from shelters, first-year young were most numerous, followed by second-year young, and successively old age groups.

ond clutches, but it is unlikely that this occurs in natural populations as far north as Kansas.

Table 67 represents an attempt to categorize every individual of my 50-year sample according to sex, size, and most probable annual age cohort. Age-size correlation is based upon the growth rates of individuals marked and recaptured. For all categories records were most concentrated in spring, late April, May, and early June. For 22 spring records of first-year young, mean SVL was 236 mm; they were estimated to have gained an average of 18 mm per month in 2 months of active life since hatching in early September. Twenty-five second-year young in spring had a mean SVL of 345 mm, and thus had gained an average 109 mm in about 7 months of active life—15.6 mm per month. Twenty-three third-year young in spring had a mean SVL of 450 mm and thus had gained, on average 105 mm—about 15.0 mm per month. After the fourth year and attain-

ment of sexual maturity, growth slows rapidly in both sexes but especially in females.

Figure 22 shows sizes (SVL) of immature milk snakes in spring. Three annual cohorts are discernible, with first-year young in the range 198–273 mm, well set off from second-year, but with second- and third-year young probably overlapping in the range 400–420. Later growth in partly grown young and adults is shown in Table 68. Growth continues in adults, but at slowing rates. It is noteworthy that four of the adults in Table 68 had records spanning 5 to 8 years and attained probable ages of 11, 13, 14, and 14 years. Table 69 attempts to show the most typical size for each cohort through the 9th year but many individuals do not conform. The smallest mature male (420 mm SVL) was presumably in his 3rd year whereas the smallest demonstrably mature female (514 mm SVL) was probably in her 4th.

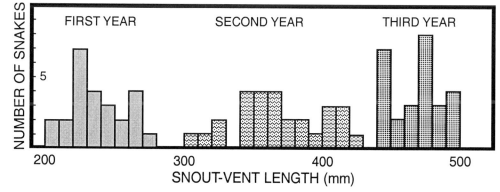

Figure 22. Sizes (SVL) of immature milk snakes; first-year, second-year, and third-year young form fairly distinct size groups.

TABLE 68. Selected Growth Records of Individually Marked and Recaptured Milk Snakes

Sex	Original Record			Recapture Record(s)			Probable Age (in Years)
	Date	SVL (mm)	Weight (g)	Date	SVL (mm)	Weight (g)	
♂	4–30-66	220	4.5	7–5–66	245	5.5	1–
♂	4–15–86	243	7.8	5–27–86	263		1–
♂	6–21–78	347	11	7–16–78	370	15	2+
♂	4–12–78	444	22	7–25–78	497	43	3–
♂	6–17–77	493	45	9–25–78	645	95	5
				5–24–80	710	98	7–
♂	6–12–89	612	64	5–28–91	734	120	7
♂	5–19–79	618	69	8–3–81	705	107	8
				9–11–82	709	99	9
				6–4–84	760	102	11–
				10–5–86	758	140	13
				5–12–87	786	94	14–
♂	5–22–82	623	52	6–20–83	627	60	7–
				6–4–84	683	69	8–
				4–27–90	720	87	14–
♂	9–11–82	709	99	5–12–87	780	100	13–
♀	6–1–84	413	16	6–5–85	471	36	4–
				9–15–86	553	41	5
♀	11–6–84	488	39	9–26–85	556	58	5
				4–1–86	597	72	6–
				10–15–86	608	56	6
				5–15–88	618	83	8–
				10–6–89	662	75	9
				10–10–90	703	133	10
				4–17–91	692	100	11–
♀	9–25–78	523	56	4–2–81	591	62	7–
♀	10–11–84	550	58	10–8–86	607	90	7
♀	5–28–89	592	87	6–11–91	740	138	7–
♀	5–23–62	640	86	10–10–62	675	73	7

Numbers

In the region of my study *L. triangulum* is a relatively uncommon species and few records were obtained annually. Clues to its actual numbers were provided by the ratio of its capture records to those of commoner snakes which were censused by Petersen Index. In the northwestern pen area (9.46 ha) of NESA, annual samples of milk snakes trapped 1990 through 1997 were: 6, 4, 1, 1, 2, 1, 3, and 0. From their ratio to garter snake records from the same area used for Petersen Index census, the milk snake records were estimated to represent a population ranging from 0.19 to 0.80 on the same area. From a similar comparison with records of racers higher figures were obtained, with a range of 0.41 to 1.31. Over the seven seasons combined the milk snake to prairie kingsnake ratio was 18 to 56. Average milk snake density per ha was estimated as 0.52 (from garter snake records) and 0.73 (from racer records).

Geographic Differentiation

Occurring from the north temperate zone into the tropics, the milk snake is subject to much geographic variation in size, color pattern, and ecological traits (Williams, 1978). Tryon and Murphy (1982) collected data concerning reproduction in captivity comparing nine of the subspecies. Females of *L. t. arcifera, L. t. elapsoides, L. t. hondurensis,* and *L. t. sinaloae* produced two clutches within a season; a female from near Zapotitlan, Puebla, Mexico produced three clutches (on 30 May, 19 July, and 4 September). Mean SVL (mm) and weight (g) in hatchlings from clutches laid in captivity were as follows, in order of increasing size: *elapsoides* (South Carolina) 163, (no weight recorded); *gentilis* (Colorado, Kansas, Nebraska) 166, (no weight recorded); *amaura* (Louisiana, Texas) 170, 5.8; *arcifera* (Jalisco, Mexico) 205, 7.7; *sinaloae* (Sinaloa, Mexico) 231, 9.7; *spp.* (Zapotitlan, Puebla, Mexico) 234, 9.8;

TABLE 69. Tentative Age-Size (SVL) Correlation in Milk Snakes

Age	SVL (mm)	
	Male	Female
Hatchling	200	200
First spring	239	239
Second spring	351	351
Third spring	463	463
Fourth spring	537	519
Fifth spring	611	563
Sixth spring	656	607
Seventh spring	701	631
Eighth spring	721	655
Ninth spring	732	679

annulata (western Texas) 249, 10.1; *nelsoni* (southern Mexico) 271, 8.2; *hondurensis* (Honduras) 318.2, 22.5. Comparable figures for hatchlings of the local population of *L. t. syspila* in northeastern Kansas are: SVL 201 mm, weight 3.01 g; thus the small subspecies *elapsoides* and *gentilis* have hatchlings estimated to be only 55% of the bulk of local *syspila* whereas the large *hondurensis* has hatchlings more than 7 times larger than *syspila*. Clutch size averages near five or six in most of the northern subspecies but is greater in the large subspecies of tropical and subtropical regions. Also, clutch size is relatively high in the large milk snake, *L. t. triangulum,* of the northeastern part of the range (12.8 in 24; Fitch, 1985). Mitchell's (1994) data for *L. t. triangulum* in Virginia indicate that adults of both sexes are markedly larger than their Kansas counterparts and have more sexual size dimorphism, but that Virginia hatchlings are markedly smaller than those in Kansas. Adults of all the northern United States populations are much smaller than those of the tropics such as *nelsoni* of southern Mexico 36 to 42 inches (est. 782–906 mm SVL), *hondurensis* of Honduras 40 to 48 inches (est. 861–1043 mm SVL), *gaigeae* of Costa Rica and Panama 54 to 60 inches (est. 914–1136 mm SVL), and *micropholis* of Ecuador 60 to 72 inches (est. 1304–1564 mm SVL). Total length measurements in inches are those of Markel (1990) followed by my conversion to SVL on the metric scale allowing 14.5% of the total for tail length.

Plate 1. *Agkistrodon contortrix phaeogaster* Osage copperhead. Adult female. FNHR, May 1975. H. S. Fitch.

Plate 2. *Agkistrodon contortrix phaeogaster* Osage copperhead. Adult female. FNHR, May 1996. Chester W. Fitch.

Plate 3. *Agkistrodon contortrix phaeogaster* Osage copperheads. Mutant, patternless adult male and normally patterned adult female. FNHR, October 1958. H. S. Fitch.

Plate 4. *Agkistrodon contortrix phaeogaster* Osage copperheads. Neonate mutant, patternless male and normally patterned female littermate. FNHR, September 1958. H. S. Fitch.

Plate 5. *Carphophis vermis* Western worm snake. NESA, November 1967. Charles W. Myers and Donald R. Clark.

Plate 6. *Coluber constrictor flaviventris* Yellowbelly racer. Adult female. NESA, May 1996. Chester W. Fitch.

Plate 7. *Coluber constrictor flaviventris* Yellowbelly racer. Adult female. NESA, May 1996. Chester W. Fitch.

Plate 8. *Coluber constrictor flaviventris* Yellowbelly racer. First-year young. FNHR, May 1996. Chester W. Fitch.

Plate 9. *Crotalus horridus* Timber rattlesnake. Adult female. NESA, May 1996. Chester W. Fitch.

Plate 10. *Crotalus horridus* Timber rattlesnake. Adult female. NESA, May 1996. Chester W. Fitch.

Plate 11. *Diadophis punctatus arnyi* Prairie ringneck snake. An adult spiralling its tail in sematic display. NESA, November 1967. Charles W. Myers and Donald R. Clark.

Plate 12. *Elaphe emoryi* Great Plains rat snake. First-year young. CWF, April 1996. Chester W. Fitch.

Plate 13. *Elaphe emoryi* Great Plains rat snake. Adult male. CWF, May 1986. H. S. Fitch.

Plate 14. *Elaphe obsoleta obsoleta* Black rat snake. Adult female. NESA, May 1996. Chester W. Fitch.

Plate 15. *Elaphe obsoleta obsoleta* Black rat snake. Adult female. NESA, May 1996. Chester W. Fitch.

Plate 16. *Elaphe obsoleta obsoleta* Black rat snake. Showing scars on clipped ventral and subcaudals with the formula: V 2r SC 51 8r. Adult female. NESA, May 1996. Chester W. Fitch.

Plate 17. *Elaphe obsoleta obsoleta* Black rat snake. First-year young. NESA, April 1996. Chester W. Fitch.

Plate 18. *Elaphe obsoleta obsoleta* Black rat snake. Immature, constricting a prairie vole. NESA, May 1996. Chester W. Fitch.

Plate 19. *Lampropeltis calligaster calligaster* Prairie kingsnake. Adult male. NESA, April 1996. Chester W. Fitch.

Plate 20. *Lampropeltis calligaster calligaster* Prairie kingsnake. Adult male. NESA, April 1996. Chester W. Fitch.

Plate 21. *Lampropeltis getula holbrooki* Speckled kingsnake. Suzanne L. Collins and Joseph T. Collins.

Plate 22. *Lampropeltis triangulum syspila* Red milk snake. Adult male. FNHR, May 1975. H. S. Fitch.

Plate 23. *Lampropeltis triangulum syspila* Red milk snake. Adult male. NESA, May 1996. Chester W. Fitch.

Plate 24. *Nerodia sipedon sipedon* Northern water snake. Adult female. FNHR, May 1975. H. S. Fitch.

Plate 25. *Nerodia sipedon sipedon* Northern water snake. Adult female. NESA, May 1996. Chester W. Fitch.

Plate 26. *Pituophis catenifer sayi* Bullsnake. Adult male. NESA, May 1975. H. S. Fitch.

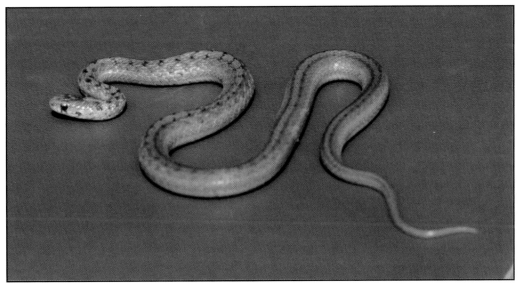

Plate 27. *Storeria dekayi texana* Texas brown snake. Adult female. NESA, BSA, April 1996. Chester W. Fitch.

Plate 28. *Storeria occipitomaculata occipitomaculata* Northern redbelly snake. Suzanne L. Collins and Joseph T. Collins.

Plate 29. *Tantilla gracilis* Flathead snakes. A group of adults. Suzanne L. Collins and Joseph T. Collins.

Plate 30. *Thamnophis sirtalis parietalis* Red-sided garter snake. Adult female. NESA, BSA, April 1996. Chester W. Fitch.

Plate 31. *Thamnophis sirtalis parietalis* Red-sided garter snake. Adult female. NESA, BSA, April 1996. Chester W. Fitch.

Plate 32. *Thamnophis sirtalis parietalis* Red-sided garter snakes. The one on the left lacks red marks. The one on the right is showing aggression in a sematic display, with head and body flattened and skin stretched to show the red marks. NESA, May 1996. Chester W. Fitch.

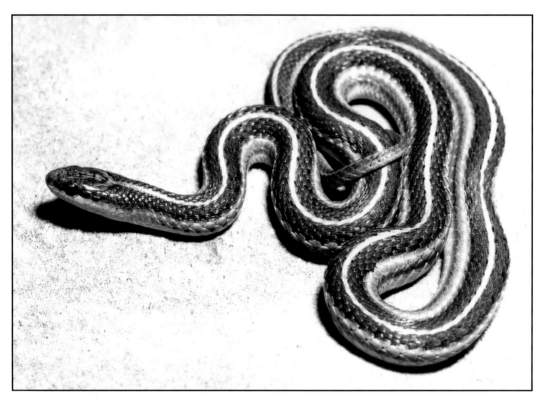

Plate 33. *Tropidoclonion lineatum* Lined snake. Suzanne L. Collins and Joseph T. Collins.

Plate 34. *Virginia valeriae elegans* Western earth snake. Williamstown, Jefferson County, Kansas, June 1949. H. S. Fitch.

Nerodia sipedon

Traits of the Species

The northern water snake is a medium-size natricine that occurs in a variety of aquatic habitats in eastern North America. The color pattern consists of a series of mid-dorsal reddish-brown blotches on a grayish-brown background; young are brightly patterned but in old adults the markings are obscure. (See Plates 24 & 25.) The belly is heavily speckled with reddish-brown spots. The dorsal scales are heavily keeled. Compared with other local snakes this species has the largest broods of young (mean 19.9), the greatest differential between adults and young (neonates average less than 2% of female weight), and the greatest size difference between the sexes (male average 34% of female weight). These snakes are widely known as fish eaters, and seem to take any kind of fish that is available. However, the population studied, living along intermittent headwater streams and small ponds, took relatively few fish (only two records) and depended mainly on anurans (14 records, six species of frogs and toads eaten). In their day-to-day movements water snakes were less vagile than most other local species (average distance moved per day: 4.5 m) but over periods of months and years individuals travelled extensively, even following intermittent watercourses to the upland heads of drainage systems. Young are born in early fall, with approximately equal numbers of males and females, and the 1:1 ratio seems to be maintained in older snakes. Defense tactics against natural enemies include swimming and diving, escape into dense vegetation, aggressive display, biting, smearing the body with musk and feces, and tail autotomy.

Behavior

Water snakes uncovered beneath shelters were easily captured, as they tended to freeze, flattening the head and body. Others were active in escaping. Those that were near water dove and swam away or hid beneath objects on the bottom. In tall grass these snakes were nearly as elusive as racers. Those caught in live traps were aggressive when approached, flattening the head and body in sematic display and lashing out at a person still well out of range—even several meters away. When grasped, a snake would flip and squirm violently to free itself, voiding semiliquid feces mixed with noxious musk, which was smeared onto the captor and over the snake itself; the tail was used effectively to smear the offensive mixture.

Tail autotomy is a final line of defense. The tail is fragile, and the caudal vertebrae probably have fracture planes, as is characteristic of other reptiles that readily shed their tails. A water snake grasped by the tail makes rapid whirling movements that quickly twist off the appendage. The freshly broken tail flips about for several seconds with lively movements that might distract a predator. The larger the snake, the more easily its tail is broken. Figure 23 shows that the largest water snakes have a high proportion of damaged tails. Table 70 shows that females, being larger, have higher incidence of broken tails than males of the same age cohort. Old females are about three times the bulk of old males. Incidence of broken tails rises sharply in large adults. Most of these large snakes with damaged tails are females. Their greater bulk permits them to autotomize more easily than males or immatures; also their burden of fetuses, borne through most of their season of activity, renders them less agile in escaping. They are more inclined to stand their ground against predators, relying on active defense, sematic display, musk and tail autotomy, and less on speedy escape than do males and immatures.

Spatial Relationships

A total of 336 captures of northern water snakes were recorded on FNHR and nearby areas. Additionally 150 young of six litters that were born in captivity were group-marked. Of the 336, 72.7% were at the FNHR pond, which was the focus of water snake activity on the area; in fact 42% were at one spot at the pond's west corner. A rowboat was usually beached there, and the snakes usually took shelter beneath it. Many of the

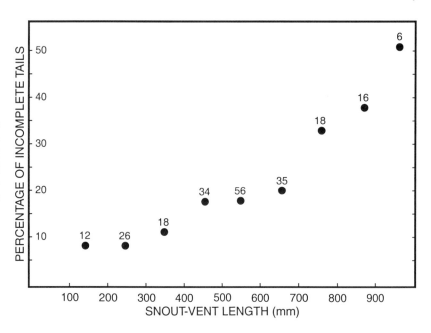

Figure 23. Ratios of incomplete tails in northern water snakes of different size groups; in large snakes (mostly females) autotomy is facilitated by greater weight, and a high proportion have incomplete tails. Sample sizes are shown by numbers over each dot.

marked snakes were found repeatedly beneath the boat or at other nearby sites around the pond's edges. They were highly localized temporary residents of the pond area, but they tended to wander; 8.2% were found in fields away from water; 6.0% were found along the small intermittent creek draining the pond, or its diversion ditch, 6.0% were found at ponds and streams beyond the borders of FNHR; 4.7% were on roads, and 2.8% were at limestone hilltop outcrops that served as hibernacula (these were found in spring and fall).

At different times four of the snakes marked at the pond were recaptured 1150 m WSW in a small pool of the intermittent creek that drained the pond, or the bridge crossing the creek. Another moved from the FNHR pond to the small pond on RET 1150 m north, and two moved to different NESA ponds, distances of about 1730 m in both cases. These last three records are of snakes that wandered, presumably following the bed of an intermittent stream to its head, suggesting the probability that the snakes often cross from one headwater to an adjacent one in another drainage system. An

adult female caught at a hilltop limestone outcrop on 8 October 1980 was recaptured at the FNHR pond on 18 June 1981, having moved 1220 m north across a flat hilltop between drainages, or else followed streambeds in a much more circuitous route. Two of the snakes that moved downstream 1150 m from the FNHR pond were females; others that made longer movements were all males. Table 71 shows that marked females were more likely to be recaptured than males and their individual records spanned longer intervals on the average. It seems that males are somewhat more vagile, but several individuals of both sexes were recaptured at or near their original location (not always associated with aquatic habitat) after periods of months or years, indicating site fidelity. However, the overall picture is that of a shifting population with individuals responding to changing water supply, food, and shelter by moving up and down stream courses.

Further insight concerning movements of water snakes was obtained from four adults (two males, and two females, one of them gravid) equipped with radio transmitters and monitored from day to day. Trailing spanned from from 5 to 27 days in different individuals. The snakes were located on 60 occasions, and in 20% of these there had been no movement since the previous day. Average movement per day (including those days of no movement) was 21 m. On half the occasions when

TABLE 70. Increasing Incidence of Tail Injuries with Age in Northern Water Snakes

Probable Age (in Years)	Males			Females		
	N	SVL (mm) Range	Incidence of Damaged Tails (%)	N	SVL (mm) Range	Incidence of Damaged Tails (%)
1st	19	163–290	0	32	172–282	0
2nd	31	300–497	6.5	33	299–499	21.2
3rd	24	500–550	8.3	28	500–600	21.4
4th	17	555–592	17.6	21	603–700	23.8
5th	13	600–639	15.4	15	701–780	40.0
6th	4	644–660	25.0	12	788–850	41.7
7th				9	853–918	44.5
8th				3	920–980	33.3

TABLE 71. Incidence of Recapture in Marked Northern Water Snakes Differing According to Sex

	Years Captured		Span of Individual Records in Years				
	2	3	2	3	4	5	6
Number of Males	7	2	6	7	1	—	—
Number of Females	13	5	14	7	1	4	1

snakes were located they were inactive, either underground or beneath sheltering objects; in 17% the snake was in the water, or dove in as it was approached; in 23% the snake was active, crawling or swimming. For three of the snakes trailing ended with disgorgement of the transmitter. The fourth, an unusually large gravid female, had been killed and partly eaten by a predator, identified as a raccoon by tracks beside the remains. Of the eight species of snakes trailed by radiotelemetry, the water snake was by far the least vagile in day-to-day movements.

Studies done elsewhere in the species' range give somewhat different impressions regarding spatial relationships. In Morgan County, Indiana, Fraken (1970) carried on a mark-and-recapture study at a fish hatchery having a pond complex. Snakes were found to be rather sedentary; 89% of those captured at small ponds (not more than 31 m across) were recaptured either at the same pond or one immediately adjacent to it. Snakes that were displaced upstream or downstream made homing movements (22 in all) from 23 to 680 m in intervals of 11 to 51 days.

Tiebout and Cary (1987) made an intensive study of the spatial relationships of *Nerodia sipedon* at the Thunderbird Recreation Area, Walworth County, Wisconsin. Ten water snakes, all females, (three in 1982 and seven in 1983) were equipped with radio transmitters and followed through their season of activity at a shallow lake of 28 ha. All water snakes at the lake used a hibernaculum about 0.5 km from the area of summer activity. Mean home range was found to be 5.4 ha, with a very concentrated core area averaging 7.7% of the entire range. Individual snakes were located from 26 to 285 times. Sizes of ranges plotted were found to be correlated with number of locations, and most of the water snakes that were followed exhibited shifting activity centers; their spatial relationships did not conform well with the traditional home range concept. Mean rate of movement was 5.2 meters per hour. Mean perch height was 10.9 cm above water level, usually on clumps of dead cattails. Cattail marshes and flooded meadows were preferred habitats. Open water was avoided.

Kinds of Prey

Fourteen of the water snakes captured had fed recently, and their prey consisted of: 6 *Rana catesbeiana,* 4 *Bufo americanus,* 2 *Rana blairi* (immatures), 2 *Acris crepitans,* 1 *Pseudacris triseriata* (adult), 1 *Hyla chrysoscelis* (adult), 1 *Cyprinella lutrensis,* and 1 *Micropterus salmoides.* The sample is notable for its paucity of fish and abundance of anurans, and perhaps this is typical of populations living in upland habitats. Red shiners are the only fish in the FNHR pond. The bass was eaten by a large female water snake at a NESA pond; its mass exceeded that of all other prey items combined. Eight

of the snakes that contained food were first-year young, but with the small sample available no clear-cut differences in food preferences can be shown between young and adults.

One result of frog-eating is parasitism by lung flukes (Plagiorchidae) that also infest aquatic snails and tadpoles during the aquatic stages of the flukes' life histories; these histories are complex. Each species of lung fluke is host-specific for a particular species of snail, anuran, and snake. In contrast to the flukes found in other kinds of local snakes, those parasitizing water snakes were much smaller and usually more numerous. They were found only in adult water snakes, and only in May and early June when they had migrated from the snakes' lungs to their mouths. Eggs laid in the snakes' mouths pass through their digestive tracts into the water, and the miracidia that hatch from them swim in search of the snail hosts. Of 13 water snakes checked in May and the first week of June, nine had lung flukes in their mouths, but others including three in July and four in September, did not.

Reproduction and Growth

Gravid female water snakes kept in confinement in different years gave birth to litters on 24 and 29 August, 3, 4, and 10 September, and 13 October, with an average date of 8 September. A female found dead as a traffic casualty on 6 September 1995 contained full-term fetuses. Litters averaged 27.4 (22–34) young. The largest female (1070 mm SVL) had 23 young, and in giving birth she also extruded yolks of 29 infertile eggs. Litter counts were obtained from 13 females that were palpated, 5 that gave birth in captivity and one found as a traffic casualty. For the entire group of 19 fecund females litters averaged 19.9±2.1 (5–36). The combined litters had 72 males and 64 females. Some of the embryo counts from females that were palpated may have included infertile eggs.

Males averaged larger in three litters and females in one, with differences small and not statistically significant. One hundred neonates averaged 193.57 mm SVL (178–209) and 4.92 g (2.9–6.8). These figures did not include three very stunted young, one of 135 mm whose littermates averaged 202, and two of 138 and 165 mm whose littermates averaged 187. For different litters SVL averaged 183, 187, 198 and 202 mm.

Table 72 shows sizes in water snakes including neonates and those in the early stages of growth. It shows that those found in October and November and some found in spring were within the size range of neonates. Seemingly growth is slowed in the cool weather of fall and spring and is much faster in warm weather, but even in warm weather some marked young made little or no growth over periods of weeks or months. In some

TABLE 72. Sizes of Northern Water Snake Young Showing Early Growth

| | SVL (mm) | | Weight (g) | | |
	Mean	Range	Mean	Range	N
Neonate	191.7	(165–210)	4.78	(2.8–6.8)	136
First-Year Young					
Sept.	187.2	(170–203)	3.83	(2.5–4.8)	10
Oct.	196.6	(175–212)	3.80	(3.0–5.3)	22
Apr.	200.0	(184–206)	4.33	(3.3–5.8)	9
May	228.4	(176–264)	6.44	(4.9–8.8)	6
June	231.0	(195–278)	7.28	(3.9–11.7)	17
July	289.0	(258–310)	13.75	(5.0–17.8)	15
1-Year-Old					
Aug., Sept., Oct.	313.0	(236–372)	18.7	(7.8–27.0)	40

instances their stunting may have been caused by the trauma of repeated capture and handling. For example, a juvenile male captured five times within the 27-month period 7 June 1961 to 2 September 1963 only grew from 221 to 258 mm SVL; if he had grown at a normal rate, he would have been about 452 mm and sexually mature.

None of the males marked as juveniles were recaptured as large adults. Better records were obtained from females because of their lesser vagility. One marked at SVL 282 mm (first year) on 17 July 1961 was recaptured on 22 July 1967 at 874 mm. One marked at 453 mm (second year) on 24 May 1956 was recaptured on 1 September 1961 at 957 mm (age approximately 7 years). A large adult of 930 mm on 25 August 1949 (probably 7 years old if she conformed to the growth pattern of the preceding individual) was recaptured on 30 April 1952 (1025 mm) and again on 10 June 1953 (1042 mm) and may have been in its tenth and eleventh years on these dates. These combined records indicate that the largest females, those having lengths exceeding a meter SVL, have probably survived for a decade or more. The largest male (SVL 748 mm) may have reached comparable age; he was markedly larger than the second (702 mm) and third (660 mm) largest.

Tables 73 and 74 allocate individual records into sex-size-age categories on the basis of the growth records shown in Table 75 but with adjustments in recognition

TABLE 73. Sizes (SVL) and Tentative Age Assignments in a Sample of 295 Northern Water Snakes

| Probable age-group (Year) | Males | | Females | | |
	N	SVL Range (mm)	N	SVL Range (mm)	Percentage of Sample
First	42	169–290	41	172–282	28.3
Second	32	300–497	33	294–499	22.0
Third	24	500–550	21	500–600	15.3
Fourth	18	555–592	24	603–700	14.2
Fifth	9	600–630	17	701–780	8.8
Sixth	3	644–660	16	788–850	6.4
Seventh			9	853–918	3.0
Eighth	1	746	2	920–980	1.0
Ninth			3	1042–1050	1.0

TABLE 74. Sizes of Northern Water Snakes in a Local Population in Northeastern Kansas

	N	SVL (mm)	Weight (g)
Adult Male	81	543.0±7.0 (416–748)	98.2±5.0 (50–180)
Adult Female	71	755.5±13.9 (585–1050)	286.5±16.1 (104–720)
Neonate	136	191.7±2.2 (165–210)	4.78±0.10 (2.8–6.8)
1-Year-Old	28	351.8±5.6 (258–438)	7.64±1.56 (14–42)

that some grew slower or faster than the average, that growth slows progressively with each passing year, and that each successively older age-group has fewer individuals than younger age-groups. Six body temperatures from active water snakes were: 29.5°C (22 May), 28.3° (10 September), 27.0° (20 May), 26.4° (18 November), 24.0° (3 September), and 16.6° (16 April). The last record was from a snake at a hilltop limestone outcrop, evidently just emerged from its hibernaculum.

Geographic Differentiation

As yet no detailed comparisons have been made to show how *Nerodia sipedon* varies in body size over its extensive range. It is one of the most prolific of North American snakes. Comparison of litter size in many samples showed the largest litters in Missouri, with a mean of 25.7 (9–66 in 95) and the smallest in Texas, of 18.0±2.6 (7–35 in 9) (Fitch, 1985). In Virginia, Mitchell (1994) recorded larger litters, averaging 28.5 (11–66 in 24). Virginia neonates (SVL 171.3±12.7 mm in 109) were smaller than those in Kansas (SVL 193.8±2.2 mm in 101). In Arkansas, Trauth et al. (1994) found mean litter size of 24.3±6.5 (6–46) from counts of yolked follicles and embryos in 12 females of *N. s. pleuralis.*

TABLE 75. Growth in Marked Individuals of Northern Water Snakes

Sex	Capture Dates	SVL (mm)	Weight (g)	Probable Age (in Years)
♂	6/1/73–9/20/74	348–575	24–120	3
♂	4/3/74–9/10/74	388–448	32–42	2
	5/1/76	503	52	3+
♂	5/8/85–6/21/88	446–572	46–130	5+
♂	10/21/64–6/23/66	506–600	77–134	4+
♂	9/27/68–9/11/69	525–620		4
♂	5/20/57–6/1/59	616–660	138–190	7
♀	6/7/61–7/17/61	218–260	5.3–14.0	1−
♀	6/19/78–6/4/79	277–536	14–80	2−
♀	8/1/63–5/27/64	254–387	8–28	2−
♀	7/17/61–10/9/63	282–740	12.3	3+
♀	8/27/62–9/5/65	356–668	36–225	4
♀	9/20/74–7/4/76	400–616	30–122	3−
♀	5/18/62–5/10/65	458–755	45–195	4+
♀	5/24/56–9/1/61	453–957	445–543	7
♀	9/15/63–8/25/64	470–655	74–245	3
♀	10/30/78–8/22/79	508–756	122–297	3
♀	6/3/55–9/6/57	574–693	119–303	4
♀	8/25/49–6/10/53	930–1042	370–615	11−

Pituophis catenifer

Traits of the Species

The bullsnake is the largest species of snake native to the United States. The species' range extends from southern Canada across the central and western United States, south to Guatemala. West of the Rocky Mountains, several subspecies are known as gopher snakes; they are distinguished by minor differences in scalation and pattern but all are similar in appearance and habits. All have a yellow ground color and a series of mid-dorsal, chocolate brown blotches, with several series of progressively smaller marks alternating on the sides. (See Plate 26.) The several eastern pine snakes are closely related and have been considered conspecific by some authorities (Conant, 1956). Except for the melanistic *P. melanoleucus lodingi,* they differ from bullsnakes chiefly in having cream, dull white, or pale tan rather than yellow ground color, and in having the dorsal blotches and lateral spots fewer and more widely spaced, black instead of brown. Gopher snakes, bullsnakes, and pine snakes are similar in their ecology and are each others' geographic representatives. Whether they are classed as separate species or conspecifics depends upon not only findings in the zones where their ranges meet or approach each other, but also on the prevailing species concept at a particular time and the individual viewpoints of investigators. Taxonomic arrangements within the genus *Pituophis* may change in the future as they frequently have in the past.

Behavior

The bullsnake is a slow-moving terrestrial hunter. Much of its predation takes place underground. Through morphological and behavioral adaptation it is able to penetrate the earth plugs sealing off the burrow systems of pocket gophers, the favorite prey, which is located by olfaction and killed by constriction. Most adult bullsnakes bear prominent scars inflicted by struggling victims. In burrows where space does not allow the prey to be enveloped in the snake's coils, it is forcibly pressed against the tunnel wall until its

struggles cease. Individual bullsnakes vary in aggressiveness; some are inoffensive when approached or even when they are handled, whereas others defend themselves vigorously. Young are usually more aggressive than adults. A bullsnake on the defensive elevates its forebody in an S-shaped loop ready to strike, writhing, hissing with explosive exhalations, flattening its head to triangular shape, darting out its tongue and vibrating its tail. Loud hissing is produced by forcible expulsion of air from the lungs against the enlarged, membranous epiglottis. The sematic display is a good imitation of that of a prairie rattlesnake, and bullsnakes are often killed because they are mistaken for prairie rattlesnakes, despite the lack of a rattle. The bullsnake's rapidly vibrating tail heightens the illusion, and in dry grass or leaves it may resemble the sound of the rattle. Extensive laboratory tests of pine snake hatchlings have demonstrated that they trail conspecifics by olfaction, but avoid the trails of a predator, the common kingsnake (Burger, 1989).

Responses to Succession

The bullsnake is characteristic of short-grass habitats. Its ecology seems to be closely linked with that of the pocket gopher (*Geomys bursarius*) locally, and with alternative species and genera of pocket gophers in other parts of its extensive geographic range. Like the gopher, the bullsnake dwindled and disappeared from FNHR within a few years after 1948, as successional changes eliminated the short-grass habitat. The species has persisted in small numbers on NESA and CWF where short-grass habitat has been maintained by mowing.

A total of 156 records of 123 individuals was obtained; one snake was recorded six times, another four times and still another three times, others were recaptured only once. Sixty-six of the records were obtained from hilltop rock outcrops where, presumably, the snakes had come to hibernate. On FNHR bullsnakes continued to appear in such places in autumn many years after summer residents had disap-

105

peared from the area. The study area was marginal for a population that lived mostly in lowland fields and pastures of the Kaw River Valley; 27 of the snakes obtained were on county roads, and 13 of these were traffic casualties. In a survey of Kansas snakes the bullsnake was found to be the only species occurring in all nine of the state's major faunal subdivisions, and it ranked fourth, after the ringneck, racer, and common garter snake, in an "index of abundance" (Fitch, 1993).

Body temperature of 12 active bullsnakes averaged 28.2°C (23.4°–37.6°) and averaged 3.8°C above ambient air temperature. Only one of the 12 had body temperature below air temperature (on 8 October 1956).

Spatial Relationships

Thirty marked bullsnakes recorded on successive occasions had made shifts ranging up to 1390 m. These movements were divisible into three categories: those between points on the snakes' summer ranges, those between points along hilltop rock outcrops in hibernation areas, and those between hibernacula and summer ranges. The latter averaged 434 m (21 to 1390; N=10), whereas movements on summer ranges averaged 354 m (54 to 1140; N=11) and movements associated with hibernacula averaged 165 m (0 to 575; N=7).

Most recaptures were made a year or more after the snake's original record and obviously the snakes had travelled much farther than the distances between successive capture points. The trend of the records suggests that most bullsnakes tend to stay within an area of a few hectares from month to month and from year to year, and that they return regularly to the same rock outcrop and perhaps to the same crevice to hibernate. If all the summer movements recorded are construed as being within the snakes' home ranges, and the mean of 354 m is equated with a home range radius, an average

home range area of 39.4 ha is suggested. However, some of the longer movements recorded may represent shifts in range. If the movements of three individuals taken from roads and released in strange surroundings, and another recaptured after 3 years, are eliminated, the remaining nine average 203 m suggesting a circular home range of 12.9 ha. Parker and Brown (1980) maintained that the circle method may grossly overestimate home range; ranges are probably never perfect circles, and to the extent that they depart from circular toward elliptical shape, they are overestimated. On the other hand ranges plotted from capture points in a convex polygon consistently underestimate the true range size, especially if there are only a few capture points. It is unlikely that New Jersey pine snakes have home ranges 31 times as large as those of Utah gopher snakes (Table 76).

My estimate of 12.9 ha for Kansas bullsnakes is about 7.4 times as large as the figure for Utah gopher snakes but less than one-fourth the estimated size for New Jersey pine snakes. Further study is needed to clarify these geographic differences and the spatial relationships in diverse populations of *Pituophis*.

I found an adult female at approximately the same spot beside a hibernation outcrop on 1 October 1949 and 7 October 1951, and beside the same outcrop 90 m northeast on 27 October 1950. She was also recorded 122 m west of this last site on 21 July 1951, probably indicating that she was a permanent resident of the general area. The longest time spans between captures were: 6 years for a female first captured in her first year that moved from a hilltop outcrop (30 October 1952) 640 m to an adjacent valley (21 June 1958) and an adult female that had moved from the same field (13 June 1953) to the same outcrop (8 October 1958). A first-year female found on the county road within FNHR (28 November 1962) was recaptured at approximately the same place on 26 August 1966.

TABLE 76. Traits of *Pituophis* Populations in Various Parts of the Geographic Range

Area of Study	Mean Size of Adult SVL (mm)	Mean Clutch	Mean Size of hatchling SVL (mm)	Hatchling Sex Ratio ♂/♀	Home Range (ha)	Migration to Hibernaculum (m)
Douglas Co. NE Kansas	1296 in 91 (1310 in 42 ♂ 1282 in 49 ♀)	11.2±1.9 8–13 in 5	412.7 in 29	1.9 to 1 in 29	12.9 in 9	434 (21–1390 in 10)
Harvey Co. S-Central Kansas	1010 in 196 (991 in 105 ♂ 1014 in 91 ♀)		363±1.6 in 9			
Cherry Co. Nebraska	1257 in 36	12.8 (5–28)	300–350 x̄=335	0.8 to 1		
Tooele Co. Utah	1048 in 77 (1063 in 59 ♂ 998 in 18 ♀)	8.37 (4–15) in 19	300–380 x̄=334.4	1.6 to 1	1.74 in 6	509 in 15
Ocean Co. New Jersey	1309 in 79 (1332 in 42 ♂ 1281 in 37 ♀)	9.5±2.0 (4–16)	337–526 x̄=416		55 (22–161 in 6)	

Kinds of Prey

The bullsnake obtains its prey by active search, guided by both odor and visual cues. Often prey is obtained by raiding nests. The pocket gopher, known to be an important prey, was not represented among the food items found in my study because it disappeared early from FNHR as a result of successional changes and deterioration of habitat.

Two adult bullsnakes each had eaten a vole (*Microtus ochrogaster*), another had eaten a bird (unidentified). Two first-year young in September and November had each eaten a white-footed mouse (*Peromyscus leucopus,* one of them a newborn young) and a third had eaten a bird's egg. Sixteen additional prey items were identified from scats, all collected in 1959 and 1960. There were six voles (*Microtus ochrogaster*), one each of cottonrat (*Sigmodon hispidus*), cottontail (*Sylvilagus floridanus*), and mole (*Scalopus aquaticus*); two race-runners (*Cnemidophorus sexlineatus*), and in three scats there were eggshells tentatively identified as house wren, meadowlark, and dickcissel, respectively.

In a study of bullsnakes at the Crescent Lake Wildlife Refuge in western Nebraska, Imler (1945) found that 42% of 274 duck nests were destroyed by these snakes. A total of 111 bullsnake stomachs contained only birds and mammals as prey: 36 voles, 9 pocket gophers, 4 kangaroo rats, 2 young rabbits, 2 harvest mice, 2 ground squirrels, 2 shrews, 29 duck eggs, 11 eggs of other birds (meadowlark, blackbird, avocet, ringneck pheasant) and 8 nestling birds including meadowlarks, blackbirds, and short-eared owls.

Reproduction

In the bullsnake, as in many other colubrids male rivalry and combat have been observed, and evidently sexual selection is involved. Shaw (1951) observed "ritual combat" in captive *Pituophis,* and he suggested that homosexuality was involved. Ritual combat has been observed mainly in captive snakes, and is triggered when males are closely confined together, sometimes in the presence of females. Under natural conditions chance meetings between males are not likely to precipitate combat. The larger snake is almost certain to dominate and the smaller may attempt to escape without putting up a fight. Observations of ritual combat in free-ranging *Pituophis catenifer* were recorded by Bogert and Roth (1966), but the beginning of the encounter was not seen and the observer interrupted before the snakes could resolve their conflict. The two large males (both slightly exceeding 2 m in overall length) were observed on a grassy bank on the outskirts of the small town of Portal, Arizona, in the foothills of the Chiricahua Range. For more than an hour they were observed to be locked in combat, and seemed totally engrossed in each other. They were lying extended with bodies and tails interlaced in corkscrew fashion, writhing and twisting, each trying to hold down the opponent. Heads were close together and slightly raised. There was no biting, but there was frequent loud hissing. The extent of interlacing varied, as the snakes were in constant motion, straining against each other, and moving forward about 9 m. No female was seen in the vicinity.

Bullsnakes probably utilize the excavations of burrowing mammals for egg laying, and may make their own nest chambers branching from the main tunnel. Nesting of the northern pine snake, *Pituophis m. melanoleucus* in the pine barrens of New Jersey is known from the observations of Leszczynski and Zappalorti (1996). These snakes dig their own nest burrows in the sand in open, sunny places. The gravid female may spend hours digging, scraping away the sand with her sharp snout, and from time to time after many scrapes, drawing out a loose pile with a loop of her forebody, with head turned at a right angle. The average combined tunnel and nest cavity is about 1 m long, but some may be double that length; the average depth is 0.1 to 0.12 m. Two or more (up to five) females may use the same burrow but with separate nest cavities. Females marked for individual recognition most often (75%) returned to the same spot to re-excavate the burrow for successive clutches. One female, marked as a hatchling returned 6 years later to the maternal nest to deposit her own clutch. Often females abandoned their partly excavated burrows, sometimes because a barrier such as a tree root hindered their digging, and sometimes for no obvious reason. After abandoning a partly excavated nest burrow the female would usually start another burrow nearby.

In my study five egg clutches (including three laid by females held in confinement and two counts of eggs dissected from females that were traffic casualties) averaged 11.2 (7, 11, 12, 13, 13). Laying dates were: 21 and 22 June 1962 and 27 June 1963. Average dimensions of eggs in one clutch were 50.5 × 30.2 mm, and in another, 53.1 × 34.3 mm. In the first clutch average egg weight was 33.0 g. A clutch laid on 27 June hatched on 18 August. For 29 hatchlings of these clutches mean SVL was 412.7 mm, weight 24.8 g. with little difference between the sexes (males 411.7 mm, 23.9 g. females 414.6 mm, 23.9 g).

At the Valentine National Wildlife Refuge in north-central Nebraska, Gutzke, Paukstis & McDaniel (1985) found that 92 (67%) of 137 adult bullsnakes collected and removed over a 3-year period were males, and that males likewise constituted 67% of 96 young from eight clutches laid by females from the same area. However, in a later study of bullsnakes from the Valentine Refuge, Iverson (1990) found hatchling ratios of males to be 44.6% (not significantly different from 1:1 by chi-square test) for five clutches with an average of 11.2 (10 to 13) eggs. At the Crescent Lake Refuge in western Nebraska, where 2100 bullsnakes were captured over a 5-year period, males made up three-fourths of the catch in April and early May, but the proportion of females progressively increased until in June they outnumbered males. In my own records males constituted 56% of the adult snakes, 66% of first-year young, and 66% of hatchlings from the clutches of two captive females. In an earlier study at the San Joaquin Experimental Range in central California I found 70% of 238 gopher snakes were males (Fitch, 1949), and of 86 first-year young 53% were males.

Growth

Table 77 shows growth in 16 bullsnakes that were individually marked as juveniles or adolescents and recaptured in subsequent years. Adolescent size of 900 to 1050 mm SVL is usually attained at an age of 1 year. Average SVL of about 1300 mm is typically attained in the fifth year, and near-maximum of 1600 mm may be attained by the eighth year. Growth rate differs widely among individuals. Table 78 with each snake assigned a most probable age on the basis of size, suggests age structure of the composite population over the 50-year span of my study. Among 116 bullsnakes of adolescent or adult size percentages in successive year classes are construed as follows: second year, 19.8%; third year, 16.4%; fourth year, 14.7%; fifth year, 13.8%; sixth year, 12.9%; seventh year, 11.2%; eighth year, 6.9%;

TABLE 77. Growth in Individually Marked Bullsnakes

Sex	Capture Dates	SVL (mm)	Weight (g)	Probable Age at Last Capture (in Years)
♂	5/31/62–5/5/64	448–855	18–190	3rd
♂	7/24/63–7/25/66	868–1447	188–956	4th
♂	9/2/58–5/2/59	925–1015	245–375	3rd
♂	10/25/54–9/25/56	975–1470	270–	4th
♂	10/28/60–5/17/62	1320–1432	800–930	7th
♀	9/9/62–6/5/63	435–630	32–80	1st
♀	11/28/62–8/26/66	530–1375	46–1150	5th
♀	10/30/52–6/21/58	562–1330	47–497	6th
♀	6/25/54–7/5/56	978–1275	267–685	4th
	10/20/58	1365	700	7th
♀	10/18/56–7/13/57	995–1072	–378	3rd
♀	10/17/50–9/1/52	1030–1410	359–	4th
♀	6/13/53–10/8/58	1042–1600	366–	8th
♀	10/11/49–10/27/50	1045–1257	201–598	3rd
	10/29/51	1330	603	4th
♀	10/20/53–8/31/56	1066–1405	260–678	5th
♀	9/30/78–5/9/81	1250–1450	557–560	6th
♀	11/2/55–9/15/56	1282–1383	520–1040	6th

TABLE 78. Tentative Age Assignments of 115 Adult Bullsnakes on the Basis of Recorded Growth in Marked Individuals

Probable Age (in Years)	N	Male SVL (mm)	N	Female SVL (mm)
2nd	11	989.7±17.5 (900–1055)	11	1018±11.4 (957–1066)
3rd	10	1123±13.0 (1082–1180)	9	1118±8.8 (1062–1160)
4th	9	1218±6.0 (1193–1250)	8	1247±17.8 (1170–1275)
5th	8	1291±13.7 (1260–1335)	8	1303±5.7 (1280–1320)
6th	6	1380±6.7 (1343–1407)	7	1349±6.9 (1327–1375)
7th	8	1422±5.5 (1407–1447)	6	1408±6.4 (1385–1430)
8th	5	1476±9.1 (1455–1495)	4	1504±28.5 (1450–1560)
9th	3	1615±7.4 (1600–1624)	2	1596±4.0 (1592–1600)

ninth year, 4.3%. Thirty-two of the bullsnakes recorded in my study were identifiable as first-year young. Since all hatch at about the same time (in late August) growth could be inferred by comparing sizes of hatchlings with sizes of young of various ages. Table 79 shows mean sizes (SVL) at different times of year and compares data from my study with those of Platt (1984) in Harvey County, Kansas, based on larger samples. Platt commented on the extremely rapid growth of first-year bullsnakes, faster than in other kinds of snakes that had been studied at the time of his writing. Growth in the bullsnakes of Harvey County and those of my study show parallel trends, but those from northeastern Kansas are consistently larger. They are 13% larger at hatching and 12% larger as adults. At the age of a year the snakes of my sample were more than double their length at hatching, and they averaged a gain of about 78 mm per month for an estimated 6 months of the year that they are active. Platt (1984) found an average monthly gain of 70.4 mm. He called attention to the apparent discrepancy in growth rates from marked individuals recaptured vs. gains made by cohorts of young sampled at different times during a season. There is differential mortality of the less successful and slower growing young sampled at different times during a season. Elimination of the slower growing young in samples caused the cohorts to increase in average size more rapidly than individual snakes.

TABLE 79. Growth in First-year Bullsnakes in Northeastern Kansas and Central Kansas

	NE Kansas, Present Study		Central Kansas, Platt, 1984	
	N	SVL (mm)	N	SVL (mm)
Hatchling	29	412.5±6.8 (324–445)	9	363±1.6
September	3	487±35.2 (442–552)	128	443±2.8 (363–523)
October	9	477±26.7 (355–680)	121	464±3.3 (365–566)
November	9	512±15.3 (455–590)	—	
May	4	538±57.0 (450–688)	43	537±8.2 (397–622)
June	7	679±56.1 (515–761)	77	630±6.1 (522–740)
July	3	811±17.1 (770–868)	49	736±14.3 (607–860)
August			35	788±11.9 (660–911)
September	4	949±13.8 (925–985)		
October	14	991±21.2 (807–1066)		

Geographic Differentiation

Table 76 summarizes and compares data from five studies of the Great Plains bullsnake and its representatives to the east and west. These studies were well separated in time and space. Also, the purpose and point of view differed. Imler's (1945) study was carried on at a Nebraska waterfowl refuge where the bullsnake was regarded as a pest and predator requiring control. Zappalorti's (1992) study of the northern pine snake in the New Jersey pine barrens was carried out as a basis for protecting the snakes from the habitat impact of road-building activities. A study by Parker and Brown (1980) on the desert gopher snake in Utah was centered on denning aggregations and the movements of individuals. Platt's (1984) study in the sandhills of south-central Kansas concentrated on the early growth of the snakes, showing differences between individuals, between the sexes, and between annual samples.

Significant ecological differences between populations are suggested. Body size, especially, is subject to geographical change. The relatively large bullsnakes of northeastern Kansas are nearest to the smallest (Harvey County in central Kansas) which average less than two-thirds of their bulk. In order of declining size, the largest snakes, in New Jersey, are followed by those of northeastern Kansas, Nebraska, Utah, and central Kansas. Evidence that these size differences have a genetic basis and are not merely the results of climatic and food effects on individuals, is found in the fact that hatchling size also differs among populations and tends to be proportional to the mean size of adults.

Sexual size difference is slight in the bullsnake but is to be expected because male combat is known to occur. It seems that sexual size difference itself is subject to geographic variation. With a sample of 105 males and 91 females Platt (1984) found a male to female SVL ratio of 93.7%, whereas other studies have found males to be larger than females (ratio 102.5% in northeastern Kansas, 106% in both Utah and New Jersey). Many published records of clutch size indicate that there is much geographic variation, with means from 8.0 in eastern pine snakes to 12.4 for Great Plains bullsnakes and 8.9 for West Coast subspecies.

Storeria dekayi

Traits of the Species

The diminutive brown snake is secretive, living in dense vegetation in damp places. The geographic range encompasses the eastern Deciduous Forest Biome, but also extends westward onto the Great Plains, and south through eastern Mexico and Guatemala to Honduras. The several subspecies are similar in appearance and habits. The head is relatively small and blunt, lacking a loreal plate; dorsal body scales are keeled; the color is dull brown with a pale gray, narrow and indistinct vertebral stripe. On each side the dorsolateral area bears two alternating rows of black spots. Also on the dorsolateral area there are pale flecks on loose skin between the scales. There are dark occipital marks, and a dull white or yellow collar. Facial markings may include a dark bar above the angle of the jaw and a dark spot beneath eye. (See Plate 27.) The prey consists of invertebrates, especially earthworms, with some slugs, snails, soft-bodied insects, and newly metamorphosed frogs and toads.

Records of the Texas brown snake have averaged less than five per year during the decades of the study; some were trapped, some were found beneath natural or artificial shelters, and some were found on roads, either alive or as traffic casualties. With such small numbers it is difficult to judge population trends; the snakes do not seem to have declined or increased markedly, but there seems to have been a shift in distribution. In the early 1950s all records were from open woodland that had been subject to grazing, but subsequently the formerly open pastures became suitable habitat as they accumulated dense ground vegetation and were invaded by woody plants.

A total of 172 brown snakes including 13 neonates were individually marked by scale-clipping but only three were recaptured. One of these, an adult male, was recaptured the day after its release and it had moved about 15 m. Another adult male was recaptured after 386 days and was 60 m from the original capture point. A second-year male released on 16 April 1966 was retaken 19 days later at a distance of 37.5 m.

During the 1960s several brown snakes were equipped with radioactive tantalum wires and attempt was made to monitor their daily movements by following them with a scintillator. In contrast with similarly equipped ringneck snakes, which were successfully monitored over periods of weeks or months, the brown snakes were invariably lost, either overnight or within a few days, because of their greater vagility. The few that were relocated consistently made daily movements of more than 30 m.

Reproduction and Growth

Counts of young in 49 litters were obtained from those born to captive females, from females that were traffic casualties, and from those palpated for embryos. Litters averaged 10.63±0.64 (4–20) young, and more than half of these litters (26) were in the range 6 to 9. Relatively small litters were produced by small, primiparous females, whereas larger and older females produced litters with about twice as many young (up to 20). For 10 litters born in captivity 3 August was the mean of birth dates that ranged from 26 July to 13 August.

Other species of local snakes are born or hatched in late August, September, or even October. The brown snake is notable for its early birth dates, made possible by cold tolerance with early emergence from hibernation. The gestation period is relatively short, with the result that the young have several weeks of activity and growth before the young of other species appear. In September and October of 5 different years, 11 young, substantially larger than the largest newborn but so small that they positively identified with the first-year cohort, were captured. Assuming each to have been of average size at birth and assuming further that all were born on the mean birth date of 3 August, these young had grown at the following rates in mm SVL per day: 0.33, 0.36, 0.38, 0.40, 0.41, 0.51, 0.65, 0.66, 0.66, 0.69, 0.86 (mean=0.54).

Table 80 represents a tentative effort to allocate all available records into age-size groups indicating growth

TABLE 80.   Tentative Age-Size Groupings in Texas
Brown Snakes

Age-group	SVL (mm)	N	Weight (g)	N
Neonate				
Male	81.5±0.57 (72–88)	55	0.29±0.08 (0.21–0.31)	49
Female	83.4±0.65 (71–90)	43	0.30±0.09 (0.22–0.47)	40
1st-Year				
Young	121.5±5.7 (84–139)	13	0.74±0.09 (0.20–1.2)	13
(Fall-Spring)				
2nd-Year				
Young				
Male	173.6±2.2 (148–198)	36	2.22±0.08 (1.8–3.2)	22
Female	183.7±3.1 (154–202)	22	2.56±0.02 (1.5–3.6)	13
Adult				
Male	218.7±2.2 (159–254)	79	4.29±0.14 (1.8–6.0)	61
Female	254.5±3.1 (199–300)	97	7.53±0.43 (3.5–16.2)	71

rate in the local population. Growth is extremely rapid in the first few months, and by the time of hibernation the largest young have attained lengths (SVL) up to 139 mm. In spring there may be some size overlap between accelerated first-year young and retarded second-year young.

Evidently sexual maturity is attained early in the second year, in time for the spring breeding season, at least in males. Motile sperm was obtained from males of 159, 161, 164, 166, 178, 179, 182, 182, and 184 mm SVL from 13 April to 5 May in different years, but was not found in eight other males of the same size range that were checked. A female of 199 mm SVL produced a litter and others of 206 and 216 mm had enlarged follicles in May. Twenty-two gravid females averaged 256 mm (206–307).

Brown snakes emerged as early as mid-March and remained active as late as mid-November; 239 records were distributed by months as follows: 25 in March, 69 in April, 37 in May, 18 in June, 11 in July, 17 in August, 27 in September, 27 in October, and 8 in November. Only 13 (6.1%) of the brown snakes captured were active when found, three each in March, April, and October, two in June, and one each in August and November. The summer records were of individuals found in the early morning or evening, but in fall and spring individuals were found active at various hours and were often in sunshine. Body temperatures of three active individuals were 24.5°, 23.8°, and 20.4°C with ambient air temperatures of 12.8°, 16.2° and 19.1°C, respectively.

Spatial Relationships

The population density of brown snakes is difficult to judge; the fact that less than five records per year, on the average, were obtained indicates that it is not very abundant. Perhaps the best basis for estimating density is a comparison of its numbers with those of ringneck snakes. In 1966 and 1967 small funnel traps were set in the House Field-Quarry Field area. In 1966 the ratio of captures was 1661 ringnecks to 55 brown snakes and in 1967 the ratio was 551 to 18; in both years brown snake numbers were about 3.3% of the number of ringnecks. For the ringnecks six Petersen Index calculations over a 3-year period indicated numbers ranging from 719 to 1849 per hectare and averaging 1266. If brown snakes were in fact 3.3% of the density of ringnecks, there would be on the average approximately 42 per hectare. However, brown snakes are more vagile, and therefore may be more at risk of capture in randomly distributed traps. It is tentatively concluded that brown snake populations occur in densities of several or many per hectare probably exceeding numbers of the larger snake species that are considered moderately common.

Kinds of Prey

An adult male captured on 23 May, 1993 had eaten 2 small slugs (*Deroceras laeve*) and another captured on 5 April, 1994 had eaten one. Like *Storeria occipito-maculata*, *S. dekayi* probably tends to be a slug specialist in its feeding, but according to published accounts the food also includes earthworms, frogs, toads, certain insects, and spiders. Of local amphibians only *Acris crepitans*, *Pseudacris triseriata*, and *Bufo americanus* have young small enough to be eaten by *Storeria*, and such predation would be limited to large adult brown snakes eating the newly metamorphosed amphibians. Wright and Wright (1957) referred to *Storeria dekayi texana* as terrestrial and semi-aquatic. In my study no snakes of this species were found associated with water, although they were most often found in damp places.

Geographic Differentiation

Ranging from southern Canada into the tropics of Central America, the brown snake is subject to geographic variation in size, details of pattern and ecological traits. Wright and Wright (1957) in their description of *S. d. texana*, the local subspecies, indicated adult male lengths of 190–455 mm, which, allowing for the tail, would represent 148–356 mm SVL, a maximum much bigger than any that I have seen in Kansas. Perhaps *S. d. texana* attains greater size in the southern part of its range, but Wright and Wrights' stated female length of 246–341 mm (ca. 202–281 mm SVL) is not much different from my measurements for Kansas females (199–300 SVL, mean 253.5). Mitchell's (1994) figures for the brown snakes (*S. d. dekayi*) in Virginia indicate that the average litter size (10.8, 3–26) corresponds with that in Kansas (10.63, 4–20), but that individually, the Virginia neonates are markedly smaller (68.9 mm SVL vs. 82 mm) and are about 59% of the weight of the Kansas neonates.

Storeria occipitomaculata

Traits of the Species

The redbelly snake is a diminutive natricine of terrestrial-secretive habits in forest habitats. The geographic range corresponds approximately with the Deciduous Forest Biome of the eastern United States, but extends into southern Canada in the Maritime Provinces and Quebec, Ontario, and Manitoba and includes most of the Dakotas. Geographic variation is slight. The dorsal scales are heavily keeled in 15 longitudinal rows, there is a broad, pale brown vertebral stripe edged with black; the head is dark, with a white spot below and behind the eye. The ventral surface is red. (See Plate 28.) The food consists of invertebrates and is alleged to include slugs, snails, insects, earthworms, myriapods, and sowbugs (Wright & Wright, 1957). Defensive behavior consists of secretiveness, and smearing the foul-smelling musk from the anal glands. Also, a peculiar defense behavior has been observed in which the maxillary bone is rotated so that the teeth are turned outward and the points are pressed against an offending object. Like other North American natricines, redbelly snakes are viviparous; litters have from one to more than 20 young. Most litters are born in late summer (as early as late June) and young mature in the second year. My study area was on the extreme western edge of the species' range and only one redbelly snake was found — on HB.

The ecology and demography of the redbelly snake are best known from field studies in Michigan (Blanchard, 1937) and South Carolina (Semlitsch and Moran, 1984), and significant differences between these geographic populations are apparent. On average the Michigan snakes were larger with SVL of adult males averaging 187 mm (169–223) and adult females 194 (169–245), neonate 72 (58–81). In South Carolina adult males averaged 150 mm (118–184), adult females 157 (126–211), neonates 61 (58–64). Mean litter size was 9 in South Carolina and 7 (1–13) in Michigan. In both populations both sexes matured and reproduced at the age of 2 years, with annual reproduction. Although various types of invertebrates have been recorded as prey, the redbelly snake is a slug specialist. In South Carolina stomachs examined (N=10) contained only philomycid and limacid slugs. Pulses of snake activity seemed to involve the following of moisture gradients in search of the slug prey.

Tantilla gracilis

Traits of the Species

The flathead snake is the smallest species of the local ophifauna, and the only one that is mainly insect-ivorous. It was found in the early years of fieldwork, but soon disappeared from FNHR as a result of successional changes. Two small isolated colonies that were known were at xeric, limestone hilltop outcrops with southern exposure, and they were eliminated when invading trees and brush shaded their habitat. Late April captures on FNHR included two adult females (203 and 207 mm SVL, 3.6 and 3.7 g), five adult males (153 to 163 mm SVL, having motile sperm) and five immatures (84, 94, 133, and 137 mm SVL, 0.37, 0.40, 1.12, and 1.72 g). On 27 May 1986 one was found in an open, xeric site at CWF, and probably the species is still present locally in dry, rocky, open places.

These are secretive snakes most often found when flat rocks are turned exposing them. The dorsal surface is golden brown, the belly is bright pink. The head is darker than the body, narrow and not well set off from the neck. (See Plate 29.) Eyes are small. Dorsal scales are smooth, in 15 longitudinal rows. Ecology and demography of the flathead snake is best known from an early study by Force (1935) in the vicinity of Tulsa,

Oklahoma. Among 499 flathead snakes collected there were 289 males and 200 females, along with 10 of undertermined sex. Contents of 73 stomachs consisted of "centipedes and earth-dwelling insect larvae such as cutworms, wireworms and leatherjackets (larvae of the Tipulidae or crane flies)" (Force, 1934). Young are hatched in August; by the following spring they average 115 mm (95 to 125) in length. By the second spring males are 125 to 175 mm and they mature in the third year. Adult males average 190 (185 to 205) mm and adult females average 201 (190 to 230) mm. Eggs are usually laid in the second half of June and there are usually two or three per clutch. Two hatchlings were 77.5 and 92.0 mm in total length; SVL is about 76.5% of total length in males and about 78.5% in females.

Twelve Kansas females averaged 1.75 oviductal eggs: 2 in 7, 1 in 4, 3 in 1 (Fitch, 1985), but in Arkansas Trauth et al. (1994) found an average of 4.9 ± 0.13 for 16 females including those with previtellogenic follicles, and 3.1 ± 0.7 for seven with oviductal eggs. In a Texas population prey was found to consist of beetle larvae (82% of items) and centipedes (11% of items; Arnold, 1993; Cobb, 1989). The prey is also alleged to include spiders, sowbugs, and slugs (Wright & Wright, 1957).

Thamnophis sirtalis

Traits of the Species

This most ubiquitous of North American snakes is usually associated with wetlands. The garter snake ranges hundreds of kilometers farther north than other snakes by virtue of its ability to survive temperatures several degrees below freezing. There is striking geographic variation in size, color pattern, and ecological traits over its transcontinental range. The basic pattern of a yellow vertebral stripe and a pair of pale lateral stripes on a dark ground color is especially variable. (See Plates 30, 31 & 32.) The mid-dorsal stripe may be faint or intense, broad, narrow, or lacking. Lateral stripes may be missing, or may be pale yellow, gray, blue, or partly red. The dark dorsolateral areas may be jet black, or paler (sepia, gray, or brown) showing on each side two alternating rows of superimposed dark spots. Crescent shaped markings on loose skin between scales on the dorsolateral areas may be large or small, yellow, blue, gray, or red, or may merge to form a continuous longitudinal stripe. Except in populations of the eastern United States there is usually some red in the pattern and it functions in sematic displays. A garter snake confronted with a predator flattens its body, stretching the skin to expose red marks normally concealed between the scales, at the same time flattening its head, and coiling to threaten its adversary and to strike, either as a bluff or to deliver an actual bite. On a transcontinental scale there is a trend for the red markings and associated display to become better developed from east to west.

In the local population there are differences between the sexes and between young and adults in choice of habitat and choice of prey. First-year young favor wet lowland sites and feed on earthworms. Many kinds of amphibians are preyed upon whenever and wherever they are available, but large adults, especially the females, often resort to grassy uplands where voles, deer mice, and other small rodents make up much of the food.

Breeding is limited to cool weather of fall or early spring. It may occur as soon as the snakes emerge from hibernation. Males are attracted by pheromones produced in the female's liver. Males find females by olfactory trailing. Normally only one male of a courting group succeeds but a female may mate two or more times during the course of the breeding season and litters often have more than one sire.

In summer, individuals tend to stay in small areas of about 0.5 ha, but in fall they shift on average a little more than 0.5 km to hibernacula at hilltop limestone outcrops. Home ranges are ephemeral, with frequent shifts, so that over periods of weeks the garter snakes on a local area may move away, one by one, and be replaced by newcomers.

Behavior

Garter snakes often frequent the edges of ponds and streams. They swim and dive well, and take to the water both to obtain food and to escape when danger threatens. In finding prey they rely on olfaction via Jacobson's organ. The prey is swallowed at once, while still alive and struggling. Following of scent trails from skin odors of conspecifics is a prominent aspect of behavior and is employed in sexual search but also leads to nonsexual aggregations. Many males may court the same female simultaneously, jostling for position but with no overt hostility. Various aspects of the behavior have been described by Constanzo (1989), Fitch (1965), Ford (1985), Ford and O'Bleness (1986), Gartska and Crews (1981, 1985), Gibson and Falls (1975), Gillingham, Rowe, and Weins (1990), Gregory (1974), Joy and Crews (1985), Kephart (1982), and Whittier and Crews (1986).

Size Relationships

Table 81 shows sizes of adult garter snakes and how they changed over 50 years. Range in weight is shown for each annual sample of each sex. For SVL only the means and maxima are shown; 410 mm is considered the minimum for adult males and 500 mm for adult females. The two smallest males demonstrated to be

TABLE 81.   Variation in Sizes of Adult Garter Snakes, 1949 to 1997

	Males					Females				
Year	N	Mean SVL(mm)	Max.	Mean Weight(g)	Range	N	Mean SVL(mm)	Max.	Mean Weight(g)	Range
1949	8	491.0 ± 14.0	573	35.1 ± 2.3	20–67	6	618.7 ± 38.8	780	113.6 ± 28.6	54–225
1950	16	485.3 ± 10.0	573	35.1 ± 2.3	27–52	18	624.0 ± 20.8	808	105.5 ± 15.7	41–225
1951	17	487.7 ± 12.8	603	46.5 ± 7.5	22–67	13	566.4 ± 13.3	630	62.7 ± 6.9	32–87
1952	11	493.8 ± 23.1	592	36.3 ± 3.4	23–55	14	589.5 ± 19.8	614	71.8 ± 6.7	51–110
1953	5	454.7 ± 19.1	513	25.8 ± 6.1	14–42	6	630.8 ± 32.8	718	83.2 ± 21.9	38–153
1954	5	466.0 ± 13.8	510	30.6 ± 2.8	21–38	3	530.0	618	60.0	38–50
1955	6	468.8 ± 16.3	512	31.3 ± 2.5	24–40	4	624.3	705	110.6	78–155
1956	7	539.1 ± 21.6	599	49.7 ± 4.4	25–61	7	727.3 ± 32.8	865	140.0 ± 15.1	100–217
1957	21	513.1 ± 6.4	625	45.7 ± 4.6	20–97	13	683.9 ± 56.6	838	150.8 ± 16.2	63–235
1958	37	566.2 ± 12.3	678	61.4 ± 3.8	20–108	41	712.6 ± 20.4	937	159.0 ± 6.1	35–308
1959	107	498.2 ± 5.7	630	38.5 ± 5.7	18–91	101	640.3 ± 11.6	944	102.9 ± 6.1	30–290
1960	78	490.6 ± 5.9	683	38.0 ± 1.7	15–110	105	628.0 ± 10.3	950	95.1 ± 5.4	40–410
1961	85	493.3 ± 5.5	678	39.7 ± 1.6	18–83	80	633.7 ± 10.3	850	103.7 ± 6.5	40–240
1962	53	475.4 ± 6.8	610	40.0 ± 2.0	18–74	37	609.3 ± 10.4	790	70.8 ± 4.5	46–145
1963	22	474.9 ± 7.3	520	33.0 ± 1.6	24–52	68	611.8 ± 6.7	930	65.0 ± 11.0	30–290
1964	21	476.2 ± 7.6	540	35.2 ± 2.5	16–63	30	614.4 ± 11.6	779	74.7 ± 5.4	35–177
1965	17	479.1 ± 28.5	602	41.4 ± 2.5	25–66	33	629.9 ± 11.4	760	103.0 ± 6.7	56–178
1966	20	512.2 ± 12.6	640	41.3 ± 2.8	24–68	14	627.2 ± 16.0	770	88.9 ± 8.7	40–160
1969	8	515.0 ± 17.5	569	42.6 ± 3.2	28–51	13	635.6 ± 23.3	831	101.5 ± 12.3	42–218
1977	44	506.4 ± 6.6	590	42.9 ± 1.7	20–70	47	617.2 ± 50.8	908	91.8 ± 6.3	30–250
1978	45	530.4 ± 9.2	648	47.9 ± 1.9	20–80	72	664.2 ± 12.1	910	112.6 ± 6.2	20–340
1979	40	513.5 ± 6.7	598	42.5 ± 2.0	20–70	52	668.9 ± 21.6	908	120.9 ± 8.2	20–330
1980	17	483.5 ± 28.1	558	40.7 ± 3.0	20–60	28	643.3 ± 29.0	963	104.6 ± 7.8	40–260
1981	23	508.3 ± 14.4	650	41.9 ± 4.0	20–90	30	641.9 ± 13.8	860	92.3 ± 6.2	40–210
1982	12	491.2 ± 15.8	595	32.5 ± 3.2	20–60	33	632.2 ± 13.6	828	79.8 ± 6.2	30–210
1983	23	479.0 ± 11.8	630	37.1 ± 4.8	20–60	55	630.2 ± 10.7	828	94.4 ± 15.3	31–400
1984	13	486.5 ± 14.9	595	38.0 ± 3.7	30–50	27	619.3 ± 12.9	740	90.4 ± 6.7	30–180
1985	26	515.0 ± 8.9	598	40.7 ± 2.4	25–83	29	634.1 ± 16.5	880	94.7 ± 6.8	37–238
1986	17	486.1 ± 9.3	577	39.1 ± 2.4	27–63	16	717.3 ± 34.1	970	125.4 ± 7.5	46–300
1987	24	514.2 ± 9.1	620	33.3 ± 2.2	21–50	42	659.3 ± 15.5	880	107.1 ± 9.5	24–300
1988	6	483.3 ± 19.9	570	44.6 ± 2.6	37–63	20	591.6 ± 9.9	670	86.6 ± 14.4	23–150
1989	6	441.7 ± 13.1	492	30.8 ± 3.5	19–44	9	687.9 ± 28.8	820	126.0 ± 21.9	54–218
1990	73	517.8 ± 10.2	640	40.7 ± 2.2	30–80	79	641.1 ± 17.6	860	93.5 ± 8.7	39–210
1991	44	518.6 ± 6.1	693	43.1 ± 1.7	26–65	80	676.8 ± 9.4	523	127.2 ± 5.7	32–252
1992	45	496.4 ± 8.4	535	43.3 ± 2.4	24–92	52	661.2 ± 14.3	585	118.0 ± 8.1	48–290
1993	65	510.4 ± 7.6	640	47.7 ± 2.4	22–58	88	626.7 ± 13.8	853	102.9 ± 13.8	42–244
1994	29	516.3 ± 9.6	636	46.3 ± 2.7	21–79	44	625.4 ± 10.2	908	109.9 ± 6.4	37–270
1995	30	477.6 ± 6.8	605	33.6 ± 1.3	21–50	46	647.2 ± 12.3	783	115.9 ± 6.2	47–190
1996	53	484.6 ± 7.0	645	40.7 ± 1.9	21–88	63	606.7 ± 10.9	810	103.3 ± 6.7	35–265
1997	24	485.6 ± 11.4	653	42.5 ± 2.8	26–77	74	603.8 ± 9.1	840	106.6 ± 5.8	41–330

sexually mature (having motile sperm) were 389 and 387 mm (SVL) and weighed 21.5 and 19.0 g. The largest adult female was 35 times the bulk of the smallest adult male. A typical male is about 490 mm SVL and weighs about 38 g whereas a typical female is about 640 mm and weighs about 100 g. However, the smallest gravid female was only 490 mm., weighing 74 g while the largest was 963 mm and maximum weight was 490 g. Average size changed from year to year reflecting trends in environmental factors favorable or unfavorable to the snakes. During the late 1950s, 1978 through 1981, and 1986 through 1988, snakes averaged markedly larger than at other times. Alternate periods of relatively unfavorable conditions, when average and maximum sizes were smaller than usual, were 1953–1955, 1961–1965, and 1982–1984. Weather, through its effect on prey populations is the chief environmental variable, causing snake populations to thrive or languish, with time lag in the snake response. In a summer with consistently humid weather and frequent rains,

conditions favor reproduction and survival of frogs (*Rana catesbeiana* and *R. blairi*), which metamorphose in great numbers at almost every pond, and disperse in swarms after every rain. Ground vegetation becomes dense and lush, providing abundant shelter and escape cover for the snakes and their prey. State of the garter snake population depends to a large extent on environmental conditions of the previous year, and to a lesser degree on conditions 2 years earlier. While the abundance and distribution of frogs is critical, the first-year snakes depend mostly on earthworms for food. The availability of earthworms as food likewise depends on frequent and heavy precipitation during the warmer half of the year. For adult female garter snakes, especially those above average size, small mammals are increasingly important in the diet. The tendency in large females to switch from amphibians to a diet of "mice," voles, and occasional shrews reduces competition with smaller garter snakes and allows them to survive and reproduce.

Tolerance of a wide range of habitat conditions by this species was demonstrated by the fact that it was moderately common on FNHR in 1948 when field work was begun and remained so 50 years later in 1997 despite striking successional change. Field observations have indicated that every part of the 239 ha reservation and the adjoining 163 ha NESA is used by the garter snake, but the extent of activity varies according to certain habitat features, and also depends upon the sex and age-class of the snake. Both areas have major habitat divisions between woodland and grassland. The snakes favor more open areas and spend relatively little time in forest; open woodland is preferred to closed canopy forest. In moving from summer range to hibernacula in fall or the reverse in spring the snakes may travel hundreds of meters through woodland, but these migrations are made before trees are fully leafed out in spring, or after leaves have been partly shed in fall, so that basking is still possible and a high level of activity can be maintained.

Outside the forest, habitat preference seems to coincide with a moisture gradient with relatively wet conditions preferred. Creek and pond margins with dense sedge or grass are most preferred. Native tall-grass prairie and weedy brome-grass pasture, especially in the vicinity of ponds or intermittent streams, are attractive. Dry upland pasture and prairie are used less than corresponding habitat in moister bottomland. There is some tendency for immature snakes to be more closely limited to moist habitats, while older and larger ones are more likely to use drier upland habitat.

Pattern Types

The vernacular "red-sided" garter snake is not wholly appropriate; many lack red in the pattern. In a typical specimen of *Thamnophis sirtalis parietalis* every other scale of the third longitudinal scale row (counting up from the lowermost) is bordered above and anteriorly by a red crescent that is confined to loose skin between the scales. Another set of red crescents border the corresponding scales of the fifth row. Three other series of red crescents border scales of the sixth, seventh, and eighth rows, respectively, and this series of small crescents on the upper part of the dorsolateral area alternates with the larger crescents on its lower part. Many of the crescents contact those above or below to form H-shaped markings separating scales. In the eastern subspecies *Thamnophis sirtalis sirtalis,* which lacks red in the pattern but has the same crescentic markings, they are usually ivory colored or dull yellow. In the local population the amount and distribution of red in the pattern is highly variable. Among 600 adults 12.9% had no red and their patterns were like that of the eastern subspecies (Table 82). In a few others red was unusually

TABLE 82. Color of Dorsolateral Crescentic Markings in Red-sided Garter Snakes

| | | Percent of Sample | | |
	N	Red in All Series	One or More of Upper Series Pale, Lacking Red	Pale, Lacking Red in All Series
Male	219	27.0	53.9	19.1
Female	381	35.7	55.1	9.2
Combined	600	32.5	54.6	12.9

extensive and was not confined to the small crescents, but invaded the area of the lateral stripe and even the edges of the ventral surface. However, in more than half of these snakes red was confined to one or two or three series of the lower crescents and series of more dorsal crescents were pale colored. The pale markings are delicately tinted. In those snakes which lacked red, crescents were classed as yellow in 46.4%, green in 34.7%, blue in 16.0%, and ivory in 2.9%, but often the shading was subtle and seemed to consist of mixtures of these colors.

Table 82 shows that the sexes differ slightly in frequency of red in the pattern; males lack red more than twice as often as females. The red crescents between the scales are ordinarily concealed, but may serve in sematic display. The usual response to danger is an escape dash into dense vegetation or into the water, but if the snake is caught or cornered, it may bite viciously, may twist off its tail and may resort to sematic display in which the body is greatly flattened, stretching the skin and revealing the red crescents. The cornered snake may behave aggressively with mock strikes while exuding musk from its vent and writhing to draw its vent over the dorsal surface which becomes thoroughly smeared with a mixture of musk, liquid feces, and anal uric acid deposits. Besides being larger than males, adult females are more aggressive. Perhaps the greater frequency of red in the pattern of females is correlated with their aggressiveness and their tendency to stage sematic displays, whereas males are more inclined to rely on escape and concealment. Major predators that might be affected by the sematic displays of red markings include hawks (*Circus, Buteo*) and herons (*Ardea, Botaurus, Bubulcis, Butorides, Casmerodius, Egretta, Nycticorax* species). As the climate becomes more arid westward, the snakes are increasingly limited to marshy and riparian habitats where they are exposed to heron predation, and this may be correlated with better development of red markings in the western United States.

Tail Functions

Like some other snakes, garter snakes resort to caudal autotomy to avoid predation (Fitch, 1965). Accompanying morphological adaptations have not been described, but in lizards that autotomize, each caudal vertebra has a transverse fracture plane where a break can occur easily. Presumably such a mechanism exists in snakes, also. A garter snake that is grasped by the tail rotates its body in a whirling motion that rapidly gains momentum and twists off the tail. Cooper and Alfieri (1993) tested this autotomizing response in a series of *Thamnophis s. sirtalis* from Seabrook Island, South Carolina. Six adults all performed the whirling motion but a juvenile did not. I have seen the whirling response in snakes of both sexes and all sizes including neonates, but it is better developed and more effective in larger individuals. The broken tail flips and wriggles vigorously for a few seconds, but activity subsides rapidly to a feeble twitching and then to inertness.

Tail autotomy is of obvious survival value. A predator that catches a garter snake by the tail suddenly finds itself struggling to subdue the broken appendage, and the snake itself can take advantage of the momentary distraction to escape. The strategy often succeeds in saving the snake's life. The larger and older the snake, the less likely it is to have an intact tail. In the oldest cohorts of males about one quarter have lost parts of their tails, while in the largest females the ratio exceeds 50%. The difference between the sexes is significant. The largest females, being almost four times as heavy as the largest males, can snap off their tails with relative ease.

There is no regeneration. Measurement of remaining stubs indicate that a break can occur anywhere along the length of the tail with almost equal probability. In one female the entire tail was missing from immediately behind the vent. In 5% of the females with tails missing, the break had occurred on the basal 18% of the tail length, but none of the males had breaks so near the body, and if they did occur, such breaks might interfere with reproductive function since the hemipenes are lodged in the tail base. The invagination of each hemipenes extends to approximately the level of the eighth subcaudal and hemipenial muscle insertions extend to vertebrae even farther posteriorly. An individual snake might break off its tail on two or more occasions, being reduced to a shorter stub after each break but it seems that this rarely occurs, as stubs were not relatively shorter in older snakes than in younger ones, and a short broken stub would not be an effective decoy. In general, tail autotomy is a one-time escape mechanism.

The tail serves as a propulsive organ in swimming and in moving through dense vegetation. It also serves a tactile function in courtship, orienting the male to bring his vent into position beside the female's. Loss of the tail, while functioning as a decoy, must involve some sacrifice of speed in locomotion and perhaps also some loss of efficiency in mating.

There is ontogenetic change in defense and escape reactions. Small juveniles move swiftly to find hiding places in the water or in dense vegetation, but ordinarily they do not react with sematic display and they are not heavy enough to twist off their own tails easily when they are handled. Garter snakes that are too cold to escape, or to defend themselves effectively, rely on passive defense — hiding the head beneath body coils while exuding musk and smearing it over the body. Aggressive behavior increases with increase in temperature (Schieffelin and de Queiroz, 1991).

In 256 neonate males of 23 litters tail length averaged $32.27 \pm 0.15\%$ of SVL while in 156 females it averaged $30.12 \pm 0.28\%$. However, tails are subject to allometric growth, and as shown in Figure 24, tail length becomes relatively shorter in the larger snakes. The change is greater and more rapid in females (to $25.9 \pm 0.43\%$) than in males (to $31.5 \pm 0.34\%$). Relative tail length is subject to substantial individual variation. Also, significant differences were found in average tail length between litters (30.8% to 33.9% in males; 28.1% to 32.4% in females).

Spatial Relationships

Among 600 garter snake recaptures 32 (5.35%) coincided with the site of a previous capture of the same individual, i.e., was in the same trap or beneath the same shelter. The percentage was highest for immatures (11.1%, N=72), less for adult females (5.44%, N=358) and least for adult males (2.35%, N=170).

Table 83 summarizes records of movements for the 528 adults recaptured. Regardless of elapsed time, relatively short movements (less than 100 m) are more numerous, and for longer movements the numbers taper off rapidly, with females a little more vagile than males. The most abrupt decrease is between 200 and 300 m. The relatively few movements exceeding 300 m are believed to represent shifts by which a snake changes its range from one area to another. The supposition that garter snakes have home ranges of sorts is supported by the fact that the records for any individual tend to be clustered in areas less than 500 m in diameter. In most cases individual ranges plotted from recapture are unsatisfactory because only two to four capture sites are available and the area enclosed is obviously much too small to represent the snake's full range. In Table 83 an attempt is made to show range size on the basis of mean snake movement. The mean distance between random capture sites of an individual is visualized as equivalent to a home range radius, and

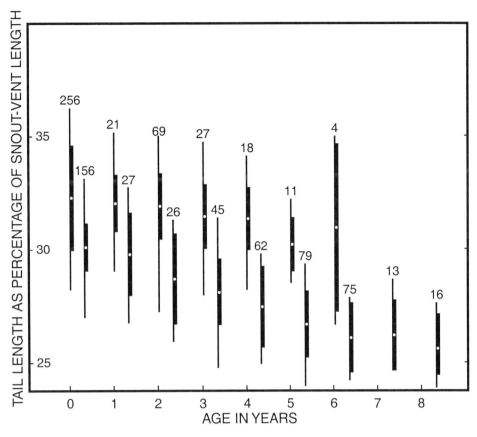

Figure 24. Relative tail length in red-sided garter snakes, showing mean, range and standard error for each series. Males of all sizes have longer tails than their female counterparts. Through ontogenetic change the tail becomes relatively shorter in both sexes as larger size is attained. For each age cohort male records are shown on the left, females on the right. Sample sizes are shown by numbers at top of each column.

the area encompassed is calculated from the formula for area of a circle (πr^2). The areas calculated varied from 0.21 ha in immatures to 0.72 ha in adult males and averaged 0.54 ha for all of the 600 recorded movements. Obvious sources of error in these calculations arise from the facts that routine movements within a home range cannot be distinguished from movements that involve range shifts (300 m is arbitrarily selected as the upper limit of movement within a range) and that ranges deviate to varying degrees from circular shape.

Nearly two-thirds (64%) of long shifts were within the same season as an earlier capture (mean 46 days); 20% occurred after a hibernation and 16% occurred after two or more hibernations.

Most garter snakes of the local population make an annual migration, from summer range in the valleys or fields of the flat cuesta top, to hilltop limestone outcrops with south exposure to find hibernacula. Usually the sites chosen are wooded and the migration may

TABLE 83. Mean Distances Moved Between Capture Points and Estimated Mean Home Range Areas for Red-sided Garter Snakes

Sex or Age-Class	Time Elapsed Between Captures	All Distances		Short Distances (<100 m)		
		N	Mean Distance Moved (m)	N	Mean Distance Moved (m)	Estimated Area (ha)
Adult ♀	< 1 Month	127	162	37	41.0	0.527
Adult ♀	1–6 Months	94	139	33	42.4	0.565
Adult ♀	2 or More Seasons	137	244	46	45.7	0.656
Adult ♀	Combined	358	185	142	43.3	0.570
Adult ♂	< 1 Month	77	151	29	46.1	0.670
Adult ♂	1–6 Months	52	186	16	52.1	0.851
Adult ♂	2 or More Seasons	47	200	17	46.8	0.689
Adult ♂	Combined	170	173	62	48.0	0.722
*Young	First Year	51	107	28	28.8	0.260
*Young	Second Year	21	157	12	19.8	0.123
*Young	Combined	72	121	40	26.1	0.214
All Categories	Combined	600	175	218	41.4	0.539

*Both sexes

involve travel across wooded slopes that are not occupied by the snakes at other times, but when the snakes retire into hibernation in November, and when they emerge in late March or April, trees are leafless and sunshine reaches the forest floor. In choosing a hibernaculum, the snake usually travels much farther than necessary to reach the nearest suitable outcrop. No aggregations have been found at hibernacula; evidently individuals hibernate either alone or in pairs or small groups. In 64 instances of individuals captured both at hibernacula and on presumed summer ranges, mean distance was 551 m. Mean movements for males, 747 m (200–1355 m, N=15), was somewhat greater than for females, 480 m (116–1365 m, N=49). Several other exceptionally long shifts that were recorded were probably related to hibernation but were not included in the figures presented above because occurrence in fall or early spring was not associated with a hibernation outcrop. First-year young, usually 200–300 mm SVL at the time of hibernation, have never been found at the hilltop outcrops sought by adults, but have been found in early spring associated with ant tunnels where they had evidently spent the winter — the same habitat where they occur in late summer and autumn.

Further information concerning spatial relationships of garter snakes was obtained from 8 adults equipped with transmitters for radiotelemetry (Figure 25). All were females, since males, even adults, were not large enough to accommodate the transmitters used. Five of the females monitored were gravid; they were remarkably sedentary and often spent several days in succession at the same place. Also, they had a tendency to return to certain favorite sites and shelters. The female

with the most complete records was monitored from 5 June to 15 August 1967 in an upland grassy field (Quarry Field) where it ". . . centered its activity about a strip of old sheet metal, and was found beneath it 21 times. At first this snake was found 9, 8, 4.5, and 1.5 m away from the metal sheet to which it returned each time, then it moved to a new area nearly 80 m from the metal sheet. When captured for battery renewal and released at the metal strip, it promptly returned to the new area. When last recorded it was 98 m from the metal sheet, 63 m from the second cluster of stations, but within 4.5 m of its original capture site" (Fitch & Shirer, 1971).

Kinds of Prey

Food habits were studied from a total of 412 prey items, palpated from stomachs of 339 garter snakes representing each year from 1950 through 1997. A total of 20 prey species included eight of amphibians, six of mammals, three of birds, and one of earthworms. The trend did not differ noticeably over the 48-year period. Prey identified included: 173 earthworms (mostly or entirely *Allolobophora caliginosa*), 69 *Rana blairi*, 43 *Bufo americanus*, 21 *Rana catesbeiana*, 19 *Microtus ochrogaster*, 19 *Acris crepitans*, 15 *Hyla chrysoscelis*, 12 *Bufo woodhousii*, 8 *Peromyscus leucopus*, 7 *Pseudacris triseriata*, 5 *Reithrodontomys megalotis*, 5 'frogs', 5 *Blarina hylophaga*, 2 *Synaptomys cooperi*, 2 *Gastrophryne olivacea*, 1 *Cryptotis parva*, 1 *Melospiza lincolni*, 1 *Cardinalis cardinalis*, 1 *Cistothorus platensis*, 1 unspecified bird, 1 *Deroceras laeve*, and 1 *Diadophis punctatus*. Table 84 shows differences according to age and size of the snakes. Most of the earthworms eaten were taken by first or second-year young. The smallest snakes also took newly metamorphosed *Acris* and *Bufo*. On the other hand, the six kinds of small mammals eaten were taken by adult or (a few) by adolescent garter snakes.

The 27 voles and white-footed mice were all taken by adult female snakes, most of them gravid; these and other small mammals were calculated to make up about 26.2% of the total food biomass taken and are the main

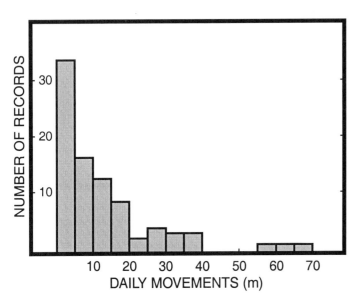

Figure 25. Day-to-day movements and relative frequency (number of records) of different distances in adult garter snakes carrying radio transmitters.

TABLE 84. Prey Eaten by 339 Garter Snakes Showing Differences Between Age-Groups (based on SVL) in Choice of Food

| | | Percentage of Prey Items Taken By Each Age-Group | | | |
Kind of Prey	N	First Year	Second Year	Third Year	Fourth Year/Older
Earthworm	173	55.5	32.4	12.1	—
Frog (*Rana*)	95	10.5	37.0	38.2	14.3
Hylid and Microhylid	43	30.6	36.2	16.6	16.6
Toad (*Bufo*)	55	18.6	38.4	20.6	22.4
Mammal	40	—	14.3	50.0	35.7

TABLE 85.   Seasonal Changes in Relative Numbers of Different Types of Prey Taken by Garter Snakes

	N	March	April	May	June	July	Aug.	Sept.	Oct.	Nov.
					Monthly Percentages					
Earthworm	173	—	4.5	19.7	21.0	20.6	15.7	10.5	8.0	—
Mammal	40	—	9.1	43.1	11.4	9.1	23.0	2.3	2.0	—
Frog	95	—	2.3	12.2	10.2	16.2	12.2	24.4	27.3	1.2
Hylid, Microhylid	43	3.1	15.6	31.6	3.1	3.1	6.4	12.4	21.7	3.1
Toad	55	4.5	8.9	14.5	18.0	16.0	10.7	18.0	9.3	—

source of sustenance for the growing embryos in summer. Earthworms make up only 13.3% of the food biomass taken, are eaten mostly by first-year snakes, and are the mainstay of the young until they have become large enough to exploit a variety of vertebrate species. Total biomass of the prey animals recorded was estimated to be more than 3 kg with the following percentages: *Rana blairi* 21.9%, *Bufo americanus* 13.6%, *Microtus ochrogaster* 12.0%, *Rana catesbeiana* 13.3%, earthworm 13.3%, *Bufo woodhousii* 3.8%, *Hyla chrysoscelis* 4.7%, *Peromyscus leucopus* 3.9%, *Synaptomys cooperi* 1.9%, *Acris crepitans* 1.8%, *Reithrodontomys megalotis* 1.6%, unspecified "frog" 2.4%, *Blarina hylophaga* 1.6%, with other kinds of prey including "bird," *Cardinalis cardinalis, Cistothorus platensis, Deroceras laeve, Diadophis punctatus, Cryptotis parva, Gastrophryne olivacea, Melospiza lincolni,* and *Pseudacris triseriata* each less than 1%.

Table 85 shows changing utilization of prey species through the season of activity. Hylids and small mammals were taken mainly in spring. Frogs and toads were most heavily preyed upon in summer when their newly metamorphosed young provided an abundant food supply for both young and adult garter snakes. Thirteen prey items, less than 4% of the total, were from snakes captured at hilltop outcrops that serve as hibernacula, in fall (10) or early spring (1) or summer (2). This prey included 6 *Rana*, 4 *Hyla*, and one each of *Microtus, Peromyscus,* and *Cryptotis.*

Garter snakes continue feeding up until the time they enter hibernation, whereas other kinds of snakes usually cease feeding before they move to their hibernacula. All of the bullfrogs taken and most of the leopard frogs and toads were immature as were some of the cricket frogs. Other kinds of prey including tree frogs, chorus frogs, voles, mice, and shrews were taken mainly as adults. Seemingly in most cases the garter snakes catch their prey in the course of active hunting rather than finding it concealed in nests or shelters.

Table 86 shows changing percentages of different prey categories during the 1990s. The most conspicuous change was the scarcity of frogs during the relatively dry years of 1992 and 1994 and their abundance in the wet year of 1993. Earthworms were relatively scarce in the diet in 1990 and relatively abundant in 1994, 1995 and 1996. Small mammals were best represented in 1990 and 1992 but were relatively scarce 1993–1995.

In a study at the Squaw Creek National Wildlife Refuge, in northwestern Missouri, Richard A. Seigel (1984) compared the food habits of *Thamnophis sirtalis* and *T. radix* in marshy lowland habitat. He found broad overlap, especially in the young, which fed mainly upon earthworms. For *T. sirtalis* the 58 food items recorded were: 26 earthworms, 16 *Rana blairi,* 3 unidentified rodents, 3 caterpillars, 2 each of *Rana catesbeiana, Rana* tadpoles, *Bufo woodhousii,* and *Ambystoma texanum,* and 1 each of *Hyla* and an unidentified fish. For *T. radix,* the 74 items that were recorded included 27 earthworms, 16 *Rana catesbeiana,* 10 *Rana blairi,* 4 each of *Rana* tadpoles and leeches, 3 each of *Peromyscus* sp. and *Pomoxis* sp., 2 each of *Ambystoma texanum* and slugs, and 1 each of *Bufo woodhousii, Blarina hylo-*

TABLE 86.   Year-To-Year Variation in Percentage-Frequency of Main Prey Types of Garter Snakes

	Year							
	1990	1991	1992	1993	1994	1995	1996	1997
Type of Prey	N=33	N=19	N=21	N=46	N=52	N=29	N=32	N=29
Earthworm	4.2	35.3	72.0	36.3	82.0	77.8	78.0	48.4
Frog (*Rana*)	46.0	29.4	4.0	43.2	4.4	7.4	6.3	23.2
Hylid/Microhylid	16.5	11.8	—	9.1	2.3	3.7	—	19.2
Toad (*Bufo*)	12.5	17.6	4.0	9.1	9.0	7.4	6.3	—
Mammal	20.8	5.9	20.0	2.3	2.3	3.7	9.4	9.2
Weather (April–Sept.)								
Precipitation (mm)	588	374	517	1046	553	761	845	641
Days of Rain	48	47	48	68	47	55	69	56

phaga, and *Lepomis* sp. Juveniles of both species fed almost entirely on earthworms. Relative prey mass showed no ontogenetic variation for either species. Both species fed heavily on earthworms in spring and fall, but relied heavily on frogs in summer. Both types of prey varied seasonally in their availability, being least available in spring and more available in summer and fall. Feeding niche overlap showed only minor seasonal variation. Spatial niche overlap varied more, and was highest in spring, lowest in fall. Findings did not clearly indicate whether interspecific competition between *T. sirtalis* and *T. radix* was a factor in the local community. Overlap in feeding was found to be much greater in juveniles than adults, causing Seigel to suggest that examining adult foraging patterns to detect interspecific competition may be fruitless in this case. Instead, comparisons should be concentrated on juveniles.

In general, the food habits of *Thamnophis sirtalis* are well known and there are important differences between regions, depending on availability. In Virginia and the Carolinas, salamanders, including *Plethodon glutinosus, Plethodon cylindraceus, Desmognathus fuscus, Eurycea bislineata, Gyrinophilus porphyriticus, Pseudotriton* sp., and *Ambystoma opacum,* predominate in the food, which also includes frogs (*Rana*), toads (*Bufo*), hylids, earthworms, and allegedly, spiders, millipedes, and various insects (Mitchell, 1994). In a sample of 1059 stomachs from marshlands of the Interlake Region of Manitoba, Gregory and Stewart (1977) found *Rana sylvatica* to be by far the most frequent prey (155) with relatively small numbers of *Pseudacris triseriata* (24), *Hyla versicolor* (8), *Rana pipiens* (4), and *Bufo americanus* (2). Other food included earthworms, leeches, dragon fly nymphs, nestling birds, and one each of snail, slug, and caterpillar.

In an earlier paper I summarized many literature records (Fitch, 1965). In New York, earthworms, anurans, and salamanders, in that order of importance, were found to be the main prey but with occasional slugs, snails, moths, beetles, dipteran larvae, grasshoppers, crickets, small mammals, and fish. Of more than 500 prey items taken by *Thamnophis* in Michigan, earthworms were by far the most frequent, with fish second and anurans third and with slugs, snails, various insects, and small mammals making up small percentages.

In an earlier study of West Coast garter snakes (Fitch, 1941), I obtained 72 prey items from 48 stomachs of *T. sirtalis* with the following numbers and percentage frequencies: toads (*Bufo, Scaphiopus*) 22 (30.5%), earthworm 17 (23.6%), tree frog (*Hyla regilla*) 15 (20.8%), tadpole (*Rana?*) 7 (10.0%), frog (*Rana boylii*) 5 (6.9%), leech 3 (4.0%), fish (minnow) 2 (2.8%), slug (1.4%). These records were from well-scattered localities in Oregon and California. Com-

pared with other geographical samples, this one was notable for the absence of mammals, birds, salamanders, and insects among the animals eaten.

Compared with these diverse geographical samples, mine from Kansas is noteworthy for the absence of insects, fish, and salamanders, and the relative frequency of small mammals.

Reproduction

Sexual activity is especially prominent in garter snakes that have recently emerged from hibernation. Males may remain in the vicinity of a hibernaculum for days or weeks, patrolling the immediate area, investigating each other, and returning frequently to the den entrance (Sexton & Bramble, 1994). Emerging females may be courted by several or many males simultaneously. Males are stimulated to court by an estrogen-controlled pheromone produced in the liver of the female. This pheromone is circulated through the female's body and passes through her skin where the epidermis is thinnest, in the hinge areas beneath the scales (Gartska & Crews, 1981). In some far northern populations that form huge denning aggregations, "female mimicry" has been noted in certain males, which are able to produce the same attractive skin odors that females have (Mason & Crews, 1985). When many males simultaneously compete for a female, these female mimics confuse and divert competitors and so increase their own chances for successful mating. There is no hostility among competing males, but each jockeys for position atop the female, with his vent next to hers. When a successful male accomplishes intromission, other suitors promptly disperse, as the semen contains an antiaphrodisiac hormone (Schwartz, McCracken & Burghardt 1989). Within 20 minutes of mating a gelatinous seminal plug is formed, distending the female's cloaca for a day or more—up to 2 weeks, depending on the temperature (Ross & Crews, 1977). Emergent females promptly disperse from denning areas, so the inhibitory effects of the anti-aphrodisiac hormone and the seminal plug prevent multiple matings during the brief period when the female is most likely to meet potential mates. Nevertheless, there is evidence that the majority of litters have multiple paternity. Series of litters from Michigan and Wisconsin tested by paternity-exclusion techniques with electrophoretic data demonstrated that multiple paternity was frequent (Schwartz et al., 1989).

In the local population ovulation occurs in May and births occur from late July through September. Young average 16.2 (4 to 59) per litter and individually average 1.69% of female weight in the population that I studied. More than 60% of neonates are males, but there is differential mortality, and by age 6 nearly all

TABLE 87. Seasonality of Multiple Trap Captures Indicative of Scent Trailing in Garter Snakes.

Sex Combinations in Traps	Month							
	April	May	June	July	Aug.	Sept.	Oct.	Nov.
Heterosexual								
Male and Female	—	9	—	3	3	42	50	12
Two or More Males and a Female	—	2	—	—	1	8	16	1
Two or More of Each Sex	—	—	—	—	—	3	2	—
Two or More Females with a Male	—	—	—	—	—	1	1	1
Homosexual								
Two Males without Females	1	2	1	5	2	25	23	2
More Than Two Males without Females	—	—	—	—	1	11	6	1
Two or More Females without Males	—	3	6	5	2	4	12	1

survivors are females. By the time of the second hibernation, after one full growing season, males are maturing. About two-thirds of females do not mature until their third spring, but thereafter may produce litters annually.

Olfaction is highly developed in garter snakes; males may find females by utilizing airborne odor but the following of scent trails is the main basis for interaction between individuals. Such trailing sometimes resulted in multiple captures, with as many as nine garter snakes in the same trap. Multiple captures may have occurred by chance occasionally, when two or more snakes wandered into the same trap independently, but the odds against that happening were great. Table 87 shows multiple captures by months. Most multiple captures involved both sexes, and presumably resulted from males following females. Such mixed captures were infrequent during late spring and summer; 91% of them were in September-October-November, which seems to be the time of year when the snakes are most active in sexual search. Single-sex combinations totaled 113 (41.5%). Of the single-sex capture combinations, 88% were males, and like the mixed captures, they were mostly in fall. It seems that males trail each other as well as females. When the odor is faint, the trailing snake may not be able to discern the sex of the one being followed. Female-with-female records in the absence of males were relatively few (12.2%) and were distributed throughout the season of activity but were concentrated in early summer, indicating a tendency for gravid females to aggregate.

Hawley and Aleksiuk (1976) studying the behavior of recently emerged garter snakes in enclosures, found that the attractiveness of females on the basis of number of courtships by males was related to size — the larger the female, the more attractive she was to prospective mates. Female receptivity depends on follicular development. Immature females that do not have enlarging follicles are only briefly courted and mating is not consummated.

Table 88 and Figure 26 show various parameters of reproduction in female garter snakes. At an age of 1 year, usually in August, they are approaching adult size and continue to grow rapidly in the fall. By the following spring most have passed 500 mm SVL and many become inseminated. A little more than one-third produce their first litters at an age of 2 years, and these primiparae are a little less than one-third of the breeding population. Their litters average about 13 young. As females grow older and larger, their litter size tends to increase. The largest and oldest produce litters that average more than twice as large as those of primiparae. However, in each age class there are some that produce small litters, near the minimum number. There are few litters, even of the largest snakes, that have more than 30 young. However, the maximum is around 50 in the local population, so it seems that an unusual combination of environmental and genetic factors is necessary for such large litters to be produced even by old and large females. Overall, some 71% of females are reproductive, but the ratio varies widely from year to year. Two-year-olds are

TABLE 88. Reproduction in Size-Age Classes of Garter Snake Females

Most Probable Age Class (in Years) on Basis of SVL	Mean and Range of Litter Size	Percentage of Total Egg Complement Contributed	Percentage Reproductive	Reproductive Females (N)	Percentage of Breeding Population
2	12.9 ± 0.43 (5–21)	23.8	35.2	101	31.5
3	16.4 ± 0.42 (4–27)	41.0	78.8	125	39.0
4	19.2 ± 0.72 (11–29)	22.4	83.5	64	19.7
5	20.0 ± 1.99 (12–26)	7.1	57.7	19	6.0
6	16.6 ± 3.21 (12–26)	2.0	71.0	5	1.6
7	15.8 ± 5.60 (8–22)	1.9	87.5	5	1.6
8	38.5 (12–51)	1.8	83.5	2	0.6

Figure 26. Size (SVL) and number of ova or embryos in female garter snakes (small dots each represent one record, large dots represent two records, triangles three records, and squares four records).

more liable to be unproductive than are females of older age classes. Two-, 3-, and 4-year-olds produce about 87% of the young in the annual crop. Females 6 years old or older produce less than 6% of the annual crop because, despite their large litters, they are relatively few.

Aleksiuk and Gregory (1974) found that mating behavior could be induced by keeping garter snakes cool (4 °C) and dark for 4 months, then warming them to 25 °C, with 12 hours of light and 12 of dark. Concentrated mating activity lasts for about 10 days, with feeding inhibited for the first 3 days and gradually increasing thereafter.

In 280 male neonates mean SVL was 164.2 ± 0.97 mm (133–191) and weight was 1.67 (0.7–2.34) g. For 175 female neonates comparable figures were 163.6 ± 0.66 mm (132–182) and 1.78 (1.0–2.25) g. The differences are not statistically significant. Presumably, size of the neonate is determined by the amount of yolk allotted to the follicle by the female. In many litters there are one or more neonates that are markedly smaller than the average. Excluding 40 such "runts" the remaining 415 neonates averaged 167.87 mm in SVL—smaller than most of those found in the field during the birthing season. The largest neonates were more than three times the bulk of the smallest. Extremely rapid growth with high incidence of mortality characterizes the first few weeks after birth.

Figure 27 compares average litter sizes in 18 years between 1959 and 1996. It is shown that in most years litter size was between 14 and 18, but occasionally was

somewhat higher (22.6 in 1978, 22.9 in 1979) or lower (11.3 in 1963).

During late spring and early summer the majority of adult females were found to be gravid, but this ratio varied from a low of 52.9% in 1977 to a high of 100% in 1979. It seems that the environmental factors that affect litter size are much the same as those that affect the changing incidence of gravid females, as these two reproductive parameters showed parallel trends (Figures 26 & 27). The years 1978 and 1979 when litter size was largest, also had highest ratios of gravid females (93.1% and 100%) and 1977 with by far the lowest litter size (9.8) also had the smallest percentage of gravid females. Average adult female size ranged from 572 mm SVL in 1977 to 694 and 710 mm in 1978 and 1979. Years of low litter size occur when there is a high percentage of recently matured females.

Of 24 litters born in captivity, 19 had more males than females; only three had more females than males and two had equal numbers of each sex. These captive-born litters had a total of 514 young with 321 (62.4%) males and 193 (37.6%) females.

In northwestern Minnesota, studying a series of 85 litters of *T. s. sirtalis* Dunlap and Lang (1990) found that the sex ratio of young within litters is influenced by female size. Relatively large females produced male-biased litters whereas litters of small females were female-biased.

The females studied by Dunlap and Lang (1990), averaging 497.8 mm SVL (422–552), were much smaller than the *T. s. parietalis* females of my study,

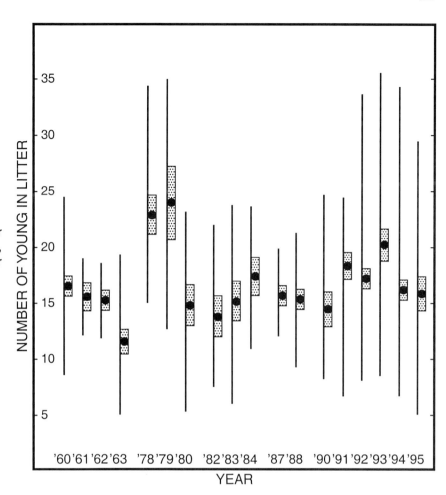

Figure 27. Year-to-year variation in litter size in red-sided garter snakes. Mean, standard error, and range is shown for each annual sample.

which averaged from 566 to 727 mm in different years. Dunlap and Lang recorded 217 males to 214 females (50.3%) in the litters they examined. In my study litters from females of all sizes were male biased but with no clear-cut trend. Male ratios were: 58.5% from females 541 to 598 SVL; 58.0% from females 611 to 695 SVL; 54.0% from females 701 to 770 SVL; 64.1% in females 830 to 873 SVL.

As shown in Figure 28, the sex ratio changed with age with fewer males in each successively older group, until in the ninth-year group, all were females. Actually, the selective elimination of males appeared to be most rapid in the first year of life. The graph in Figure 28 was constructed by assigning each of the 3086 snakes in the sample a probable age on the basis of the average growth shown by marked individuals recaptured. Sex ratio approaches parity only in the first- and second-year age classes, and is heavily weighted to females in older groups.

Growth

Most births occur from the end of July through early September; neonates average 164 mm SVL and the *smallest* 1-year-olds are more than twice their length (Table 89). One-year-olds average about 405 mm SVL in males and 444 in females. In about 7 months of active life before hibernation they must have made average monthly gain of 34 mm (males) or 40 mm (females). Table 90 based on individual records of 97 young adults recaptured, shows that growth slows rapidly in both sexes, but females grow faster than males of corresponding size. As young adults, males grow on the average 14.1 mm per month and females 27.5, but in large old adults the rates have slowed to 4.6 mm and 5.5 mm, respectively. Exceptionally large garter snakes, males of more than 667 mm SVL and females more than 876 were approximately 1% of the sample (Table 91). It is estimated that a female, growing at the average rate of marked individuals recaptured, would reach 900 mm in its 7th year, and by then 99% of adults would have been eliminated. However, one female captured 11 November, 1955 (SVL 378 mm, presumably a 1-year-old,) was recaptured five years later at SVL 900 (Table 92). Perhaps most of the snakes that attain 900 mm are like this one — exceptionally fast-growing so they reach near maximum size before their 7th year.

Table 91 represents an attempt to show composition of the population by age cohorts, based on all available

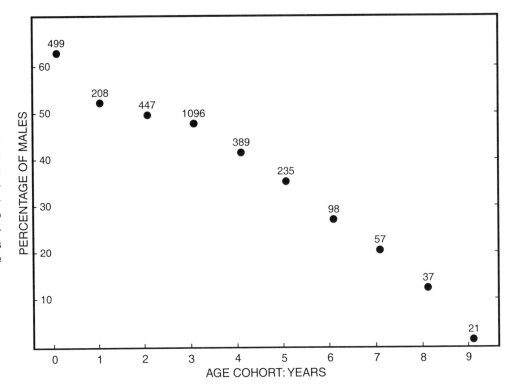

Figure 28. Sex ratios in red-sided garter snakes of different age cohorts (age deduced from size and from the growth of marked individuals) showing that males are more numerous at birth, but their ratio decreases with each successively older cohort. Numbers over the dots show sample sizes.

TABLE 89. Mean Monthly Sizes (SVL) of Young Garter Snakes Showing Early Growth

	N	Male SVL (mm)	N	Female SVL (mm)
First-Year				
Captive-				
Born				
Neonates	280	164.2 ± 1.0 (133–191)	175	163.6 ± 0.6 (132–182)
August	6	185.7 ± 8.8 (158–224)	5	169.6 ± 3.4 (162–182)
September	11	221.3 ± 7.4 (163–250)	12	227.0 ± 5.6 (194–253)
October	10	273.3 ± 11.7 (208–351)	16	268.3 ± 10.8 (205–338)
April	9	274.0 ± 7.7 (242–325)	23	278.3 ± 6.3 (218–338)
May	7	293.1 ± 9.1 (258–330)	15	314.0 ± 3.6 (250–393)
June	28	302.4 ± 7.3 (225–356)	21	328.4 ± 7.8 (265–393)
July	12	375.3 ± 7.2 (322–435)	4	389.0 (283–448)
Second-Year				
August	31	431.2 ± 5.4 (324–477)	9	421.6 ± 15.7 (370–498)
September	18	447.9 ± 7.8 (352–495)	21	489.5 ± 9.7 (382–540)
October	9	470.2 ± 7.7 (351–502)	19	525.1 ± 8.0 (400–558)

TABLE 90. Growth as Indicated by Recapture Records in Adult Garter Snakes Showing More Rapid Rates in Females and Progressive Slowing in Both Sexes as Larger Size Is Attained

	Male		Female	
		Average Gain per Month		Average Gain per Month
SVL range (mm)	N	in SVL (mm)	N	in SVL (mm)
400–449	12	14.1 (6.7–31.5)	—	—
450–499	9	9.5 (4.0–12.7)	—	—
500–549	11	7.9 (0.3–25.3)	11	27.5 (10.6–72.0)
550–599	6	4.6 (2.1–13.6)	12	17.2 (7.0–23.7)
600–649	—	—	8	10.9 (3.4–15.3)
650–699	—	—	13	11.5 (3.0–23.5)
700–900	—	—	15	5.5 (2.5–45.0)

records of adults, and the assumption that each snake had grown at the average rate for its size and sex. An obvious flaw in the data is the relatively small number of first-year snakes, because these were able to escape from live traps. The quarter-inch wire mesh of the traps permitted juvenile garter snakes to pass through easily, and spreading apart of the wires that occurred with prolonged use allowed even small adults to escape, also. Many of them were found stuck between the wires, part way out of a trap.

First-year young can ordinarily be distinguished from other age classes, and early growth can best be shown by comparing the average sizes in different months (Table 89). All litters are born within a period of a few weeks but litters differ markedly in average size of young and often there are one or several runts that are much below average size. Young grow at different rates and by the time of hibernation, the largest are 40% longer than the smallest. Most rapid growth is in the summer, and by July the average length is more than double that at birth. By August, when they are a year old, the most successful young are overtaking the most retarded 2 year olds.

Numbers

During the 13-year period 1985 through 1997, intensive sampling of garter snake populations was carried on within two separate areas, each calculated to cover

TABLE 91. Composite Sample of Red-Sided Garter Snakes 1949–1992 Grouped According to Sex, Size (SVL), and Tentative Age-Class

Annual Age-Class (Years)	Males			Females			Combined	
	N	SVL Range (mm)	%	N	SVL Range (mm)	%	N	% of Sample
First	150	156–410	12.6	397	156–449	22.4	547	18.5
Second	495	411–499	41.7	560	450–600	31.8	1055	35.6
Third	362	500–559	30.5	458	601–690	26.0	360	27.8
Fourth	137	560–607	11.5	223	691–765	12.6	102	12.2
Fifth	29	608–639	2.4	73	766–829	4.3	41	3.5
Sixth	11	640–666	0.9	30	830–875	1.7	17	1.4
Seventh	4	667–683	0.4	13	876–909	0.7	4	0.6
Eighth	–	–	–	5	910–940	0.3	5	0.2
Ninth	–	–	–	4	941–970	0.2	4	0.1

TABLE 92. Growth from First-Year or Early Second-Year to Adult Sizes in Individually Marked Garter Snakes

Sex	Original Record		Recapture Record	
	Date	SVL(mm)	Date	SVL(mm)
♂	7/31/89	322	5/16/90	412
♂	7/21/60	342	9/18/61	528
♀	8/05/59	190	6/20/61	608
♀	10/25/50	279	7/28/53	718
♀	10/03/88	212	6/15/90	403
♀	7/14/60	360	8/01/61	586
♀	5/12/86	292	5/23/87	546
♀	11/11/55	378	10/08/60	900
♀	5/14/59	370	9/11/59	646
♀	11/14/58	390	7/11/59	570

TABLE 93. Demographic Parameters in a Sample of 707 Hand-Caught Garter Snakes, House Field, 1990–1997

Most Probable Annual Age-Class (Years)	Males		Females		Combined	
	N	SVL Range (mm)	N	SVL Range (mm)	N	% of Sample
First	118	136–400	171	190–445	289	41.0
Second	118	410–494	147	464–600	265	37.5
Third	41	502–557	63	612–673	104	14.7
Fourth	14	564–592	27	700–760	41	5.7
Fifth	3	621	2	809–820	5	0.7
Sixth	2	640	1	843	3	0.4

approximately 10 ha — the north-central part of NESA, with mowed grassland, two small ponds, a residence and several other buildings used as storage and workshops, and two fenced rodent enclosures, the fences used as sites for placing wire funnel traps. The second area was 1.8 km south of the first one and included the headquarters of FNHR; House Field was an elongate, irregular lowland field of former brome-grass pasture overgrown with brush and trees, with a pond and intermittent stream. Forty artificial shelters in this area were checked frequently as a means of sampling snakes (Table 93). In Tables 94 and 95 a total of 65 Petersen Index censuses are shown for the House Field area (where all size-age cohorts were represented in the samples from artificial shelters, as snakes were captured by hand), and the NESA pens (where the snakes were captured in live-traps of quarter-inch wire mesh, and only adults were represented). Fourteen of the censuses were each based upon a single recapture and presumably were less reliable than those calculated from larger samples. Excluding these censuses based on single recaptures,

TABLE 94. Census of Garter Snakes Based on Petersen Index, from Live-Trap Captures at Fenced Enclosures on Northwestern Quadrant of NESA (9.65 ha)

Time	No. Snakes in Primary Sample	(Dates Collected)	No. Snakes in Secondary Sample	(Dates Collected)	No. of Recaptures	Estimated Population	Density/ha
1990 Season	27	(8 May–29 July)	60	(12 Sept.–3 Nov.)	6	270	28.0
1990 Spring/Summer	14	(8 May–6 June)	19	(29 June–29 Aug.)	3	89	9.2
1990 Fall	42	(12 Sept.–29 Sept.)	28	(1 Oct.–3 Nov.)	10	118	12.2
1991 Season	41	(27 April–19 June)	34	(17 Sept.–9 Oct.)	5	276	28.6
1991 Season	55	(27 April–30 Sept.)	20	(1 Oct.–15 Oct.)	5	220	22.8
1991 Spring	22	(27 April–1 May)	18	(2 May–30 June)	5	79	8.2
1991 Fall	14	(1 Sept.–30 Sept.)	19	(1 Oct.–31 Oct.)	4	133	13.8
1992 Season	36	(3 May–25 June)	34	(8 Sept.–22 Oct.)	7	175	18.1
1992 Spring	29	(8 May–6 June)	9	(7 June–25 June)	2	130	13.5
1992 Spring	33	(8 May–27 May)	14	(28 May–25 June)	2	230	23.9
1992 Fall	20	(18 Sept.–26 Sept.)	16	(27 Sept.–22 Oct.)	3	114	11.8
1993 Season	22	(19 April–26 June)	58	(15 Sept.–22 Oct.)	4	324	33.6
1993 Spring	15	(1 April–31 May)	8	(1 June–30 June)	1	120	12.4
1993 Fall	20	(1 Sept.–30 Sept.)	38	(1 Oct.–31 Oct.)	3	254	26.4
1993 Fall	32	(1 Sept.–5 Oct.)	27	(6 Oct.–22 Oct.)	4	216	22.4
1994 Season	27	(13 May–6 July)	19	(13 Sept.–6 Oct.)	2	256	26.5
1994 Spring	9	(13 May–31 May)	14	(1 June–29 June)	1	126	13.0
1994 Fall	6	(15 Sept.–20 Sept.)	15	(22 Sept.–6 Oct.)	3	30	3.1
1996 Season	27	(24 April–6 Sept.)	24	(7 Sept.–5 Oct.)	2	162	16.8
1996 Fall	11	(1 Sept.–9 Sept.)	19	(10 Sept.–5 Oct.)	4	32	2.3
1997 Spring/Summer	13	(26 April–26 June)	3	(10 Aug.–25 Aug.)	1	39	4.0

TABLE 95. Censuses, Based on Petersen Index, of Garter Snakes Captured from Artificial Shelters in House Field Area (10 ha)

Time	No. Snakes in Primary Sample	(Dates Collected)	No. Snakes in Secondary Sample	(Dates Collected)	No. of Recaptures	Estimated Population	Density/ha
1985 Season	10	(1 May–30 Sept.)	14	(1 Oct.–30 Nov.)	2	70	7.0
1985 Fall	4	(Sept.)	14	(1 Oct.–30 Nov.)	1	56	5.6
1986 Season	11	(1 April–31 May)	13	(1 Aug.–31 Oct.)	1	143	14.3
1987 Season	14	(30 April–31 May)	6	(1 June–31 July)	1	84	8.4
1988 Season	19	(13 April–13 June)	17	(15 June–5 Nov.)	2	162	16.2
1988 Spring	19	(13 April–13 June)	8	(15 June–30 June)	2	76	7.6
1989 Season	9	(26 March–27 May)	15	(6 June–17 Oct.)	1	135	13.5
1989 Spring	9	(26 March–27 May)	4	(June)	1	36	3.6
1989 Fall	6	(24 July–30 August)	6	(2 Sept.–17 Oct.)	1	36	3.6
1990 Season	9	(31 March–16 May)	25	(17 May–29 Oct.)	1	225	22.5
1990 Spring	8	(1 March–8 May)	8	(9 May–30 June)	1	64	6.4
1990 Fall	10	(27 Sept.–15 Oct.)	5	(16 Oct.–29 Oct.)	1	50	5.0
1991 Season	25	(1 March–30 June)	32	(1 July–31 Oct.)	3	267	26.7
1991 Season	18	(1 March–31 May)	42	(1 June–31 Oct.)	5	151	15.1
1991 Spring	17	(1 March–31 May)	11	(June)	3	62	6.2
1992 Season	47	(2 March–26 June)	66	(21 July–17 Oct.)	11	282	28.2
1992 Spring	32	(1 March–31 May)	27	(1 June–31 July)	6	144	14.4
1992 Fall	27	(1 Aug.–11 Sept.)	28	(12 Sept.–31 Oct.)	8	95	9.5
1993 Season	50	(1 April–30 June)	33	(1 July–31 Oct.)	13	127	12.7
1993 May	8	(5 May–21 May)	9	(23–27 May)	2	36	3.6
1994 Season	85	(1 April–30 June)	41	(1 July–31 Oct.)	12	292	29.2
1994 Spring	61	(23 March–31 May)	37	(1 June–31 July)	8	283	28.3
1994 Summer	52	(1 June–31 July)	30	(1 Aug.–31 Oct.)	8	195	19.5
1994 April	19	(April)	39	(May)	5	148	14.8
1994 May	39	(May)	25	(June)	6	162	16.2
1994 June	39	(June)	16	(July)	5	77	7.7
1994 July	16	(July)	8	(Aug.)	1	128	12.8
1994 August	8	(Aug.)	28	(Sept.)	3	75	7.5
1994 Sept.	27	(1 Sept.–22 Sept.)	19	(27 Sept.–18 Oct.)	2	274	27.4
1995 Season	26	(1 April–30 June)	49	(1 July–31 Oct.)	3	424	42.4
1995 Spring	15	(May)	14	(June)	1	210	21.0
1995 July	16	(July)	17	(Aug.)	2	136	13.6
1995 Summer	24	(1 June–30 July)	31	(1 Aug.–31 Oct.)	6	124	12.4
1996 Season	39	(20 April–30 July)	41	(1 Aug.–20 Oct.)	5	316	31.6
1996 Summer	21	(2 May–27 June)	35	(1 July–27 Aug.)	3	245	24.5
1996 July	12	(1 July–27 July)	25	(1 Aug.–27 Aug.)	2	150	15.0
1997 Season	72	(April through June)	69	(July through Oct.)	8	621	62.1
1997 Spring & Summer	26	(April–May)	92	(June–July–Aug.)	5	478	47.8
1997 Summer	26	(April–May)	53	(June–July)	5	276	27.6
1997 April	9	(April)	14	(May)	2	63	6.3
1997 May	14	(May)	41	(June)	2	287	28.7
1997 June	45	(June)	7	(July)	2	157	15.7
1997 July	7	(July)	41	(Aug.)	2	143	14.3
1997 August	45	(Aug.)	17	(Sept.)	3	255	25.5

there remain 9 House Field censuses from samplings extending over the entire season and these averaged 287.0 ± 54 (70–424); 12 censuses based on shorter sampling periods (of 1 to 3 months) averaged 185.3 ± 36.0 (36–478); 14 censuses with sampling periods either based on consecutive months or within a single month averaged 149.4 ± 20.6 (36–287) Censuses from the NESA pens area reveal parallel trends: 227.9 ± 36 for 7 sets extending over the entire season; 162.6 ± 27 (62–283) for 9 having sampling periods of 2 or 3 months; 125.3 ± 15.9 (75–162) for 6 censuses having 1-month samplings; 158 (42–294) for 2 censuses based on sampling periods of less than 1 month. Collectively these figures bear out the idea that the longer the sampling period, the higher is the census figure obtained, presumably because the snakes that are captured and marked eventually emigrate and are replaced by newcomers.

Thus the figures that are obtained from relatively short and consecutive sampling periods are more reliable than those obtained from an entire season. It seems that in favorable habitat locally garter snakes often occur in densities of 10 to 20 per hectare, but in the course of a year such an area may have a much larger number of temporary residents (often more than 20), most of which are present for only a few weeks.

If some of the snakes that were caught and marked moved off the study area during or before the follow-up sampling, too few of them would be recaptured, their ratio would be erroneously low, and the census figure obtained would be correspondingly inflated. An obvious remedy for avoiding such distortion is to have short and concentrated census periods; however, this results in reduced sample size.

Regardless of actual numbers, habitat partitioning according to sex and size is strongly indicated where snake samples were obtained from artificial shelters and were not subject to the biases of trap captures. On BSA — a relatively xeric, grassy upland habitat, mowed, but with islands and edges of tall weeds and thickets — 70 garter snakes were recorded over the years 1986–1992, of which 91.5% were adult females and 8.5% were adult males. But in later years, 1992 through 1997, after two small reservoirs were installed near the northern edge of BSA creating more mesic conditions, a sample of 192 garter snakes consisted of 63.1% adult females, 24.8% adult males, and 12.1% first-year young. Quarry Field, another somewhat xeric upland grassy area, being invaded by trees and brush, had a similar ratio in the 42 garter snakes recorded over the 8-year period 1990–1997, with adult females 55%, adult males 24%, and first-year young 21%. In contrast, the relatively mesic lowland area of House Field and several adjacent fields yielded 644 garter snake captures over the same 8-year period, with 27.8% adult females, 27.1% adult males and 45.1% first-year young. It seems that adults, especially large females, are more likely to prey upon mammals and to choose grassy upland sites, whereas first-year young prey mainly upon earthworms and prefer mesic, lowland habitat. Rapid population turnover is indicated by the fact that of 403 snakes captured in 1990, 1991, and 1992 in House Field and NESA, only 58 (14.4%) were recaptured in a second year on their respective areas, and only 10 of 238 from 1990–1991 (4.2%) were recaptured in a third year. Perhaps most shifts occur when snakes move off their home ranges to find a hibernaculum and move to a new area when they emerge in spring. However, substantial within-season shifting occurs also. Snakes recorded on the study areas were more likely to be recaptured there within the first few days than after longer periods. Of 200 recaptures on the combined study areas 31 were made during the first week after the original capture, 24 in the second week, 19 in the third, 15 in the fourth, 10 in the fifth, 9 in the sixth, 8 in the seventh, 4 in the eighth, 5 in the ninth, 11 in the tenth, 6 in the eleventh, 7 in the twelfth, and 1 to 7 in each of the next 10 weeks (Figure 29).

Juvenile garter snakes born from late July through early September must be present in large numbers in early fall, and it is remarkable that so few are seen. They must be relatively secretive, and the maturing crop of ground vegetation provides abundant hiding places. Many of those found were on the margins of the FNHR pond, but these must have been only a minuscule part of the population on the area. There was no concentration of gravid females in the pond vicinity in the weeks before birth of young. The young require moisture and an ample supply of earthworms for food, but often in late summer there is hot, dry weather with little or no dew at night.

In the late 1960s miniature funnel traps were used with 3.5 m sheet metal drift fences; the juvenile garter snakes captured reveal habitat preference. There were 37 trap sites in the west-central part of FNHR, in both lowland and upland habitat. Of these sites only 17 yielded *Thamnophis*. Of 16 traps within 40 m of the small intermittent creek draining the pond, three-fourths yielded juvenile garter snakes, sometimes with multiple captures, but of 12 traps in the same general

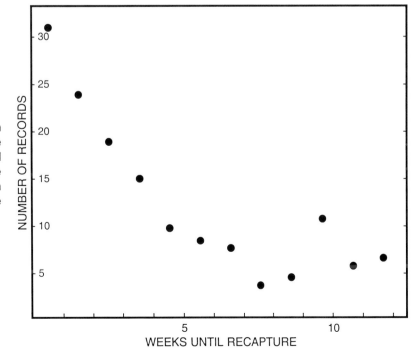

Figure 29. Elapsed time until recapture in marked garter snakes, showing that capture frequency (number of records) undergoes rapid reduction for several weeks, evidently because individuals shift their ranges frequently and soon move away from the area where they were marked, reducing the likelihood of recapture.

TABLE 96. Numbers of Garter Snakes Captured and Recaptured, 1950 to 1992

	Males		Females		Combined	
	N	Percent of Male Sample	N	Percent of Female Sample	N	Percent of Combined Sample
Captured, Marked, & Released	957	100.0	1293	100.0	2250	100.0
Marked but Never Recaptured	810	84.6	1062	82.1	1872	83.2
Recaptured Only in Year of Marking	94	9.8	113	8.7	207	9.2
Captured in 2 Years	48	5.0	101	7.8	149	6.6
Captured in 3 or More Years	5	0.5	17	1.3	22	1.0

area more than 40 m from the creek only one-third caught garter snakes, and of nine traps placed in upland, in or near an old quarry site, only two yielded garter snakes. It seems that moist, lowland habitat is preferred.

A high percentage of the garter snakes captured and marked were never seen again, and the most plausible explanation is that they were transients which soon moved away from the places where they were found and hence were not at risk of capture — unless they happened to travel to another area where studies were in progress. Over the 20-year period, 1975 through 1994, 1223 garter snakes were marked in the northwestern part of FNHR and NESA; 72.5% were caught only once; 15.0% were recaptured only in the year that they were marked; 8.8% were captured in 2 consecutive years; 0.75% were captured in 3 consecutive years; 3.0% were captured in 2 or more years but were missing in some intervening years.

As shown in Table 96 a total of 2250 garter snakes were captured and marked (not including neonates born to females held in confinement). A little less than 17% of those marked were recaptured. Even after years of live trapping on specific areas, the catch always consisted predominantly of new unmarked individuals, with a rather rapid population turnover resulting from relatively high vagility and short life span. Only 7.6% were recaptured in a year subsequent to that of marking; 62% of the snakes recaptured were females. Of the 171 snakes captured in more than 1 year, 51 were missed for 1 or more years between the first and last record. The longest sequence of records spanned 9 years. Two individuals each spanned 6 years, five spanned 5 years, 13 spanned 4 years, and 31 spanned 3 years. From the sizes, and assumed ages of these individuals at the time of first capture and marking, their ages at the time of their last records were deduced as follows: fifth year in 13, sixth year in seven, seventh year in 12, eighth year in three, ninth year in four, tenth year in one, and eleventh year in one.

The areas where I sampled garter snake populations with intensive trapping or shelter-checking were relatively small, 3–20 ha, and not adapted to showing long

movements, but the rate of population turnover — much more rapid than could be expected from normal mortality, and replacement by reproduction — suggested many long but unrecorded movements. In contrast, long distance dispersal was found by Gregory and Stewart (1977), studying movements of snakes to and from the great hibernation dens at Inwood in the Interlake Region of Manitoba. The thousands of snakes concentrated at the hibernacula of limestone sinks were found to migrate south to vast marshland areas where they spent the summer. In two seasons some 3000 snakes were marked at the dens and more than 1000 were captured and marked in the marshlands. Twenty-six marked snakes were recaptured in the marshes; 20 from the dens and six from marshland. Mean distance moved by snakes from the dens was 10.7 ± 0.73 (4.3–17.7) km.

Geographic Differentiation

The common garter snake's geographic variation in lepidosis, color, and pattern over its extensive range has been studied in detail. Variation in body size, sexual dimorphism, reproduction, habitat, and ecological traits are less known. Comparisons of figures from local garter snakes *Thamnophis sirtalis parietalis* with Mitchell's (1994) data for Virginia *T. s. sirtalis* show some striking differences. In the Kansas snakes mean SVL mm for adult males, adult females, and neonates were, respectively, 440.0, 639.4, and 164.2, whereas in the Virginia snakes corresponding figures were 408.7, 515.3, and 131.2. Thus the Virginia snakes were relativley small, with less sexual dimorphism. Litter size is notably higher in Virginia, 26.2 vs. 16.2 in Kansas. In an earlier study of geographic variation in litter size I found population means ranging from 10.5 to 29.0. Relatively low means were found on the West Coast, 11.3 (*fitchi*), 13.1 (*concinnus*), 13.9 (*infernalis* and southern *fitchi*), and 13.1 (*pallidula* in New Hampshire). Highest means, 20.6 to 29.0, were found in the mid-Atlantic states and in the Great Lakes region (Fitch, 1985). In Arkansas Trauth et al. (1994) found an average of 26.6 ± 4.0 (16–33) yolked eggs or embryos in eight females.

Tropidoclonion lineatum

Traits of the Species

The lined snake is a dwarfed garter snake relative, occurring in the Great Plains from southern Minnesota to southern Texas. The general appearance is that of a small garter snake, brown, with a dull yellow vertebral stripe involving the mid-dorsal scale row and half of the adjacent row on each side, and a pair of paler lateral stripes that involve the second and third scale rows on each side. (See Plate 33.) Dorsal scales are keeled, in 15 rows. Proportions differ from those of a typical garter snake; the head is relatively narrow, not distinct from the neck, and the tail is relatively short (about 19% of SVL in males and 14% in females). Each ventral scute bears a pair of black spots on the anterior half and sometimes the spots of a pair are in contact or merged. The monotypic genus *Tropidoclonion* is separated from the garter snakes (*Thamnophis*) on the basis that each hemipenis is slightly bilobed, and each lobe bears a solid awn. The lined snake is known to prey on earthworms, perhaps to the exclusion of other kinds of prey.

Much of what is known about lined snakes is based upon the early studies of Blanchard and Force (1930) and Force (1934) on large series from the vicinity of Tulsa, Oklahoma. Young are born in August; for 132 neonates mean length was 111 (70–125) mm. Average adult male length was found to be 260 (185–325) mm and adult female length 304 (235–425) mm. In spring lengths were bimodal, with little overlapping between young born the previous August, 120–200 mm, and reproductive adults of 240–350 mm. As in some other natricines (e.g., *Thamnophis*) the lined snake in the course of its ontogeny develops knobs along the keels of its supranal scales. These are associated with courtship, and appear in males that are nearing sexual maturity, but in females they appear relatively late in life.

Reproduction in the lined snake is well known through the studies of Krohmer and Aldridge (1985) in the region of St. Louis, Missouri. Like other American natricines this snake is a live-bearer. Young are born about mid-August, and average 7.1 ± 0.52 (2–12) per litter, with larger females having relatively large litters. Females' fat bodies are reduced at the time of parturition, but they enlarge rapidly to their maximum size by mid-September. Mating occurs in fall immediately after parturition; adult females are 221 to 320 mm in SVL. Follicles are ovulated in June at an average diameter of 14.1 mm. Feeding tapers off during pregnancy. Female neonates average 84 mm SVL, but gain about 1.0 mm per day and by the time of hibernation they average 124 mm.; they mature and give birth as 2-year-olds. Males are larger than females at birth (95 mm SVL) and average 145 mm by the time they enter hibernation. They reproduce as 1-year-olds. "If sexual maturity is defined as the onset of spermatogenesis, the lined snake could be considered sexually mature two months after birth" (Krohmer and Aldridge, 1985).

In the course of my study lined snakes were found only on NESA, but one was found in the stomach of a racer that was beneath a shelter only 10 m from the north edge of FNHR. David Reber while employed in botanical research in 1992 saw several dozen lined snakes in a field of brome grass in the northeastern corner of NESA (personal communication, 1992). The snakes were attracted to places where plantings had been made and were burrowing in the loose soil of recently filled excavations.

Lined snakes are usually found in grassland, but occur in a variety of habitats, and have often been recorded in urban and suburban surroundings in gardens and in vacant lots hiding beneath trash.

Virginia valeriae

Traits of the Species

The western earth snake is a diminutive natricine of secretive-fossorial habits in deciduous forest habitats of the eastern United States and west to eastern Kansas, where it has been found in nine counties clustered around the Kansas City area. In this stubby-bodied little snake the head is narrow, not well set off from the neck; the body is uniform golden brown dorsally, with head darker and ventral surface pale yellow. (See Plate 34.) The dorsal scales are in 17 longitudinal rows, mostly smooth, but lightly keeled on the rear of the body and the tail. The pale ventral color extends up onto the labial scales. The tail is relatively short. Moist woodland or woodland edge habitat is preferred. The prey consists mainly of earthworms, but possibly includes some other invertebrates. As in other natricines there is a pronounced sexual size difference, with females being larger. In Virginia, Mitchell (1994) recorded an average of 214.5 (183–276) mm SVL in 30 females vs. 171.4 (153–200) in 20 males. Earth snakes are live-bearers. Litters from a composite sample of 41 females from nine states, mostly from the eastern part of the range, averaged 6.4 (5–14) (Fitch, 1985). In my study only three earth snakes were found. One was on a wooded, south-facing slope near the middle of FNHR on 24 May 1964. One found under a massive flat rock on 18 April 1954 had a body temperature of 31.0 °C when air temperature was 24.2 °C. A gravid female having seven embryos was found in a lowland meadow habitat on FNHR on 27 May 1978. This snake measured 268 mm SVL and weighed 9.5 g. In Arkansas Trauth et al. (1994) found an average of 5.8 yolked follicles and oviductal eggs in seven females. In their study mean adult SVL was found to be 202.6 ± 9.4 (175–237) in seven snakes.

Discussion and Conclusions

The 50-year span of the present study has resulted in a better understanding of the ecology and demography of common species of snakes. Abundant data has been accumulated to show mean adult size of male and female, and of hatchlings or neonates, clutch size, longevity, and types of prey in local populations and how all these traits are affected by the course of ecological succession and environmental extremes in years that are unusually hot or cold, wet or dry. The plethora of data from a specific locality provides a basis for comparison and contrast with data from other remote localities or areas in species' ranges, revealing geographic variation in ecological traits.

Species Diversity in Diet and Demography

In this local study of snakes in northeastern Kansas 18 species were found, five of which were near the centers of their transcontinental ranges. Eight other species, most characteristic of deciduous forests of eastern North America, were near their western range limits. Three uncommon species were most characteristic of Great Plains grasslands. Successional changes on the 239 ha natural area where my study was centered — forest invading grassland and fallow fields — changed the ophifauna. Three species of snakes (*Crotalus horridus, Pituophis catenifer, Tantilla gracilis*) disappeared from FNHR and four others became much scarcer, but no species made noticeable gains. Seven species are characteristic of forest habitat, seven favor grassland, two are found most often at forest-grassland interface, and two have aquatic tendencies.

The following list shows prey species of the local snakes, with their scientific names arranged alphabetically under major phylogenetic groupings. Those marked with an asterisk are from my own field records. Others represent literature records that are specifically cited in the text but I have not made a complete literature survey. The capital letters following the name of the prey are acronyms for the scientific name of the

snake predator (see page 2), e.g., ACP = *Agkistrodon contortrix phaeogaster.* The literature records usually pertain to subspecies other than those that I studied, and in such cases the acronym is limited to two letters for genus and species.

List of Prey Animals of Local Snake Species

Mammals

Blarina hylophaga Elliot's shorttail shrew* — ACP, CCF, CH, EOO, LCC, LTS, TSP

Clethrionomys gapperi Northern redback vole — AC

Condylura cristata Star-nose mole — AC

Cryptotis parva Least shrew* — ACP, LCC, LTS

Didelphis virginiana Virginia opossum — AC

Dipodomys ordii Ord's kangaroo rat — PC

Geomys bursarius Plains pocket gopher — PC

Microtus ochrogaster Prairie vole* — ACP, CCF, CH, EE, EOO, LCC, LTS, PCS, TSP

Microtus pinetorum Woodland vole* — ACP, LCC

Mus musculus House mouse* — EOO, LCC

Neotoma floridana Eastern woodrat* — CH, EOO

Parascalops breweri Hairy-tailed mole — AC

Peromyscus leucopus White-footed mouse* — ACP, CCF, EOO, TSP

Peromyscus maniculatus Deer mouse* — ACP, CCF, EOO, LCC

Reithrodontomys megalotis Western harvest mouse* — ACP, CCF, TSP

Scalopus aquaticus Eastern mole* — ACP, CCF, LCC

Sciurus carolinensis Gray squirrel* — CH

Sciurus niger Fox squirrel* — CH

Sigmodon hispidus Cottonrat* — ACP, LCC

Synaptomys cooperi Southern bog lemming* — ACP, LCC

Sylvilagus floridanus Eastern cottontail* — CH, EOO, LCC, PCS

Zapus hudsonius Meadow jumping mouse* — ACP, CCF

Birds

Agelaius phoeniceus Redwing blackbird* — TSP

Archilochus colubris Ruby-throated hummingbird — AC

Asio flammeus Short-eared owl — PC

Cardinalis cardinalis Northern cardinal* — EOO, TSP

Cistothorus platensis Sedge wren* — TSP

Coccyzus americanus Yellow-billed cuckoo* — EOO

Colinus virginianus Northern bobwhite* — EOO, LCC

Corvus brachyrhynchos American crow* — EOO

Cyanocitta cristata Blue jay* — EOO

Gallus domesticus Chicken* — EOO

Melospiza lincolnii Lincoln's sparrow* — TSP

Molothrus ater Brown-headed cowbird* — TSP

Phasianus colchicus Ring-necked pheasant — PC

Recurvirostra recurvirostra American avocet — PC

Riparia riparia Bank swallow — EOO

Sayornis phoebe Eastern phoebe* — EOO

Sialia sialis Eastern bluebird* — EOO

Spiza americana Dickcissel* — PCS

Sturnella magna Eastern meadowlark* — PCS

Sturnella neglecta Western meadowlark — PC

Troglodytes aedon House wren* — EOO

Zenaida macroura Mourning dove* — EOO

Reptiles

Carphophis vermis Western worm snake* — ACP, LTS

Cnemidophorus sexlineatus Six-lined racerunner* — ACP, CCF, LCC, PCS

Coluber constrictor flaviventris Yellowbelly racer* — ACP, CCF

Crotalus horridus Timber rattlesnake* — LCC

Diadophis punctatus Ringneck snake* — ACP, CCF, LCC, LTS

Eumeces fasciatus Five-lined skink* — ACP, CCF, LCC, LTS

Eumeces obsoletus Great Plains skink* — CCF, LCC, LTS

Ophisaurus attenuatus Slender glass lizard* — ACP, CCF, LCC

Scincella lateralis Ground skink* — ACP

Storeria dekayi Brown snake* — CCF

Thamnophis sirtalis Common garter snake* — CCF

Tropidoclonion lineatum Lined snake* — CCF

Amphibians

Acris crepitans Northern cricket frog* — NSS, TSP

Ambystoma opacum Marbled salamander — TS

Ambystoma texanum Smallmouth salamander — TS

Bufo americanus American toad* — NSS, TSP

Bufo woodhousii Woodhouse's toad* — NSS, TSP

Desmognathus fuscus Northern dusky salamander — TS

Eurycea bislineata Northern two-lined salamander — TS

Gastrophryne olivacea Great Plains narrowmouth toad* — ACP

Gyrinophilus porphyriticus Spring salamander — AC

Hyla regilla Pacific treefrog — TS

Plethodon cylindraceus White-spotted slimy salamander — TS

Plethodon glutinosus Northern slimy salamander — TS

Pseudacris triseriata Western chorus frog* — NSS, TSP

Pseudotriton sp. Red and Mud salamanders — TS

Rana blairi Plains leopard frog* — ACP, CCF, NSS, TSP

Rana catesbeiana Bullfrog — ACP, NSS

Rana boylii Foothill yellow-legged frog — TS

Rana pipiens Northern leopard frog — TS

Rana sylvatica Wood frog — TS

Fish

Cyprinella lutrensis Red shiner* — NSS

Micropterus salmoides Largemouth bass* — NSS

Pomoxis sp. Crappie — NSS

Invertebrates

Acheta assimilis Field cricket* — CCF

Allolobophora caliginosa Yellow-headed earthworm* — CV, DPA, TSP

Arphia simplex Sulfur-winged locust* — CCF

Automeris io Io moth — AC

Ceuthophilus pallidus Pallid cave cricket* — CCF

Citheronia regalis Regal moth — AC

Chortophaga viridifasciata Green-striped grasshopper* — CCF

Deroceras laeve Black slug* — SDT

Magicicada septemdecin Periodical cicada* — ACP

Melanoplus bivittatus Two-striped grasshopper* — CCF

Melanoplus differentialis Differential grasshopper* — CCF

Melanoplus femurrubrum Red-legged grasshopper* — CCF

Nemobius fasciatus Striped ground cricket* — CCF

Neoconocephalus robustus Robust cone head katydid* — CCF

Orchelimum vulgare Meadow grasshopper* — CCF

Schistocerca americana American grasshopper* — CCF

Sphargemon equale Say's grasshopper* — CCF

Stagomantis carolina Carolina mantis — AC

Tibicen pruinosa Pruinose cicada* — ACP, CCF

Tipulidae Crane flies — TG

Differences in food habits mitigate interspecific competition between members of the snake community; differences in habitat and in size reduce competition between those species with most similar preferences (Henderson, 1974). Eight species prey primarily on mammals, 7 on earthworms, one each on reptiles, fish, amphibians, and insects (Table 97). Both numerically and in biomass, the earthworm *Allolobophora caliginosa* proved to be by far the most important prey species, comprising an estimated 73% of total prey biomass, followed by *Microtus ochrogaster* with 9%, and with *Sylvilagus floridanus, Peromyscus leucopus, Rana blairi, Neotoma floridana, Microtus pinetorum, Rana catesbeiana, Ophisaurus attenuatus,* and *Sigmodon hispidus* in that order making up most of the remaining small percentages.

Table 97, summarizing the food habits of local snakes, shows striking differences between species. "Mice" (including murid, cricetid, and zapodid) were eaten by 10 species, voles by 9, shrews by 8, earthworms by 7, frogs and passerine birds each by 6, rats (*Neotoma, Sigmodon*) by 5, skinks, glass lizards and snakes each by 4, birds'

TABLE 97. Diverse Food Habits of Species in a Snake Community

Prey	Agkistrodon contortrix	Carphophis vermis	Coluber constrictor	Crotalus horridus	Diadophis punctatus	Elaphe emoryi	Elaphe obsoleta	Lampropeltis calligaster	Lampropeltis getula	Lampropeltis triangulum	Nerodia sipedon	Pituophis catenifer	Storeria dekayi	Storeria occipitomaculata	Tantilla gracilis	Thamnophis sirtalis	Tropidoclonion lineatum	Virginia valeriae
Rabbit			A				B					B						
Squirrel			B															
Rat	C		B		B	B	B					B						
Vole	A	A	B		A	A	A		B			A				A		
Mouse	B	B	D		B	B	B	*	B			B				B		
Shrew	D	C	D		B	B	B		B							C		
Snake	D	C					C	A*								C		
Glass lizard	C	C	C				B	*										
Skink	D	C					B		A									
Bird	C	C				B	C					B				C		
Bird egg						B	C					B						
Frog	B	B					D				A	B*				A		
Toad											A					B		
Fish											A					*		
Earthworm		A			A								A*	B*		D	A*	A*
Slug													B*	A*		C		
Orthopteran			A															
Cicada	D		C															
Moth	C		C															
Moth larva	C		C															
Fly or beetle larva			C											A*				

A Primary food source
B Secondary food source
C Occasional food source
D Food source of first year young
* Literature record

eggs, toads, fish, moths (and their larvae), cicadas and slugs each by 2, and squirrels and grasshoppers each by 1. The most eurytrophic species were found to be *Agkistrodon contortrix* and *Coluber constrictor,* each taking 12 different types of prey. Next were *Thamnophis sirtalis* with 8 kinds of prey and *Elaphe obsoleta* with 7. *Carphophis vermis* was found to be the most stenotrophic species with only one prey category—earthworm. In four of the species with most diverse food habits— *Agkistrodon contortrix, Coluber constrictor, Crotalus horridus, Thamnophis sirtalis*—first-year young were found to utilize different types of prey than adults, with varying amounts of overlapping, but in other species no such partitioning was observed. In *Agkistrodon contortrix, Coluber constrictor,* and *Thamnophis sirtalis,* all having pronounced size differences between the sexes, males and females differed in food habits, with the larger sex taking larger kinds of prey. In *Crotalus horridus* and *Nerodia sipedon* similar partitioning is suspected but for these food samples were inadequately small.

Of seven grassland species, three (*Pituophis catenifer, Tantilla gracilis, Elaphe emoryi*) disappeared where their shortgrass habitat deteriorated with invasion of woody plants and rank herbaceous cover; *Lampropeltis getula* and *Storeria occipitomaculata* may have conformed to this trend also. *Tropidoclonion lineatum* persisted in small numbers only on mowed areas. *Coluber constrictor* and *Lampropeltis calligaster* underwent drastic reduction where their tall-grass habitat was being replaced by invading forest.

Forest-inhabiting species were not necessarily benefitted by the successional changes that occurred. *Crotalus horridus* disappeared from FNHR, as a thick forest canopy developed with lack of basking places in the rocky woodland type preferred. *Virginia valeriae* may also have been eliminated, as none was recorded over a 20-year period, but because of its rarity and secretiveness its status was uncertain. *Agkistrodon contortrix, Carphophis vermis, Elaphe obsoleta,* and *Storeria dekayi* underwent reduction in numbers and tended to shift from old, established woodland to formerly open areas where new stands of trees were developing.

Two species most characteristic of forest-grassland interface—*Diadophis punctatus* and *Lampropeltis triangulum*—both underwent reduction, which was drastic in the case of *Diadophis,* relatively slight in *Lampropeltis.* Aquatic habitats on the study areas were relatively stable. Of the two snake species with aquatic tendencies *Nerodia sipedon* has undergone marked reduction. *Thanmophis sirtalis* has undergone less reduction but has shifted from areas with most dense vegetation to more open situations.

Size Relationships

Tables 98, 99, and 100 show lengths and weights in adults of both sexes and in hatchlings (or neonates) of several species of snakes. These samples of females were mostly

TABLE 98. Size Relationships of Adults and Young in 13 Species of Snakes

Species	Adult Female		Hatchling or Neonate			Adult Male		
	N	Weight (g)	N	Weight (g)	% of Female Weight	N	Weight (g)	% of Female Weight
Agkistrodon contortrix	100	129.2 73–400	563	11.1 5.7–13.2	8.6	2238	170.6 40–530	132
Carphophis vermis	16	7.8 3.4–11.8	21	1.03 0.89–1.19	13.2	16	7.02 2.9–10.1	90
Coluber constrictor	100	161.6 51–400	118	4.6 2.3–7.8	2.8	100	118.6 87–157	73
Crotalus horridus	14	530.8 313–1100	13	26.5 19.2–29.1	5.0	14	896 260–2084	169
Diadophis punctatus	100	6.3 3.2–10.9	49	0.76 0.55–1.10	12.1	100	5.63 3.2–10.1	89
Elaphe emoryi	13	303.1 214–576	0	—	—	17	370 152–625	122
Elaphe obsoleta	100	271.9 112–1270	81	11.7 9.9–15.0	4.3	58	511 162–820	188
Lampropeltis calligaster	57	174.9 82–340	16	8.3 6.0–9.4	4.7	85	228 83–340	130
Lampropeltis triangulum	61	65.7 37–172	15	3.01 2.3–4.1	4.6	87	79.2 30–143	120
Nerodia sipedon	34	305.9 97–720	100	4.91 2.9–6.8	1.6	81	98.2 36–172	32
Pituophis catenifer	32	635.9 260–1470	29	24.8 15.6–34.1	3.9	60	705.8 375–1710	111
Storeria dekayi	30	5.85 3.3–10.0	133	0.29 0.23–0.46	5.0	61	4.3 2.7–6.0	74
Thamnophis sirtalis	100	112.8 48–248	455	1.71 0.7–2.34	1.5	100	41.5 18–110	37

TABLE 99. Contrasting Demographic Traits of Species in a Local Snake Community

Species	Mean Female SVL (mm)	Female SVL as % Male SVL	Female Wt. as % Male Wt.	Hatchling Wt. as % Female Wt.	Relative Clutch Mass
Agkistrodon contortrix	595	92	88	7.9	0.286
Carphophis vermis	287	117	145	10.2	0.345
Coluber constrictor	822	115	132	2.8	0.400
Crotalus horridus	927	93	54	4.9	0.335
Diadophis punctatus	288	113	128	11.2	0.396
Elaphe emoryi	1045	89	76	—	0.332
Elaphe obsoleta	1081	88	65	3.5	0.338
Lampropeltis calligaster	828	93	74	4.9	0.375
Lampropeltis triangulum	601	96	98	4.1	0.438
Nerodia sipedon	756	140	292	1.7	0.248
Pituophis catenifer	1280	99	89	2.7	0.454
Storeria dekayi	260	111	125	4.3	0.359
Thamnophis sirtalis	640	131	239	1.6	0.272

from October. It is noteworthy that the largest kinds, *Crotalus horridus* and *Pituophis catenifer,* are more than one hundred times the bulk of the smallest, *Diadophis punctatus* and *Storeria dekayi.* Parental investment per offspring is greatest in *Carphophis vermis* and *Diadophis punctatus,* with hatchlings weighing, respectively, 10.2% and 11.2% of adult female weight; it is least in *Nerodia sipedon* and *Thamnophis sirtalis* (neonates 1.6% and 1.5% of female weight), but in most kinds young are from 3 to 5% of female weight. The 13 species listed in Table 99 are almost evenly divided between those in which the male is the larger sex (viperids, rat snakes, kingsnake, milk snake, bullsnake) and those in which females are larger (worm snake, ringneck, racer, natricines). In the water snake and garter snake, males are only about one-third of female size, whereas in the black rat snake, males average nearly twice (188%) female size. In all the species each sex shows a wide range in adult size; in most the largest females are three

to five times the bulk of the smallest, with the greatest range in *Elaphe obsoleta* having the largest females more than 11 times the bulk of the smallest. In males, *Agkistrodon contortrix* shows the greatest size range with the largest male more than 13 times the bulk of the smallest. In hatchlings or neonates each species showed a wide size range, with the largest from 1.34 (in *Carphophis*) to 3.44 (in *Thamnophis*) times the bulk of the smallest. All these figures were, of course, influenced by sample sizes, which were small in some cases and very large in others.

Table 99 contrasts demographic traits in 13 species of local snakes; *Lampropeltis getula, Tantilla gracilis, Tropidoclonion lineatum,* and *Virginia valeriae* are not included because too little data was obtained from these relatively rare species. The greatest size differential was between the males of *Storeria dekayi* and of *Crotalus horridus,* the latter averages 204 times as

TABLE 100. Behavioral and Ecological Traits of Species

Species	Adult SVL (mm)	Microhabitat *	Time of Surface Foraging **	Strategy of Capturing Prey ***	Strategy of Subduing Prey****
Agkistrodon contortrix	389–960	ter	noc	a	v
Carphophis vermis	177–344	fos	ne	os	sa
Coluber constrictor	461–1110	ter	di	vs	sa
Crotalus horridus	681–1270	ter	noc	a	v
Diadophis punctatus	173–396	sec	ne	os	sa
Elaphe emoryi	660–1110	ter	noc, di	os	c
Elaphe obsoleta	825–1850	arb	noc, di	vs	c
Lampropeltis getula	547–818	ter	noc, di	os	c
Lampropeltis calligaster	629–1070	ter	noc, di	os	c
Lampropeltis triangulum	420–800	ter	noc, di	os	c
Nerodia sipedon	413–1050	aq	noc, di	vs	sa
Pituophis catenifer	855–1624	ter	noc, di	vs	c
Storeria dekayi	159–300	sec	ne	os	sa
Storeria occipitomaculata	—	sec	ne	os	sa
Tantilla gracilis	153–307	fos	ne	os	sa
Thamnophis sirtalis	389–970	ter	di	vs	sa
Tropidoclonion lineatum	220–313	sec	ne	os	sa
Virginia valeriae	—	sec	ne	os	sa

* aquatic (aq), arboreal (arb), fossorial (fos), secretive (sec), terrestrial (ter)
** diurnal (di), nocturnal (noc), nonemergent (ne)
*** ambush (a), olfactory search (os), visual search (vs)
**** constriction (c), swallow alive (sa), venom (v)

large. Adult female-to-male weight ratios range from a minimum of 63% in *Crotalus horridus* to a maximum of 294% in *Nerodia sipedon*.

Relative clutch mass, the weight ratio of a clutch or litter to the female's weight before egg laying or parturition, averages 35% and ranges from 25% to 45% in the 13 species. It tends to be lowest in viviparous species whose females are burdened with fetuses during most of their season of activity, highest in oviparous kinds that are sluggish and secretive, and therefore not much handicapped by a burden of eggs before laying (Seigel and Fitch, 1984).

Table 101 shows figures, some tentative, for a suite of demographic traits including mean number of eggs per clutch or young per litter, age at maturity, frequency of clutches or litters, longevity, and population density. Bracketed items represent records from the literature for information lacking from my own records because of rarity of the species in the area. Tables 98–104 are based upon various data sets and subsets, some of which have contrasting figures. In Table 98, for instance, adult female weights are shown for relatively small fall subsamples, intended to eliminate the variance introduced by including females that were gravid, or had recently oviposited or given birth.

In Table 101 the third and fourth columns, age at maturity, show that in most species males become sexually mature at least a year earlier than females, while they are still far short of average adult size. In most species males mature in their second year in time to become parents as 2-year-olds. Maturation in the third year is most common for females. In nearly all species one clutch or litter per year per female is the usual pattern, but in the copperhead, and probably in the black rat snake, females are most likely to produce biennially, some producing more often or less often, depending on the food supply and the weather. In the species that are on an annual schedule, occasionally females may miss a year.

For each species the figure for maximum recorded longevity is an estimate based on recaptures of marked individuals: the sum of intervals between captures and assumed age at the time of marking, early in life. The data is of course influenced by sample sizes and is more meaningful for the copperhead, garter snake, racer, and ringneck than for relatively uncommon species like the timber rattlesnake, bullsnake and water snake, with relatively meager samples. Of course relatively few approach the maximum life span. First-year young, because they are subject to relatively high mortality rates, were not likely to be recaptured as old adults. Most of the oldest and largest snakes recaptured were marked when they were already adult, hence their ages were not definitely known but, in some, age could be estimated with a degree of confidence. In some instances ecological succession occurring with changes in land use, or unfavorable sequences of weather, resulted in deterioration of habitat and reduction of snake populations; during these periods the ages attained were less than they were under more favorable conditions.

Greatest recorded ages were attained by *Diadophis punctatus;* several were believed to be more than 20 years old. However, the huge samples of *Diadophis,*

TABLE 101. Ages, Reproduction, and Abundance of Snake Species in a Local Community

Species	Number in Clutch or Litter	Age at Maturity (Years)		Frequency of Female Production	Maximum Recorded Longevity (Years)	Population Density/ha
		Male	Female			
Agkistrodon contortrix	5.6	2	3	Mostly Biennial	19	4.9**
Carphophis vermis	3.0	2	3	Annual	10	22.9
Coluber constrictor	11.8	2	2 or 3	Annual	11	14.8***
Crotalus horridus	9.6	3	3 or 4	Mostly Annual	15(?)	0.31
Diadophis punctatus	3.8	2	3	Annual	24	1040–1603****
Elaphe obsoleta	9.7	3	4	Biennial?	16	0.9–3.6
Lampropeltis calligaster	9.2	2	3	Annual	8	0.56–4.0
Lampropeltis triangulum	6.7	3	4	Annual	14	0.13–0.70
Nerodia sipedon	19.9	2	3	Annual	8	0.30
Pituophis catenifer	11.2	2	2 or 3	Annual	8	0.13
Storeria dekayi	11.0	2?	3?	Annual	—	15.7
Storeria occiptomaculata	9.0*	2*	2*	Annual*	—	<1
Tantilla gracilis	1.75	—	—	Annual?	—	<1
Thamnophis sirtalis	16.2	2	2 or 3	Annual	9	14.7*****
Tropidoclonion lineatum	7.1*	1*	2*	Annual*	—	<1

* Literature records
** Mean of 11 Petersen Index censuses; House Field and Quarry Field, 1977–1988
*** Mean of 7 Petersen Index censuses with 0.5 mo. sampling periods, Quarry Field and NESA pens, 1977 to 1994
**** Mean of 7 Petersen Index censuses, Quarry Field, 1966–1970
***** Mean of 28 Petersen Index censuses with sampling periods of 2 to 8 weeks; House Field, 1985–1997

the limited vagility, and concentration on relatively small study areas favored longtime records in this species. Some other kinds of snakes are believed to have even greater life expectancies, notably *Crotalus horridus* and *Elaphe obsoleta*. Life spans of about 15 years were recorded for *C. horridus* and nearly 16 years for *Elaphe*. In the milk snake, *Lampropeltis triangulum,* despite the relatively small sample, two were evidently in their fourteenth year at their last recaptures. In a sample of 321 *L. calligaster* the oldest were believed to be 9 or 10 years old. In *Thamnophis sirtalis* the sixth year cohort was less than 1% of the sample and the oldest individuals may have been about 11 years old. In *Coluber constrictor* the oldest individuals of the large sample may have been in their tenth and eleventh years. No data is available regarding longevity in *Storeria occipitomaculata, Tantilla gracilis, Tropidoclonion lineatum,* nor *Virginia valeriae,* but presumably these diminutive species are relatively short lived.

Snakes that have become adjusted to captivity, with freedom from many of the mortality factors that affect them in the wild, often surpass the life spans of their conspecifics in nature. Snider and Bowler (1992) have published longevity records for the majority of the species included in my study. Some of their records are as follows (species name folowed by age in years and to nearest month): *Agkistrodon contortrix* 29 + 2 months; *Crotalus horridus* 30 + 2; *Elaphe emoryi* 21 + 2; *Elaphe obsoleta* 23; *Lampropeltis calligaster* 25 + 9; *L. getula* 33 + 4; *L. triangulum* 21 + 4; *Pituophis catenifer* 33 + 10; *Nerodia sipedon* 9 + 8; *Storeria dekayi* 7; *S. occipitomaculata* 4 + 7; *Thamnophis sirtalis* 14; *Virginia valeriae* 6. These records suggest that the largest kinds live longest, sometimes exceeding 30 years, that even medium-size colubrids have the potential to exceed 20 years, and that natricines, especially the smallest kinds, are relatively short lived.

The least reliable figures in Table 101 are those of the last column, population density. Doubtless all have a wide margin of error and figures for the less common species are least reliable. For the copperhead, racer, ringneck, and garter snake figures are derived from a Petersen Index of capture-recapture ratios, but even for these most common species the theoretical assumptions necessary for an accurate Petersen Index could not be fully satisfied. For each species the time span required to amass an adequate sample was great enough to permit population shifts and distortion of ratios.

For each of the four species listed above, many census computations were carried out, comparing numbers on different areas, or on the same area at different times, and there were possible effects of shortening or lengthening sampling periods, as discussed in the foregoing species accounts. For the remaining species, not amenable to Petersen Index treatment, density estimates were calculated from the ratio of their numbers to one or more of the species censused by Petersen Index (Fitch, 1982). Differences in time and place and amount of activity distort such ratios. Some of the figures presented are means from different times and places. Figures were obtained from areas where the species was present in some numbers, but not necessarily in optimum habitat.

Temporal Changes

When succession and weather favored a snake population, causing it to thrive, the average adult size was greater than in less favorable periods, and this was well shown by the annual samples of the four best-sampled species. *Agkistrodon contortrix* averaged 18.2% larger in its best year (1952) than in its worst year (1977); *Thamnophis sirtalis* averaged 18.1% larger in its best year (1968) than in its worst (1962); *Coluber constrictor* averaged 16.7% larger in its best year (1959) than in its worst (1950) as shown in Figure 30. In *Diadophis punctatus* the range was much less, 6.9% larger in its best year (1994) than in its worst year (1962). Obviously each species reacted somewhat differently to changing environmental conditions.

Size of egg clutch (or litter) changed from year to year also. Figures 31 and 32 show productivity over periods of years (arranged in order from lowest to highest) for years in which adequate series were available. Range in size of brood from worst year to best was 3.33 to 4.7 in *Diadophis punctatus,* 4.0 to 7.7 in *Agkistrodon contortrix,* 10 to 13 in *Coluber constrictor,* and in *Thamnophis sirtalis* 9.8 (in 1977) to 22.0 (in 1978) with no overlapping between the samples of those 2 years.

Longtime successional changes dramatically affected the numbers and distribution of each of the snake species occurring locally. Observations were made continuously and records kept throughout the 50-year span of my study only on FNHR. The two most striking successional stages to be seen there were: early development of a dense grass-weed mixture on formerly almost barren areas of overgrazed pastures and cultivated fields, and subsequent invasions of shrubs and trees shading out this herbaceous vegetation. The grass-weed mixture was most diverse at the start, and throughout the 1950s there was progressive loss of forb species, replaced by grasses. Small mammals (mainly voles, cotton rats and deer mice) peaked in numbers in 1950 and 1951, then underwent drastic decline, with the white-footed mouse replacing them in much smaller numbers. The species of snakes preferring tallgrass habitat followed the trends of their rodent prey, with rapid increase during the early years, and gradual decline as grass replaced forbs and, in turn, woody

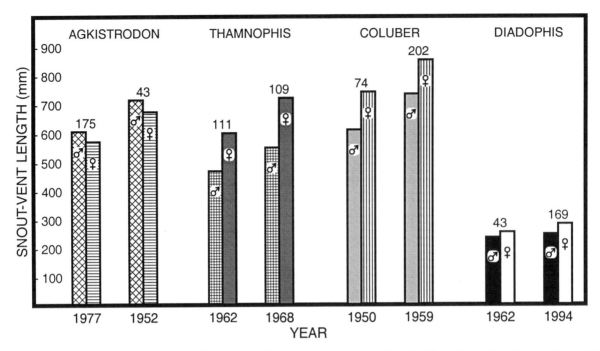

Figure 30. Mean sizes (SVL) of snakes of both sexes in annual samples, contrasting "worst" and "best" years in *Agkistrodon contortrix phaeogaster, Thamnophis sirtalis parietalis, Coluber constrictor flaviventris,* and *Diadophis punctatus arnyi.* Number of snakes in each annual sample is indicated.

vegetation replaced the grass. Table 102 documents these changes. *Elaphe emoryi, Lampropeltis getula, Storeria occipitomaculata,* and *Tropidoclonion lineatum* are omitted from the table as they were never found on FNHR but only on nearby areas. The table's fourth column, population shift from forest or edge to formerly open areas, recognizes a trend that applied to a majority of the species. The overgrazed pastures and cultivated fields had few snakes, but when shelter and food became available, many species moved in and

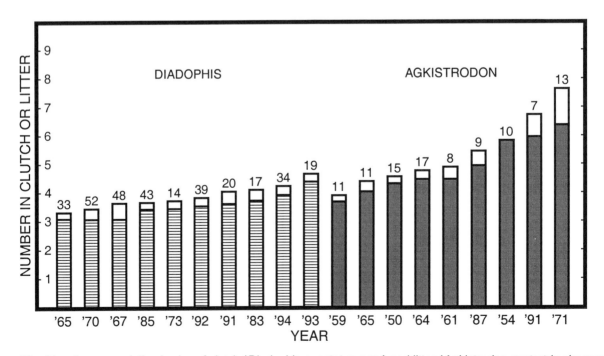

Figure 31. Year-to-year variation in size of clutch (*Diadophis punctatus arnyi*) and litter (*Agkistrodon contortrix phaeogaster*) arranged in order from "worst" to "best" year. Top of each column shows the mean, and open space shows one standard error.

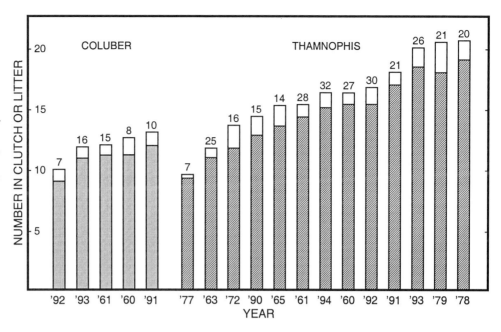

Figure 32. Year-to-year variation in size of clutch (*Coluber constrictor flaviventris*) and litter (*Thamnophis sirtalis parietalis*), arranged in order from "worst" to "best" year. Top of each column shows the sample's mean, and open space shows one standard error.

multiplied beyond the numbers present originally in other habitats.

Snake Occurrences on the Biotic Succession Area (BSA)

A small proportion of the snake records obtained were from BSA, but the systematic sampling on this area facilitated year-to-year and species-to-species comparisons. BSA was a large upland field in the southeastern part of NESA. The field, formerly cultivated, served for various interdisciplinary studies involving "islands" of natural vegetation in a replicate pattern of rectangles. The islands were of three sizes: 4 × 8 m, 12 × 24 m, and 50 × 100 m (Figure 33). The smallest rectangular islands were replicated in three rows of five, regularly spaced in an area corresponding to a large island (50 × 100 m), and the medium-size islands (12 × 24 m) were in two rows of three, also within an area corresponding with a large island. The island plots of BSA established in 1984 were in five tiers from west to east. Only the two eastern tiers were used for the snake study begun in 1986. For each of seven 50 ×

TABLE 102. Responses to Ecological Succession in Local Snakes

Species	1950s	Trends on FNHR 1960s through 1990s	Population Shift from Forest or Edge to Formerly Open Areas	Reasons for Changes
Agkistrodon contortrix	rapid increase	gradual decline	Yes	Favored initially by population explosion of voles
Carphophis vermis	gradual increase	relatively stable	Yes	Gains mainly in areas that had been unsuitable
Coluber constrictor	rapid increase	gradual decline		Benefitted by transition from over-grazed shortgrass to tallgrass, but set back by spread of forest
Crotalus horridus	decrease	disappearance		Eliminated by shading as closed canopy developed in forest
Diadophis punctatus	rapid increase	gradual decline	Yes	Favored by development of dense ground cover in overgrazed pastures but later expansion of woodland was deleterious
Elaphe obsoleta	gradual increase	relatively stable	Yes	Favored by great increase of voles in early years
Lampropeltis calligaster	increase	gradual decline	Yes	Favored by transition to tallgrass and increase of voles in early years, later set back by spread of forest
Lampropeltis triangulum	increase	gradual decline	Yes	Favored by initial increase in ground cover; set back by later spread of woodland
Nerodia spiedon	gradual increase	gradual decline	No	Favored by dredging of pond in early 1950s extending and improving aquatic habitats
Pituophis catenifer	rapid decrease	early disappearance		Shortgrass habitat eliminated
Sotreria dekayi	gradual increase	relatively stable	Yes	Favored by early development of dense ground cover
Tantilla gracilis	rapid decrease	eliminated	No	Barren rocky areas invaded by vegetation that shaded out its habitat
Thamnophis sirtals	gradual increase	relatively stable	Yes	More affected by annual weather changes than by longtime succession
Virginia valeriae	?	?	?	Population trends obscured by rarity

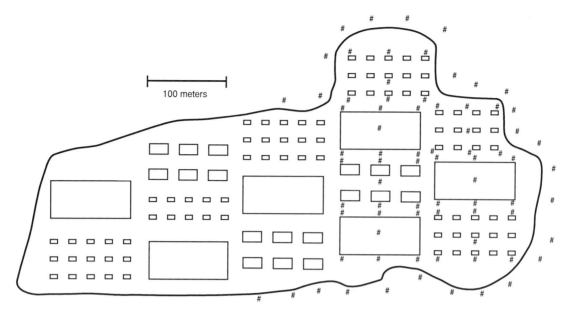

Figure 33. Pattern of islands of natural vegetation (rectangles) on NESA Biotic Succession Area and locations of shelter pairs (#).

100 m rectangles (whether it was a large island, six medium-size islands or 15 small islands), seven pairs of shelters each 0.61 × 1.22 m were emplaced, each pair including one of corrugated sheet metal and one of plywood. The original 98 shelters were set out at 49 sites encompassing tier 4—with four sets of islands, from north to south small, large, medium, large—and tier 5 with three sets: small, large, small. The intent was to test the snakes' preference for metal vs. wooden shelters and for small vs. medium vs. large islands of vegetation. At the beginning of the 1987 season an adjunct set of 26 shelter pairs was emplaced, at regular intervals in the unmowed periphery of the field, opposite tiers 4 and 5. The intent for this adjunct series was to test whether snakes favored the unmowed edges, with reluctance to cross the mowed areas in order to reach the islands of denser vegetation. At the start of the 1994 season still more adjunct shelters were emplaced. For each peripheral pair two new pairs were added, spaced in the intervals between the old pairs. One new pair of each series was placed on the ground vegetation with no preparation, but the second pair was placed on bare soil after hoeing and raking; the intent was to test the effects of substrate conditioning (Parmelee & Fitch, 1995). Thus shelters totalled 98 (49 pairs) in the 1986 season, 150 (75 pairs) from 1987 through 1993 and 254 (127 pairs) in 1994, 1995, 1996, and 1997.

By 1995 BSA had developed three fairly distinct seral communities. On the islands, perennial weeds, mainly *Aster* and *Solidago*, dominated, in a stand 0.9 to 1.5 m high, but woody vegetation, especially *Cornus drummondi, Ulmus americanus,* and *Rhus glabra* was invad-

ing, with saplings up to 3.6 m. The area around the islands was mowed frequently during the growing season, and its vegetation was mainly grass (*Poa annua, Aristida oligantha, Setaria lutescens,* and others) with herbaceous plants including *Lespedeza striata* and *Taraxacum* sp., with a height of less than 0.1 m. The peripheral strip, 2 to 50 m wide, was dominated by grass, especially *Bromus inermis,* but also with prairie tallgrasses (*Andropogon scoparius* and *Sorghastrum nutans*) 0.6 to 0.9 m high and with clumps or isolated plants of *Cornus drummondi, Rhus glabra, Gleditsia triacanthos, Rubus* sp., and others.

Over the decade 1986 through 1995 a total of 47,285 shelter checks were logged on BSA and 641 snake sightings were recorded. In most instances snakes were captured and fully processed, with individual marks, measurements, sex, and stomach contents recorded, but some (mainly racers) escaped capture and the smallest snakes, *Diadophis* and *Storeria*, were not marked. Of the 641 snakes from shelters, 29.4% were *Thamnophis sirtalis,* 24.2% were *Coluber constrictor,* 18.9% were *Diadophis punctatus,* 13.6% were *Agkistrodon contortrix,* 9.3% were *Elaphe obsoleta,* 1.4% were *Lampropeltis triangulum,* 1.0% were *Crotalus horridus,* 0.8% were *Storeria dekayi,* 0.6% were *Tropidoclonion lineatum,* 0.5% were *Lampropeltis calligaster.* These figures may reflect approximately the relative numbers of the 10 species involved. Figures 34 and 35 show how these ratios changed from year to year, with number of snakes per 1000 shelter checks used as the unit of comparison. Numbers fluctuated widely from year to year, but with some parallel trends between species. One of the most noticeable changes

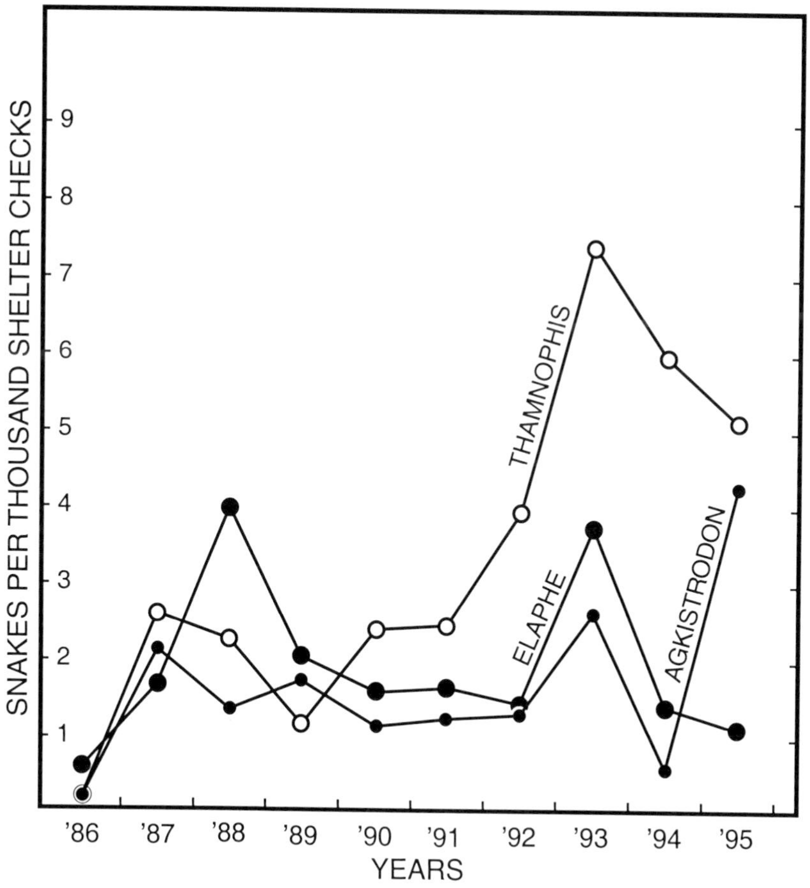

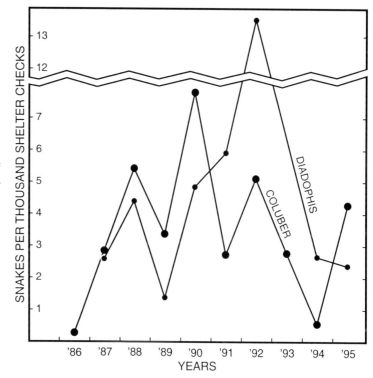

Figure 34. Year-to-year variation in numbers of *Thamnophis sirtalis parietalis, Elaphe obsoleta obsoleta,* and *Agkistrodon contortrix phaeogaster* obtained in BSA snake sampling.

Figure 35. Year-to-year variation in numbers of *Coluber constrictor flaviventris* and *Diadophis punctatus arnyi* obtained in BSA snake sampling.

was an increase in the number of garter snakes. Also, there was change in the age composition of garter snakes captured. During the first 7 years nearly all those captured were adult females, but after installation of two small reservoirs adjoining BSA in 1992, the catch each year, 1993 through 1997, included substantial numbers of males and first-year young, as explained in the species account of *Thamnophis sirtalis*.

For each species certain shelters seemed to be preferred and were known to have been used several or many times, whereas other shelters that appeared to be equally suitable were used only once or not at all. For *Elaphe obsoleta* 36.6% of captures were at 6 shelters, for *Lampropeltis triangulum* 41.2% were at 6 shelters, for *Agkistrodon contortrix* 46.0% were at 13 shelters, for *Coluber constrictor* 41.5% were at 21 shelters. The shelters that were preferred were different for different species. The most plausible explanation for preference is that use of a shelter by one individual conditioned the substrate rendering it more attractive to conspecifics following scent trails. Usually months or years elapsed between the records of use for any one shelter — too long for the scent trail of the original user to persist, but perhaps a succession of users intervened, unrecorded because they were present only on days when there was no sampling. Memory of a specific shelter site may have led individuals to return after one or more hibernations when scent trails were no longer detectable.

The shelters were used by many other kinds of animals besides snakes including insects (especially ants, crickets, and roaches), earthworms, amphibians (*Pseudacris triseriata*, *Bufo americanus*, *Rana blairi*, *R. catesbeiana*), lizards (*Scincella lateralis*, *Eumeces obsoletus*, *Ophisaurus attenuatus*), and mammals (*Microtus ochrogaster*, *Synaptomys cooperi*, *Peromyscus maniculatus*, *P. leucopus*, *Sigmodon hispidus*, *Neotoma floridana*, *Reithrodontomys megalotis*, *Blarina hylophaga*, *Cryptotis parva*). The small mammals were often permanent residents beneath specific shelters, where they had nests and food stores, and their presence was obviously an attraction for snake predators including *Agkistrodon*, *Coluber*, *Crotalus*, *Elaphe*, *Lampropeltis*, and *Thamnophis*. Allowing for difference in numbers between old and new shelters, the old shelters were more productive of mammal-eating snakes: 60% vs. 40% for new shelters. In contrast, the diminutive snakes that are not mammal predators (*Diadophis*, *Storeria*, *Tropidoclonion*) were found in nearly equal numbers at old (51.1%) and new (48.9%) shelters. Overall, metal shelters were slightly preferred over wooden, 51% vs. 49% but use of both depended on weather conditions. In hot, sunny weather metal shelters were avoided except at night and when the sun was low in early morning or late afternoon. Wooden shelters were avoided when they were soggy with

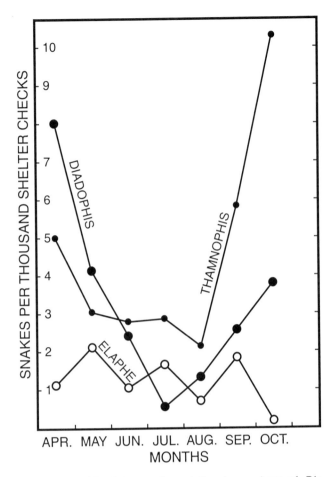

Figure 36. Month-to-month variation in numbers of *Diadophis punctatus arnyi*, *Elaphe obsoleta obsoleta*, and *Thamnophis sirtalis parietatlis* in BSA snake sampling.

condensation at times of high humidity. Old shelters, new shelters with unprepared substrate, and new shelters with bare ground (cleared substrate) yielded, respectively, 40, 34, and 24 captures in a comparison during the 1994 season.

For the decade of shelter checks on BSA changes in numbers of snakes from month to month were not great. Monthly totals per 1000 shelter checks were: April 14.6, May 16.5, June 13.7, July 10.0, August 9.9, September 10.0, October 18.5. Figures 36 and 37 show month to month changes for the five most common species that made up 92% of the total records. Each shows different trends. *Diadophis punctatus* conforms to the traditional trend for Temperate Zone snakes with maximum numbers early in the season, tapering off rapidly in the summer with a secondary peak in fall. *Thamnophis sirtalis* also showed a U-shaped seasonal curve, but with the fall peak the higher. *Agkistrodon contortrix*, dispersing slowly and tardily from its winter quarters, was never found on BSA in April but reached maximum numbers in May and then tapered off through the remainder of the season. *Coluber constric-*

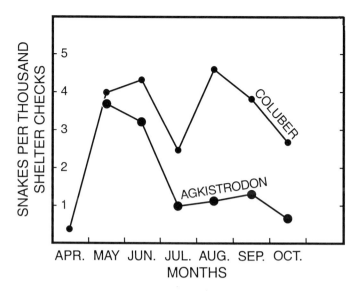

Figure 37. Month-to-month variation in numbers of *Agkistrodon contortrix phaeogaster* and *Coluber constrictor flaviventris* obtained in BSA snake sampling.

tor and *Elaphe obsoleta* showed relatively little seasonal change, but the latter was scarce at the beginning and end of the season.

Sex Ratios and Sexual Maturity

Table 103 shows observed and estimated sex ratios in 17 samples of 12 local species. It shows that sex ratios in samples are subject to a wide range of variation, with males ranging from 43% in *Thamnophis sirtalis* to more

than 70% in *Lampropeltis triangulum* and 63% in *Elaphe obsoleta*. In *Coluber* and in the natricines *Nerodia, Storeria,* and *Thamnophis,* females outnumbered males, but in crotalines, most colubrines (*Elaphe, Lampropeltis,, Pituophis*) and *Diadophis,* males outnumbered females. Sex ratios in hatchlings usually deviate from parity, depending on the species. Temperature during critical stages of embryonic development may determine sex, as has been demonstrated for turtles and crocodilians, and the sex ratio of a species may change in time and space.

It must be questioned whether the relative numbers of males and females in samples represent true sex ratios that prevail in nature. Information already presented in the species account of *Diadophis punctatus* indicates that the ratios in samples are biased by behavioral differences that change during the course of a season. In general, male snakes are more mobile and more in evidence than females during the spring breeding season. Later, gravid females spend more time basking than do males; their use of superficial shelters and their reduced agility at this time may render them more susceptible to capture. But at the time of oviposition in early summer, females may be relatively safe from capture in the underground nests where eggs are deposited.

The extent to which sex ratios of samples are biased by such behavioral differences may be judged by comparing the incidence of recaptures in the sexes. If the ratio of recaptures of marked snakes to original

TABLE 103. Sex Ratios in Population Samples and Recapture Samples of Local Snakes

Species	Origin of Sample	N	Sex Ratio %		Percentage Recaptures		♂/♀ Recapture Ratio	Calculated Sex Ratio %	
			♂	♀	♂	♀		♂	♀
Agkistrodon contortrix	fields, FNHR & NESA 1977–1996	565	51.1	48.9	67.0	53.7	1.25	45	55
Agkistrodon contortrix	hilltop outcrops, fall 1977–1995	251	63.4	36.1	22.4	31.5	0.71	71	29
Carphophis vermis	FNHR, 1949–1996	270	57.3	42.7	5.1	11.9	0.43	76	24
Coluber constrictor	NESA 1980–1996	987	48.0	52.0	64.6	46.0	1.39	40	60
Crotalus horridus	FNHR, NESA, 1949–1996 (adults and young)	128	57.0	43.0	12.3	10.9	1.13	50	50
Diadophis punctatus	FNHR, 1980s & 1990s (adults)	752	60.0	40.0	33.4	16.6	2.01	43	57
Diadophis punctatus	FNHR, 1980s and 1990s (First-year young)	314	58.5	41.5	41.5	17.6	2.36	38	62
Diadophis punctatus	FNHR, 1980s and 1990s (second-year young)	342	58.6	41.4	30.0	10.6	2.89	38	62
Elaphe obsoleta	FNHR, NESA, 1949–1996	737	63.0	37.0	24.4	42.5	0.57	75	25
Lampropeltis calligaster	FNHR, NESA, 1949–1996	115	58.5	41.5	36.8	37.5	0.98	59	41
Lampropeltis triangulum	FNHR, NESA, 1949–1996	95	70.6	29.4	23.9	17.2	1.39	63	37
Nerodia sipedon	FNHR, NESA, 1949–1996	213	47.0	53.0	21.0	24.0	0.58	60	40
Pituophis catenifer	FNHR, NESA 1949–1996	91	57.1	42.9	26.9	46.2	0.58	70	30
Storeria dekayi	FNHR, NESA, 1949–1996	194	47.9	52.1					
Thamnophis sirtalis	NESA pens (in traps) 1990s	364	43.0	57.0	26.7	36.7	1.51	33	67
Thamnophis sirtalis	FNHR, House Field, 1977–1997 (adults, hand caught)	409	43.8	56.2	28.4	50.2	0.57	58	42
Thamnophis sirtalis	FNHR, House Field, 1977–1997 (first-year young hand caught)	234	45.4	54.6	42.0	44.8	0.94	48	52

TABLE 104. Minimum Sizes of Sexually Mature Snakes of 12 Local Species

	Male			Female			Male/Female %	
Species	Date	SVL (mm)	Weight (g)	Date	SVL (mm)	Weight (g)	SVL	Weight
Agkistrodon contortrix	24 July 1960	389	22	17 August 1960	494	66	79	33.3
*Carphophis vermis**		177	2.9		237	5.8	75	50.0
Coluber constrictor	29 Oct. 1959	461	29	2 May 1961	600	80	77	36.2
Crotalus horridus	23 May 1965	682	177	12 July 1957	803	410	85	43.1
Diadophis punctatus	13 May 1966	173	1.7	20 May 1991	225	4.3	77	39.5
Elaphe obsoleta	27 May 1960	825	118	11 July 1959	960	190	86	62.0
Lampropeltis calligaster	18 May 1964	629	68	13 June 1978	715	182	88	37.4
Lampropeltis triangulum	21 April 1963	420	23	8 May 1960	514	48	82	48.0
Nerodia sipedon	1 Nov. 1960	413	36	9 July 1962	577	104	71	34.5
Pituophis catenifer	5 May 1964	855	190	13 June 1953	1042	366	77	51.9
Storeria dekayi	13 April 1968	159	1.8	8 May 1976	199	3.5	76	51.4
Thamnophis sirtalis	24 July 1960	389	22	17 August 1992	494	79	79	27.8

* from Clark (1970).

captures is different in the sexes, the figures provide a clue to the amount of bias. An attempt was made to apply a correction factor to observed sex ratios on the basis of recapture ratios. For 4 of the samples (*Crotalus horridus, Diadophis punctatus, Lampropeltis triangulum,* and *Thamnophis sirtalis*—first-year young sample) the male-to-female ratio was nearer to parity than in the observed samples of these species. In other samples, notably *Carphophis vermis* and *Elaphe obsoleta,* the supposedly corrected sex ratios departed from parity even more than in the observed samples, with a ratio of about 3 males to 1 female, and perhaps were distorted by unrecognized biases.

In each of the 12 species included in Table 104 males attained sexual maturity at smaller size and presumably at an earlier age than female counterparts. For the entire group males averaged 80.2% (72 to 88) of female SVL and 43.0% (28 to 62) of female mass. The greatest sexual size differences are in *Thamnophis sirtalis, Nerodia sipedon,* and *Coluber constrictor* and in these species the smallest mature males are only 5.0% to 5.5% of the mass of the largest females. Attainment of sexual maturity in males that are far short of mean adult size minimizes the chances that fecund females will fail to produce because of low population density and limited vagility preventing them from being found by males. In *Agkistrodon, Crotalus, Elaphe* and *Lampropeltis,* having relatively large males and male combat, male maturity is somewhat delayed and the newly matured males of these species are liable to be dominated by older and larger males, so that their chances of siring offspring are minimal. Nevertheless, they provide insurance that despite the species' low density and low vagility females will not go unmated.

Sexual maturity in males was determined by finding active sperm in seminal fluid. The cloaca was cleared of fecal and renal material by pipetting physiological saline solution into it and then flushing out the liquid and solid wastes with gentle backward pressure of the operator's thumb. A drop of cloacal fluid was then withdrawn and examined under a dissecting microscope with 60 power magnification. Results were not consistently positive even with fully mature males believed to be in breeding condition. Specific records for minimum adult sizes are shown in Table 104. In the more common species the records for minimum size presented in the table were supported by the records of several or many other individuals that were only a little larger and obviously belonged to the same age-size cohort. The samples of *Elaphe obsoleta, Lampropeltis calligaster, L. triangulum, Nerodia sipedon,* and *Pituophis catenifer* were relatively meager; more intensive sampling might reveal male maturity at somewhat smaller size in these species. Many hundreds of male snakes were checked for active sperm, and as a rule it could be found during the entire season of activity.

In females sexual maturity was determined by observing the abdomen distended with ovarian follicles, oviductal eggs or embryos, which could be individually palpated as soft lumps of fairly uniform size. In oviparous species females usually were detectably ovigerous from about mid-May to early July and the viviparous species retained their fetuses through July and early August, some even into October. It should be mentioned that maturity is detectable several weeks earlier in males than in females of the same age cohort, even though both are reproductive and will become parents at the same time. Meanwhile the females may make substantial growth. Hence the size differences between newly matured males and females may be somewhat less than indicated by the figures in Table 104.

Geographic Differentiation

Geographic variation in snakes has been studied mostly in terms of lepidosis, but comparison of my data with literature records indicates that there are far more significant geographic differences within species in body size, reproduction and other demographic traits. For instance in *Thamnophis sirtalis* a literature survey indicated a mean litter size ranging from 26.0 in Ontario to 11.3 in southwestern Oregon. A general trend was evident—from maximum numbers in the Great Lakes region to much reduced numbers in northern New England and especially in the far western states (Fitch, 1985).

Joseph C. Mitchell in his *Reptiles of Virginia* (1994) published statistics for that state on many of the same species that occur at about the same latitude in Kansas, providing a basis for comparison; for almost all species there are striking contrasts. In the copperhead for instance adult body size is somewhat larger in Virginia, but neonate size is much larger (by 57%) in Kansas and number of young per litter is correspondingly reduced in Kansas: 5.3 vs. 7.6 in Virginia (Table 105). In the racer there are even more striking differences between the two regions. The black racers of Virginia have little or no sexual size difference according to Mitchell's figures, and their weight is more than twice that of female Kansas yellowbelly racers and about three times the weight of Kansas males. Clutch size in Virginia is nearly twice that of Kansas, and Virginia hatchlings are 37% larger than those of Kansas. Timber rattlesnakes in Kansas are larger than those in Virginia, and this applies to adults of both sexes and to neonates. But the Kansas neonates are larger in proportion to adults.

In *Elaphe* the contrast between Kansas *E. emoryi* and Virginia *E. guttata* is especially striking; adult males in Kansas average 2.5 times the bulk of their Virginia counterparts. The difference is a little less in females. Clutch size was 6.43 ± 1.09 in my Kansas sample vs. 11.3 ± 5.1 in a Virginia sample of six. In the black rat snake, size is similar in the two regions but clutch size in Virginia is double that in Kansas (19.4 vs. 9.7). In the prairie kingsnake both sexes of adults are slightly larger in Kansas than in Virginia, but egg clutches average larger in Virginia (13.5 vs. 8.7) and the size of Virginia hatchlings is correspondingly reduced—to less than two-thirds that of their Kansas counterparts. The milk snake averages larger in Virginia, but its hatchlings average smaller with more per clutch than in Kansas. In the northern water snake average adult size is somewhat larger in Virginia, but neonates are smaller, with more per litter in that region (average 19.9 in Kansas vs. 28.5 in Virginia). Kansas brown snakes exceed their Virginia counterparts by about 10% in length in both sexes, with litter size nearly the same—10.6 vs. 10.8. In the common garter snake, Virginia females average only a little more than half the bulk of Kansas counterparts, but they have larger litters: 26.2 vs. 16.2, and the young are correspondingly small.

In summary, each of 10 snake species that occur both in northeastern Kansas and in Virginia were compared in the two regions and all were found to have striking but hitherto unrecognized differences in demographic traits, paralleling the known differences in color, pattern and lepidosis that are the main bases for taxonomic divisions (Table 105). Presumably the demonstrated differences in mean size between geographic populations are genetically determined. The concept that growth is "indeterminate" in reptiles has diverted attention from using size to compare species and populations, and there has been undue emphasis on maximum measurements. However, in all the snake species studied growth is "determinate" in that each has a typical adult size. After attainment of sexual maturity the rate of growth slows drastically and continues to taper off with advancing age. The largest individuals are likely to be the oldest and size provides a clue to age, but, as shown above in the accounts of *Agkistrodon contortrix* and *Elaphe obsoleta,* a surfeit of food may allow individuals to attain unusually large size.

Snakes must swallow every meal entire and no doubt one of the most critical evolutionary adaptations has been adjustment to the size of available prey. It is not surprising that the earthworm-eating ringneck snakes of Kansas are small compared with salamander-eating and ophiphagous populations in other parts of North America. In each of the local species both adult and hatchling sizes probably have adjusted through natural selection to the most available prey.

Mortality Factors

Each species of snake has attained evolutionary adjustment to diverse mortality factors including predation, accident, and disease. Despite temporary gains or setbacks, mortality is essentially in equilibrium with natality. It is difficult to identify and evaluate specific mortality factors. Much of the loss occurs in hibernation, underground, or in well-concealed sites where it is not likely to be observed. In my study the most obvious cause of mortality was traffic on the county road passing through the study area (FNHR–NESA) or along its edge for 3.4 km. With the exceptions of several of the rarest and most secretive kinds of snakes all were observed to be traffic casualties from time to time. Ringneck snakes and garter snakes were the most frequently observed traffic casualties. Racers also were often noted dead on roads, but on various occasions they were seen to escape oncoming cars by darting off onto the side of the road. Road kills were judged to be significant mortality factors only for the bullsnake and the timber rattlesnake.

For the common species an attempt was made to gauge routine mortality by calculating the rate of re-

TABLE 105.   Geographic Differences Between Kansas and Virginia in Populations of Common Snake Species

| Species | | | | | |
State	Sex	N	Mean SVL (mm)	Mean Weight (g)	Mean Clutch or Litter Size
Agkistrodon contortrix Copperhead					
Kansas	Male	960	656	170.6	
	Female	825	595	154.5 ± 5.4	
	Neonate	90	222.7	11.1	5.34 in 234
Virginia	Male	90	733	273 ± 136.4	
	Female	80	598 ± 92.6	178.1 ± 69.6	
	Neonate	17	196.5 ± 8.7	7.0	7.6 ± 3.9 in 18
Coluber constrictor Racer					
Kansas	Male	1715	707	118.6 ± 3.1	
	Female	1349	822	165 ± 3.5	
	Hatchling	107	219.3	4.6	11.4 in 60
Virginia	Male	78	1036 ± 20.3	351 ± 30.1	
	Female	82	1020 ± 16.6	350 ± 29.8	
	Hatchling	28	224.7 ± 8.4	6.3	21.0 ± 8.3 in 14
Crotalus horridus Timber rattlesnake					
Kansas	Male	45	1050 ± 6.6	868 ± 92	
	Female	37	921 ± 14.2	530 ± 39.5	
	Neonate	19	324.7 ± 3.8	26.5 ± 0.84	8.9 ± 0.88 in 13
Virginia	Male	51	956 ± 11.6	700	
	Female	30	867 ± 16.2	394	
	Neonate	62	286	no data	7.6 ± 3.2 in 8
Elaphe sp. Corn snake or Rat snake					
Kansas *E. emoryi*	Male	17	1184 ± 27.4	398 ± 31.4	
	Female	16	1040 ± 15.7	328 ± 19.8	
	Hatchling	—	—	—	6.43 ± 1.09 in 7
Virginia *E. guttata*	Male	12	870 ± 32	159 ± 6.6	
	Female	17	868 ± 26.4	159 ± 6.6	
	Hatchling	7	267 ± 29.4	7.97 ± 0.19	11.3 ± 5.1 in 6
Elaphe obsoleta Black rat snake					
Kansas	Male	233	1226	511	
	Female	184	1081	334	
	Hatchling	81	316.6 ± 2.68	11.7 ± 0.36	9.7 ± 1.19 in 87
Virginia	Male	124	1182 ± 187	—	
	Female	54	1136 ± 156	—	
	Hatchling	48	284.6 ± 14.2	11.3 ± 1.2	19.4 in 21
Lampropeltis calligaster Prairie kingsnake or Mole kingsnake					
Kansas	Male	85	893.3	228.3	
	Female	70	828.4	188	
	Hatchling	16	264.4 ± 3.8	8.3	9.14 ± 0.58 in 14
Virginia	Male	31	840.6 ± 102.9	—	
	Female	15	799.6	199	
	Hatchling	?	176–210	2.7–6.5	13.5 ± 4.8 in 4
Lampropeltis triangulum Milk snake					
Kansas	Male	81	630 ± 8.13	69.5 ± 3.0	
	Female	42	601 ± 8.9	68.2 ± 3.6	
	Hatchling	15	201 ± 2.4	3.01 ± 0.01	6.89 ± 0.36 in 18
Virginia	Male	32	738 ± 18.3	—	
	Female	12	640 ± 22.9	—	
	Hatchling	11	181.7 ± 10.1	4.1 ± 0.3	(5–20)
Nerodia sipedon Water snake					
Kansas	Male	81	544 ± 7.0	98.2 ± 5.0	
	Female	71	756 ± 13.9	286.5 ± 16.1	
	Neonate	101	193.6 ± 2.2	4.91 ± 0.10	19.9 ± 2.1 in 19
Virginia	Male	142	573 ± 9.0	196.1 ± 111.3	
	Female	52	774 ± 12.7	454.1 ± 23.96	
	Neonate	109	171.3 ± 12.5	4.7 ± 0.9	28.5 (11–56) in 24
Storeria dekayi Brown snake					
Kansas	Male	90	218.7 ± 2.2	4.3 ± 0.14	
	Female	104	254.5 ± 3.1	7.53 ± 0.43	
	Neonate	98	82.3	0.29 ± 0.08	10.63 ± 0.64 in 49
Virginia	Male	46	199.6 ± 27.0	—	
	Female	64	232.3 ± 28.2	5.2	
	Neonate	47	68.9 ± 4.5	0.28 ± 0.05	10.8 ± 4.3 in 26
Thamnophis sirtalis Common garter snake					
Kansas	Male	1048	523	44.2	
	Female	1443	639	105.7	
	Neonate	455	164.2	1.71	16.19 in 321
Virginia	Male	53	409.7 ± 56.4		
	Female	102	515.3 ± 105		
	Neonate	100	131.2 ± 7.5	1.7 ± 0.2 (in 45)	26.2 ± 16.8 in 22

Note: The Virginia records (from Mitchell, 1994) show standard deviations, whereas the Kansas records show standard errors.

cruitment. For instance a series of Petersen Index censuses for the garter snake indicated an average density of 9.1 per hectare and 20.5% of these garter snakes would be adult females. In an average year 68% of adult females are breeders. For each hectare an average of 1.27 fecund females producing 16.2 young apiece might contribute a recruitment of 20.6 neonates. Comparable quotas for other species would include 44.1 for the brown snake, 15.3 for the worm snake, 8.9 for the copperhead, 8.6 for the racer, 1.7 for the watersnake and 0.81 for the black rat snake, totalling about 100 per hectare for these seven species combined. However, the ringneck snake is far more abundant than any other species, with an estimated 1040 per hectare of which 210 (20.2%) might be adult females. With an average clutch of 3.36 the ringneck snake might contribute 706 snakes per hectare to an annual total of 806 per hectare for all species combined. The combined FNHR, NESA, and CWF areas of 563 ha indicate an annual recruitment of 453,778 snakes, and for the 50-year study the total would be more than 22 million. The figure may seem impossibly high. The ringneck snake, especially, may have been present in numbers much below the estimated 1040 per hectare at times and places for which no census samples were obtained, but undoubtedly this one species made up the greater part of the snake population studied. Censused areas consisted mainly of open fields, but there were extensive tracts of woodland that were poor habitats for most kinds of snakes. Nevertheless, snake mortality may have totalled several million on the combined study areas over the 50-year span of fieldwork.

Most of this mortality cannot be measured or categorized but some clues exist as to the fates of the thousands of snakes eliminated annually. Hibernation is known to be a time of stress in Temperate Zone reptiles. Most individuals of most species of snakes in my study left their summer ranges in autumn and migrated varying distances to seek secure hibernacula in hilltop limestone outcrops with southward exposure. Clefts and fissures in the rock, and burrows of mammals adjacent to it provided opportunities for snakes to retreat beneath the frost line. The fact that even the most cold-hardy species (garter snake) seeks such protection emphasizes the importance of suitable hibernacula where the snakes may spend almost half the year. However, the hibernaculum may become a tomb; many snakes die in hibernation. Depth of the frost line varies from year to year, depending on amount of snow cover or lack of it, high wind, and intense or prolonged cold periods. Extremes may result in mass mortality of hibernating snakes, but some species are much more susceptible than others, and young are more vulnerable than adults. In every instance when a local snake population was sampled in fall and again the following spring, major changes were noted which could have been caused in part by winter mortality.

This mortality is not necessarily a result of the rigors of extreme weather. Hibernating snakes are immobilized, helpless, and vulnerable to any small predators that are able to reach them. Two such animals are the white-footed mouse (*Peromyscus leucopus*) and Elliot's short-tailed shrew (*Blarina hylophaga*), although neither is ordinarily considered a formidable predator. In summer both are favorite prey of common snakes, including the copperhead, racer, black rat snake, kingsnakes and garter snake, but in winter the relationship may be reversed, with these small mammals preying on the snakes. Circumstantial evidence was observed on many occasions; wire funnel traps used in fall or spring when nights were cool sometimes caught a shrew or white-footed mouse along with a snake of several or many times its bulk. In such cases the mammal, lacking other food, was found to have attacked the snake and gnawed enough flesh from its tail or dorsal surface to obtain a meal, even though the snake was not fully immobilized.

Shrews and mice, having a keen sense of smell and some digging ability, could locate hibernating snakes and feed upon them, perhaps over periods of days or weeks, both before and after death. The hapless snake would be helpless at temperatures near freezing, and would be meat in cold storage for the mammal predator. The white-footed mouse ordinarily feeds on nuts and seeds but also takes some animal food; the short-tailed shrew preys primarily on invertebrates, but also takes small vertebrates. Both mammals are common in local woodland, and possibly both are major predators on several kinds of snakes in winter when other foods are scarce.

During their active season the larger kinds of snakes are safe from such small predators, but they have various natural enemies to contend with (Table 106). One such is the red-tailed hawk (*Buteo jamaicensis*). It was a permanent resident and usually several pairs were present on the combined study areas. During the first 10 years of my study disgorged pellets of the young hawks were gathered from beneath nests and a total of 541 prey items were identified of which 221 were snakes: 148 *Elaphe obsoleta*, 35 *Agkistrodon contortrix*, 23 *Diadophis punctatus*, 8 *Coluber constrictor*, 5 *Thamnophis sirtalis*, and 2 *Pituophis catenifer* (Fitch, 1974). Doubtless the number of snakes represented was somewhat less, as the remains of one snake, especially a large one, might be found in two or more pellets. Nevertheless, the sample is significant, suggesting that more than one-third of the hawks' prey in the nesting season consists of snakes and that the black rat snake is the favorite prey (see "Interactions with Birds" in *Elaphe obsoleta* account). Also, it is shown that the hawk is able to prey on the

TABLE 106. Vertebrate Predators and Their Observed or Suspected Predation on 18 Species of Local Snakes

Predators	*Agkistrodon contortrix*	*Carphophis vermis*	*Coluber constrictor*	*Crotalus horridus*	*Diadophis punctatus*	*Elaphe emoryi*	*Elaphe obsoleta*	*Lampropeltis calligaster*	*Lampropeltis getula*	*Lampropeltis triangulum*	*Nerodia sipedon*	*Pituophis catenifer*	*Storeria dekayi*	*Storeria occipitomaculata*	*Tantilla gracilis*	*Thamnophis sirtalis*	*Tropidoclonion lineatum*	*Virginia valeriae*
Mammals																		
Blarina hylophaga	S	S	S	S	S	S	S	S	S	S	S	S		S	S	S	S	S
Canis latrans			S			S	S	S	S		S		L		S	S	S	
Didelphis virginiana	m	L			m	L	S	L			S	L	L	m	S	S	S	L
Mephitis mephitis			M				L		S		M	m	m	m		S	S	S
Procyon lotor	S	S	S		S		S	S			M	m	m	S			S	S
Peromyscus leucopus	S	S		S	S		S	S	S		S	S	S	S	S		S	S
Scalopus aquaticus		S			M								S	S	S		S	S
Spilogale putorius		S			S		S		L	S	S		S					
Birds																		
Ardea herodias											M	m	s			M		
Bubo virginianus	S	S		S	m		L	L										
Buteo jamaicensis	M		m	m	m	L	M	m	S	S	m	m		L	S	L	S	
Buteo platypterus	L		m		m	S	m	m	S			S			S	S	S	S
Butorides striatus												m		S		S		
Circus cyaneus			S		S	S					S					S		
Coccyzus americanus							S							S	S	S	S	S
Coccyzus erythrophthalmus							S							S	S	S	S	S
Corvus brachyrhynchos			S		S	S			S					S	S	S	S	S
Toxostome rufum		S					S		L						S	S	S	S
Reptiles																		
Agkistrodon contortrix		m	m		m		m						m			L		S
Chelydra serpentina												m		L	L	m		
Coluber constrictor	L		m		m								L	L	S	m	m	
Lampropeltis calligaster					m													L
Lampropeltis getula	L	L	L		L	L	L	L			L		L	L		L		L

M = major predator
m = minor predator
L = literature record(s)
S = suspected

venomous copperhead with impunity and may be one of its major natural enemies. Food habits of the red-tailed hawk in the nesting season were investigated on a larger scale by Fitch and Bare (1978). A total of 195 nests in 25 counties in the eastern one-third of Kansas were located, 1960–63, and 2760 prey items were identified. Of these 661 were snakes; 431 *Elaphe obsoleta*, 79 *Thamnophis sirtalis*, 55 *Coluber constrictor*, 47 *Agkistrodon contortrix*, 25 *Diadophis punctatus*, 12 *Pituophis catenifer*, 10 *Nerodia sipedon*, 1 *Lampropeltis* sp., and 1 *Crotalus horridus*. Again the red-tailed hawk is implicated as a frequent predator of snakes, including venomous kinds, and especially as a natural enemy of the black rat snake.

In the early years of fieldwork on FNHR the broad-winged hawk (*Buteo platypterus*) was a regular summer resident, arriving soon after mid-April. Nests were kept under observation in 1954, 1957, and 1958 and 138 prey items were recorded including 23 snakes: 13 *Diadophis punctatus*, 7 *Coluber constrictor*, 2 *Elaphe obsoleta*, and 1 *Lampropeltis calligaster.* The average prey item was

estimated to weigh 19 g, in contrast to an average of 106 g for the red-tailed hawk (Fitch, 1974). After 1965 broad-winged hawks were rarely seen, and the species seems to have been eliminated from the local fauna. The coyote (*Canis latrans*) was another predator species investigated during the early years of the study (Fitch and Packard, 1955). Scats were collected from FNHR in 1948, 1949, 1950, 1951, and 1952. The total of 118 scats yielded 272 prey items among which there was only one snake. However, most of the scats represented feeding during the colder part of the year, as they deteriorate rapidly during warm and humid weather. Coyotes are opportunistic predators that prey on snakes when they are available. However, coyote use of the area decreased greatly after livestock were removed, and decreased further after small mammal populations had passed their peak and woody vegetation invaded formerly open areas.

The opossum (*Didelphis virginiana*) is omnivorous, taking a great variety of plant and animal food.

Sandidge (1953) examined the contents of 62 digestive tracts collected between 25 September 1949 and 27 March 1950. Because they were collected during the colder part of the year, the records probably do not do justice to the opossum as a snake predator, there were only two snakes (*Carphophis vermis* and *Storeria dekayi*) and together they made up only 1.2% of the total. In 1951 and 1952, 79 scats were collected from FNHR mainly from the fall months (Fitch and Sandidge, 1953), two of these scats contained copperhead remains.

The raccoon (*Procyon lotor*) was studied in Kansas by Stains (1956), and large collections of scats were made along the Wakarusa River in Douglas County. Unidentified snakes made up a little less than 1% of the items in 529 autumn scats. On FNHR in summer both opossums and raccoons are believed to be more important predators of snakes than indicated by these meager records. Both animals often attempted to remove snakes from wire funnel traps, and often succeeded. In some instances they tore the funnels off the traps, exposing captured snakes to attack. On other occasions one of these predators reached through a trap's funnel opening with a front paw to grasp a snake and pull it out of the trap. In striving to reach a trapped snake the predator usually was snagged on projecting wire points and left tufts of hair revealing its identity. Traps were often rolled or dragged for several meters and might be found with the trapped snake still safe inside. On one occasion a large female northern water snake that was being trailed by radiotelemetry was found dead and partly eaten, with raccoon tracks in the mud beside it.

Skunks (*Mephitis mephitis, Spilogale putorius*) may have been important as snake predators on the study area. The striped skunk is known to feed largely on insects, whereas the much smaller spotted skunk is more weasel-like, and preys to a greater extent on small vertebrates. In the 1950s and 1960s many skunks of both species were live-trapped on FNHR, but no spotted skunks have been seen for more than 25 years, and striped skunks have become less common than formerly. On many occasions evidence of striped skunks digging up and eating snake eggs have been found in grassland (Fitch, 1963a). Most of the nests were those of racers. Eggs from nests, usually at a depth of 7.5 to 10.0 cm, had been dug up, broken and chewed, with shell fragments littered over an area of several square meters.

Although it is generally known as a predator of invertebrates, the eastern mole may destroy more snakes than all other predators combined. The evidence is circumstantial. Eastern moles confined in terraria readily accepted as food any small snakes that were offered, including ringnecks, worm snakes, and even a small copperhead. Usually the snake was attacked from below, grasped at mid-body and pulled underground, so that its movements were restricted, then it was subdued by a series of nips severing its spinal cord. Ringneck snakes were often found to bear scars that could be interpreted as mole bites. The shelters that were most used by ringnecks often had well-used mole tunnels under them indicating that moles came there regularly to hunt. From similar evidence Clark (1970) speculated that the mole was a major predator of worm snakes on his study areas. Other diminutive snakes including the smooth earth snake, brown snake, flathead snake, redbelly snake, and lined snake, probably are equally at risk.

Large snakes prey on smaller ones. Among local kinds the copperhead, racer, prairie kingsnake, and common kingsnake all prey upon other snakes, but only the common kingsnake has a high proportion of snake in its food. The racer is the only species known to prey on young of its own kind. Of 50 snakes taken by racers locally, 16 were young racers, 16 were ringnecks, 14 were garter snakes, 4 were black rat snakes, and 1 was a water snake (Fitch, 1963a). Of 289 copperhead prey items 16 were ringnecks, 5 were worm snakes, and 1 was a racer.

Earthworm-size young of the smallest snake species may be taken by small predators such as passerine birds, that feed mainly on invertebrates. The crow, blue jay, cuckoos, and brown thrasher are suspected.

The tallgrass prairie of eastern Kansas is a fire subclimax which depends on periodic burning. On RET and NESA several separate tracts of both original and regenerated prairie were regularly subjected to controlled burning, usually in early spring. Many snakes have been found dead or moribund after the burns. Racers, especially are frequent victims because of their affinity for tallgrass habitat. Garter snakes also are vulnerable, and because of early emergence, they may be killed by fires while some other species are still safe in their hibernacula. Prairie kingsnakes have been found killed by fires on several occasions. Plants and animals of the tallgrass prairie have many adaptations to escape or resist burning. For snakes the most obvious defense would seem to be prompt retreat underground, but behavioral responses have not been recorded.

Little is known about the diseases of snakes that limit their numbers under natural conditions. Most of the snakes that were captured appeared to be healthy. Some were afflicted with a skin disorder which seemed to be the same in various species. It was especially noticeable in snakes recently emerged from hibernation; small, hard, raised nodules were scattered over the dorsal surface. Most often there were only a few nodules and the snake was not noticeably affected. Occasional individuals had more severe infections, with dozens of nodules, and they sometimes appeared weak and emaciated, giving reason to believe that they might not recover. Such skin infections were seen most fre-quently in ringneck snakes, and may have resulted from excess moisture in hibernacula. In the months after emergence the frequency and severity of infections decreased. Great Plains rat snakes had the highest incidence of infection; in fact all of those examined had at least a trace of the characteristic skin disorder.

Literature Cited

Aleksiuk, M., & Gregory, P. T. (1974). Regulation of seasonal mating behavior in *Thamnophis sirtalis parietalis.* Copeia, 1974:681–689.

Allen, J. A. (1868). Catalogue of the reptiles and batrachians in the vicinity of Springfield, Massachusetts, with notice of all other species known to inhabit the state. Proc. Boston Soc. Nat. Hist., 12:171–204.

Anderson, P. L. (1965). The reptiles of Missouri. Univ. Missouri Press, Columbia. xxiii + 330 pp.

Arnold, S. J. (1993). Foraging theory and prey-size-predator-size in snakes. *In* Snakes ecology and behavior (pp. 87–115). Richard A. Seigel & Joseph T. Collins (Eds.). McGraw-Hill, New York.

Bechtel, H. B., & Bechtel, E. (1958). Reproduction in captive corn snakes, *Elaphe guttata guttata.* Copeia, 1958:148–149.

———— (1962). Heredity of albinism in the corn snake, *Elaphe guttata guttata,* demonstrated in captive breedings. Copeia, 1962:436–437.

Blanchard, F. N. (1937). Data on the natural history of the red-bellied snake, *Storeria occipito-maculata* (Storer) in northern Michigan. Copeia, 1937:151–162.

————, & Force, E. R. (1930). The age of attainment of sexual maturity in the lined snake, *Tropidoclonion lineatum* (Hallowell). Bull. Antivenin Inst. Amer., 3:96–98.

Bogert, C. M., & Roth, C. D. (1966). Ritualistic combat of male gopher snakes, *Pituophis melanoleucus affinis* (Reptilia; Colubridae). Amer. Mus. Nat. Hist. Novit., No. 2245, 27 pp.

Brown, W. S. (1991). Female reproductive ecology in a northern population of the timber rattlesnake, *Crotalus horridus.* Herpetologica, 47:101–115.

————, Pyle, D. W., Greene, K. R., & Friedlander, J. B. (1982). Movements and temperature relationships of timber rattlesnakes (*Crotalus horridus*) in northeastern New York. Journal of Herpetology, 16:151–161.

Burger, J. (1989). Following of conspecifics and avoidance of predator chemical cues by pine snakes (*Pituophis melanoleucus*). Jour. Chem. Ecol., 15:799–806.

Clark, D. R., Jr. (1970). Ecological study of the worm snake *Carphophis vermis* Kennicott. Univ. Kansas Publ. Mus. Nat. Hist., 19(2):85–194.

Clark, H. (1953). Eggs, egg-laying and incubation of the snake *Elaphe emoryi* (Baird and Girard). Copeia, 1953 (2):90–92.

Cobb, V. A. (1989). The foraging ecology and prey relationships of the flathead snake, *Tantilla gracilis.* Unpublished master's thesis, University of Texas, Tyler.

Collins, J. T. (1993). Amphibians and reptiles in Kansas. Univ. Kansas Mus. Nat. Hist. Pub. Ed. Series No. 13, xx + 397 pp.

———— (1997). Standard common and current scientific names for North American amphibians and reptiles. Herp. Cir. No. 25, Soc. Study of Amphib. and Rep., iv + 40 pp.

Conant, R. (1956). A review of two rare pine snakes from the Gulf Coastal Plain. Amer. Mus. Novit. No. 1781, 31 pp.

Constanzo, J. P. (1989). Conspecific scent trailing by garter snakes (*Thamnophis sirtalis*) during autumn. Further evidence for use of pheromones in den location. Jour. Chem. Ecol., 15:2531–2538.

Cooper, W. E., & Alfieri, K. J. (1993). Caudal autotomy in the eastern garter snake, *Thamnophis s. sirtalis.* Amphibia-Reptilia, 14(1):86–89.

Ditmars, R. L. (1907). The reptile book. Doubleday, Page and Co., New York. pp. xxxii + 472.

Dixon, R. D., & Chapman, J. A. (1980). Harmonic mean measure of animal activity areas. Ecology, 61:1040–1044.

Dundee, H. A., & Miller, M. C. (1968). Aggregative behavior and habitat conditioning in the prairie ringneck snake, *Diadophis punctatus arnyi.* Tulane Studies Zool. Bot., 15:41–58.

Dunlap, K. D., & Lang, W. (1990). Offspring sex ratio varies with maternal size in the common garter snake, *Thamnophis sirtalis.* Copeia, 1990:568–570.

Duvall, D., Schuett, G. W., & Arnold, S. J. (1993). Ecology and evolution of snake mating systems. *In* Snakes ecology and behavior (pp. 165–200). Richard A. Seigel & Joseph T. Collins (Eds.). McGraw-Hill, New York.

Finneran, L. C. (1953). Aggregation behavior of the female copperhead, *Agkistrodon contortrix mokeson,* during gestation. Copeia, 1953:61–62.

Fitch, H. S. (1941). The feeding habits of California garter snakes. California Fish and Game, 27(2):2–32.

——— (1949). Study of snake populations in central California. American Midl. Nat., 4:513–579.

——— (1951). A simplified type of funnel trap for reptiles. Herpetologica, 7:77–83.

——— (1959). A patternless phase of the copperhead. Herpetologica, 15:10–24.

——— (1960). Autecology of the copperhead. Univ. Kansas Pub. Mus. Nat. Hist. 13:85–288.

——— (1963a). Natural history of the racer, *Coluber constrictor.* Univ. Kansas Pub. Mus. Nat. Hist., 15:351–468.

——— (1963b). Natural history of the black rat snake (*Elaphe o. obsoleta*) in Kansas. Copeia, 1963:649–658.

——— (1965). An ecological study of the garter snake, *Thamnophis sirtalis.* Univ. Kansas Pub. Mus. Nat. Hist., 15:493–564.

——— (1970). Reproductive cycles in lizards and snakes. Univ. Kansas Mus. Nat. Hist. Misc. Pub. No. 52, 247 pp.

——— (1974). Observations on the food and nesting of the broadwing hawk (*Buteo platypterus*) in northeastern Kansas. Condor, 76(3):331–333.

——— (1975). A demographic study of the ringneck snake (*Diadophis punctatus*) in Kansas. Univ. Kansas Mus. Nat. Hist. Misc. Pub. No. 62, 53 pp.

——— (1978). A field study of the prairie kingsnake (*Lampropeltis calligaster*). Trans. Kansas Acad. Sci., 81:453–463.

——— (1982). Resources of a snake community in prairie-woodland habitat of northeastern Kansas. *In* Herpetological communities (pp. 83–97). Norman J. Scott (Ed.). U. S. Fish & Wildlife Serv., Wildlife Research Report 13

——— (1985). Variation in clutch and litter size in New World reptiles. Univ. Kansas Mus. Nat. Hist. Misc. Pub. No. 76, 76 pp.

——— (1987). Collecting and life-history techniques. *In* Snakes ecology and evolutionary biology (pp. 143–164). Richard A. Seigel, Joseph T. Collins, & Susan S. Novak (Eds.). MacMillan Publishing Company, New York.

——— (1992). Methods of sampling snake populations and their relative success. Herpet. Rev., 23(1):17–19.

——— (1993). Relative abundance of snakes in Kansas. Trans. Kansas Acad. Sci., 96(3–4):213–224.

———, & Bare, R. O. (1978). A field study of the red-tailed hawk in eastern Kansas. Trans. Kansas Acad. Sci., 81(1):1–13.

———, & Fleet, R. R. (1970). Natural history of the milk snake (*Lampropeltis triangulum*) in northeastern Kansas. Herpetologica, 36:387–396.

———, & Packard, R. L. (1955). The coyote on a natural area in northeastern Kansas. Trans. Kansas Acad. Sci., 58(2):211–221.

———, & Sandidge, L. L. (1953). Ecology of the opossum on a natural area in northeastern Kansas. Univ. Kansas Publ. Mus. Nat. Hist., 7:309–338.

———, & Shirer, H. W. (1971). A radiotelemetric study of spatial relationship in some common snakes. Copeia, 1971:118–128.

Force, E. R. (1934). A local study of the opisthoglyph snake, *Tantilla gracilis.* Baird and Girard. Papers Michigan Acad. Sci., Arts, Lett., 20:645–659.

Ford, N. B. (1985). The role of pheromone trails in the sociobiology of snakes. *In* Chemical signals in vertebrates, vol. 4, pp. 261–278. D. Duvall, D. Miller-Schwartze, & R. M. Silverstein (Eds.). Plenus, New York.

———, & O'Bleness, M. B. (1986). Species and sexual specificity of pheromone trails of the garter snake, *Thamnophis marcianus.* Journ. Herpet., 20:259–262.

———, & Seigel, R. A. (1989). Phenotypic plasticity in reproductive traits. Evidence from a viviparous snake. Ecology, 70:1768–1774.

Fraken, M. A. (1970). Home range and homing in the watersnake, *Natrix sipedon sipedon.* Copeia, 1970:665–673.

Galligan, J. H., & Dunson, W. A. (1979). Biology and status of the timber rattlesnake (*Crotalus horridus*) population in Pennsylvania. Biol. Conserv., 15:13–58.

Garton, B. M., & Dimmick, R. W. (1969). Food habits of the copperhead in middle Tennessee. Jour. Tennessee Acad. Sci., 44:113–117.

Gartska, W. R., & Crews, D. (1981). Female sex pheromones in the skin and circulation of a garter snake. Science, 214:681–683.

——— (1985). Mate preference in garter snakes. Herpetologica, 41:9–19.

Gehlbach, F. R. (1974). Evolutionary relations of southwestern ringneck snakes (*Diadophis punctatus*). Herpetologica, 30:140–148.

Gibbons, J. W. (1972). Reproduction, growth and sexual dimorphism in the canebrake rattlesnake (*Crotalus horridus atricaudatus*). Copeia, 1972:222–226.

Gibson, A. R., & Falls, J. B. (1975). Evidence for multiple insemination in the common garter snake. Canadian Jour. Zool., 53:1362–1363.

Gillingham, J. C. (1979). Reproductive behavior in the rat snakes of eastern North America genus *Elaphe.* Copeia, 1979:319–331.

———, Rowe, J., & Weins, M. A. (1990). Chemosensory orientation and earthworm location by foraging eastern garter snakes, *Thamnophis s sirtalis. In* Chemical signals in vertebrates (pp. 522–532). D. McDonald, D. Miller-Schwartze, & S. Natynczuk (Eds.). Oxford University Press, Oxford.

Gloyd, H. K. (1934). Studies on the breeding habits and the young of the copperhead, *Agkistrodon mokasen* Beauvois. Pap. Michigan Acad. Sci., Arts, Lett., 19:587–604.

Gregory, P. T. (1974). Patterns of emergence of the red-sided garter snake (*Thamnophis sirtalis parietalis*) in the interlake region of Manitoba. Canadian Jour. Zool., 52:1063–1069.

Gregory, P. T., & Stewart, K. W. (1977). Long-distance dispersal and feeding strategy of the red-sided garter snake (*Thamnophis sirtalis parietalis*) in the interlake region of Manitoba. Canadian Jour. Zool., 53:238–245.

Gutzke, W. H. N., Paukstis, G. L., & McDaniel, L. L. (1985). Skewed sex ratios for adult and hatchling bullsnakes, *Pituophis melanoleucus* in Nebraska. Copeia, 1985:649–652.

Hawley, A. W. L., & Aleksiuk, M (1976). Sexual receptivity in the female red-sided garter snake (*Thamnophis sirtalis parietalis*). Copeia, 1976:401–404.

Heinrich, M. L., & Kaufman, D. W. (1985). Herpetofauna of the Konza Prairie Research Natural Area, Kansas. Prairie Nat., 17(2):101–112.

Henderson, R. W. (1974). Resource partitioning among the snakes of the University of Kansas Natural History Reservation, a preliminary analysis. Milwaukee Pub. Mus. Contrib. Biol. Geol., 1:1–11.

Imler, R. H. (1945). Bullsnakes and their control on a Nebraska wildlife refuge. Jour. Wildlife Mgt., 9:265–273.

Iverson, J. B. (1990). Sex ratio in snakes: a cautionary note. Copeia, 1990(2):571–573.

Joy, J. E., & Crews, D. (1985). Social dynamics of group courtship behavior in male red-sided garter snakes (*Thamnophis sirtalis parietalis*). Jour. Comp. Psychol., 99:145–149.

Keenlyne, K. D. (1972). Sexual differences in feeding habits of *Crotalus horridus horridus.* Jour. Herpetology, 6:234–237.

Kephart, D. G. (1982). Microgeographic variation in the diets of garter snakes. Oecologica (Berlin), 52:287–291.

Krohmer, R. W., & Aldridge, R. D. (1985). Female reproductive cycle of the lined snake (*Tropidoclonion lineatum*). Herpetologica, 41(1):39–44.

Leszczynski, Z., & Zappalorti, R. T. (1996). Pine snake (*Pituophis melanoleucus melanoleucus*). Reptiles, 4(5):25–26, 28–30, 32, 34, 36–38.

Lillywhite, H. B. (1985). Trailing movements and

sexual behavior in *Coluber constrictor.* Herpetologica, 19(2):306–308.

Markel, R. (1990). Kingsnakes and milk snakes. TFH Publications, Inc., Neptune City, NJ, 144 pp.

Martin, W. H. (1992). Phenology of the timber rattlesnake (*Crotalus horridus*) in an unglaciated section of the Appalachian Mountains. *In* Biology of the pit vipers (pp. 259–277). J. A. Campbell & E. D. Brodie, Jr. (Eds.). Selva, Tyler, TX.

Mason, R. D., & Crews, D. (1985). Female mimicry in garter snakes. Nature, 316:59–60.

Mitchell, J. C. (1994). The reptiles of Virginia. Smithsonian Inst. Press, Washington, DC, xv + 352 pp.

Neill, W. T. (1948). The caudal lure of various juvenile snakes. Quart. Jour. Florida Acad. Sci., 23:173–200.

Parker, W. S., & Brown, W. S. (1980). Comparative ecology of two colubrid snakes *Masticophis t. taeniatus* and *Pituophis melanoleucus deserticola* in northern Utah. Milwaukee Pub. Mus. Pub. Biol. Geol., 7:1–104.

Parmelee, J. R., & Fitch, H. S. (1995). An experiment with artificial shelters for snakes: Effects of material, age, and surface preparation. Herpet. Nat. Hist., 3(2):187–191.

Platt, D. R. (1984). Growth of bullsnakes (*Pituophis melanoleucus sayi*) on a sand prairie in south central Kansas. *In* Vertebrate ecology and systematics, a tribute to Henry S. Fitch (pp. 41–55). Richard A. Seigel, Lawrence E. Hunt, James L. Knight, Luis Malaret, & Nancy Zuschlag (Eds.). Univ. Kansas Mus. Nat. Hist. Spec. Pub. No. 10.

Plummer, M. V. (1977). Predation by black rat snakes in bank swallow colonies. The Southwestern Naturalist, 22(1):147–148.

Pough, F. H. (1988). Mimicry and related phenomena. Chapter 2, pp. 155–234 in Biology of the Reptilia. Volume 16 Ecology B. Defense and Life History.

Reinert, H. K. (1993). Habitat selection in snakes. *In* Snakes ecology and behavior. (pp. 201–240). Richard A. Seigel & J. T. Collins (Eds.). McGraw-Hill, New York.

———, Cundall, D., & Bushar, L. M. (1984). Foraging behavior in the timber rattlesnake. Copeia, 1984: 976–981.

———, & Zappalorti, R. T. (1988). Timber rattlesnakes of the pine barrens: their movement patterns and habitat preferences. Copeia, 1988:964–978.

Rigley, L. (1971). "Combat dance" of the black rat snake, *Elaphe obsoleta.* Jour. Herpetology, 5:65–66.

Ross, P., & Crews, D. (1977). Influence of the seminal plug on mating behavior in the garter snake. Nature, 267:344–345.

Sandidge, L. L. (1953). Food and dens of the opossum

(*Didelphis virginiana*) in northeastern Kansas. Trans. Kansas Acad. Sci., 59:97–106.

Schieffelin, C. D., & de Queiroz, A. (1991). Temperature and defense in the common garter snake: Warm snakes are more aggressive than cold snakes. Herpetologica, 47:230–237.

Schuett, G. W., & Gillingham, J. C. (1988). Courtship and mating in the copperhead, *Agkistrodon contortrix*. Copeia, 1988:374–381.

⸻ (1989). Male-male agonistic behavior in the copperhead, *Agkistrodon contortrix*. Amphibia-Reptilia, 10:243–266.

Schwartz, J. M., McCracken, G. F., & Burghardt, G. M. (1989). Multiple paternity in wild populations of the garter snake *Thamnophis sirtalis*. Behav. Ecol. Sociobiol., 25:269–273.

Secor, S. (1987). Courtship and mating behavior of the speckled kingsnake, *Lampropeltis getulus holbrooki*. Herpetologica, 43:15–28.

Seigel, R. A. (1984). The foraging ecology and resource partitioning patterns of two species of garter snakes. Unpublished dissertation, The University of Kansas Department of Systematics and Ecology.

⸻, & Fitch, H. S. (1984). Ecological patterns of relative clutch mass in snakes. Oecologica, 61:293–301.

⸻, & Ford, N. B. (1991). Phenotypic plasticity in the reproductive characteristics of an oviparous snake, *Elaphe guttata*: Implications for life history studies. Herpetologica, 47(3):301–307.

Semlitsch, R. D., & Moran, G. B. (1984). Ecology of the redbelly snake (*Storeria occipitomaculata*) using mesic habitats in South Carolina. American Midl. Nat., 111:33–40.

Sexton, O. J., & Bramble, J. E. (1994). Post-hibernation behavior in a population of garter snakes, (*Thamnophis sirtalis*). Amphibia-Reptilia, 15:9–20.

Shaw, C. E. (1951). Male combat in American colubrid snakes with remarks on other colubrid and elapid snakes. Herpetologica, 7:149–168.

Snider, A. T., & Bowler, J. K. (1992). Longevity of reptiles and amphibians in North American collections (2nd ed.). SSAR Herp. Circ., 21:1–40.

Stains, H. J. (1956). The raccoon in Kansas. Univ. Kansas Mus. Nat. Hist. Misc. Publ. No. 10, 76 pp., 4 pl.

Tiebout, H. M., & Cary, J. R. (1987). Dynamic spatial ecology of the water snake, *Nerodia sipedon*. Copeia, 1987:1–18.

Trauth, S. E., Cox, R. L. Jr., Meshaka, W. E. Jr., Butterfield, B. P., & Holt, A. (1994). Female reproductive traits in selected Arkansas snakes. Proc. Arkansas Acad. Sci., 48:196–209.

Tryon, B. W., & Carl, G. (1980). Reproduction in the mole kingsnake, *Lampropeltis calligaster rhombo-maculata* (Serpentes, Colubridae). Trans. Kansas Acad. Sci., 83(2):66–73.

⸻, & Murphy, J. B. (1982). Miscellaneous notes on the reproductive biology of reptiles. 5. Twelve varieties of the genus *Lampropeltis*, species *mexicana, triangulum,* and *zonata*. Trans. Kansas Acad. Sci., 85:96–119.

Vaughan, R. K., Dixon, J. R., & Thomas, R. A. (1996). A Reevaluation of the corn snake *Elaphe guttata* (Reptilia: Serpentes: Colubridae) in Texas. Texas Jour. Sci., 48(3):175–190.

Vitt, L. J. (1973). Observations on reproduction in five species of Arizona snakes. Herpetologica, 51(1):83–84.

Weatherhead, P. J., & Haysack, D. J. (1989). Spatial and activity patterns of black rat snakes (*Elaphe obsoleta*) from radiotelemetry and recapture data. Canadian Jour. Zool., 67:463–468.

⸻, & Robertson, I. C. (1990). Homing to food by black rat snakes (*Elaphe obsoleta*). Copeia, 1990(4):1164–1165.

Whittier, J. M., & Crews, D. (1986). Ovarian development in red-sided garter snakes, *Thamnophis sirtalis parietalis:* relationship to mating. Comp. Endocrin., 61:5–12.

Williams, K. L. (1978). Systematics and natural history of the American milk snake, *Lampropeltis triangulum*. Milwaukee Pub. Mus. Publ. Biol. Geol., 2:1–258.

Wright, A. H., & Wright, A. A. (1957). Handbook of snakes of the United States and Canada. Comstock Publ. Associates, Cornell Univ. Press, 2 vols., 1105 pp.

Zappalorti, R. T. (1992). Use of experimental man-made dens as summer basking sites and winter hibernacula by the snakes *Elaphe guttata* and *Pituophis melanoleucus* in the New Jersey Pine Barrens, with notes on their management. *In* Captive management and conservation of amphibians and reptiles. James B. Murphy, Joseph T. Collins, & Kraig Adler (Eds.). SSAR Contrib. Herpetol.

Zappalorti, R. T., & Reinert, H. K. (1986). Final report on habitat utilization by the timber rattlesnake *Crotalus horridus* (Linnaeus) in southern New Jersey with notes on hibernation. 170 pp. Report submitted for publication.

Zappalorti, R. T., & Rocco, G. (1992). Additional corn snake studies and habitat evaluations of alignment "C" of the proposed mule road extension. Berkeley Township, Ocean County, New Jersey, with special notes on an alternative road design to offset and mitigate long-term adverse impacts. Herpetological Associates. File No. 90.17 B, 130 pp. + 2 appendices. Submitted to Ocean County, New Jersey Engineering Department.

Index